STARG
SG·1 ™

FANTASTIC FRONTIERS
STARGATE SEASON ONE

WRITING

Rob Defendi
Scott Gearin
Dr. S. Alexander Gentry, PhD
Jack Kessler
Valerie Kessler
James Maliszewski
Don Mappin
Clayton Oliver
Lou Prosperi
Rodney Thompson

ADDITIONAL WRITING

Brannon Boren
Steve Crow
BD Flory
Patrick Kapera
Rob Vaux

LINE DEVELOPERS

Patrick Kapera
Rob Vaux

MECHANICS ASSISTANCE

Kevin P. Boerwinkle
Steve Crow
Scott Gearin
Patrick Kapera
Kevin Wilson
Erik Yaple

EDITING

Scott Gearin
Patrick Kapera
Rob Vaux

CREATIVE DIRECTOR

Mark Jelfo

TYPESETTING

Steve Hough

GRAPHIC DESIGN

Steve Hough

CHIEF EXECUTIVE OFFICER

John Zinser

CHIEF OF OPERATIONS

Maureen Yates

PRODUCTION MANAGER

Mary Valles

FOR MGM TELEVISION ENTERTAINMENT INC.

Tamara Blanton: Product Development Coordinator
Kobie Jackson: Product Development Coordinator
Laura Reid: Category Manager

SPECIAL THANKS

To all our online supporters and the countless *Stargate* fans out on the web. Your enthusiasm makes our work easier.

DEDICATION

To the international brotherhood of Chicago Cubs fans. Strength in adversity.

PLAYTESTERS

Tony Allen, Carl Ballard, Jon Bancroft, Kevin Barbour, Steve Barr, Clark Barrett, Matt Birdsall,
Eirik Bull-Hansen, Kyle Burckhard, Simon Campey, Chris Carlson, Richard Cattle, David Crabbe,
Joshua Cremosnik, Steve Crow, Ray Edwards, Steve Emmott, Charles Etheridge-Nunn, Jerry Ham, Rich Harkless,
Nabil Homsi, Olav B. Hovet, Ashley Jestico, Stephen Johnstone, Kalai Kahana, Christi McCray, Matt McGowan,
Angus McNichol, James McPherson, Clint Menezes, Steven Mileham, Justin Miller, David Molinar,
Jose H. Molinar, Ole Myrbakken, Jason Olsan, Kent Peet, Bob Pfeiffer, Anthony Rainwater, Rolando Rivero,
Hector Rodriguez, Dave Salisbury, Jon Sederqvist, Aaron Smith, Mandy Smith, Marshall Smith, Sonya Smith,
Catherine Spainhour, Rich Spainhour, Alasdair Stuart, Michael Surber, Andrew Fraser Taylor, Omar Topete,
David Trask, Seth Tupper, Kris Wagner, James Wiley, Marcus Wischik, Vivika McKie-Woods, Matt Wright

Contents

INTRODUCTION

The first steps are always the hardest. For years, the Stargate sat mothballed at the bottom of Cheyenne Mountain, a forgotten trinket from a long-dead civilization. Then suddenly, it sprang to life again... and the dangers of an entire universe came knocking at our door.

The missions were tentative at first; we had no idea what lay before us, and the threats which lay beyond that watery threshold looked well-nigh insurmountable. There were the Goa'uld, would-be gods who threatened to subjugate our entire species. There were hostile aliens, virulent diseases, and threats the likes of which we couldn't imagine. But their were also opportunities. For exploration. For discovery. For furthering humanity's knowledge and for the chance to greet the universe as peaceful ambassadors. The challenge had been issued. How could we not answer it?

Slowly, surely, we moved with greater confidence. The Goa'uld had to be stopped of course; their plans were too dangerous to let stand unimpeded. And there were other species out there – potential allies whose good will we needed to cultivate. It wasn't easy. The Nox, extreme pacifists with technology that dwarfed anything we had ever seen, refused to compromise on their beliefs of total nonviolence. The Unity, a race of sentient crystals, almost killed one of our own before communication could be established, and the amphibious Ohnes had their own agenda to pursue. But we made some inroads as well. Plenty of near-human cultures – our genetic cousins, abused and subjugated by the Goa'uld – stood ready to take up arms against their former masters. There were a few renegade Jaffa, weary of slavery and willing to follow the example of the *shol'va* rebel Teal'c. And here and there lay tantalizing hints of someone else – someone who might give us a big leg up in our fight against the System Lords...

As we followed these leads, we learned more and more about life beyond our little blue-green ball. We unlocked the mysteries of the ancient world, and found new brethren scattered amongst the stars. We discovered wondrous planets whose potential bordered on the breathtaking, an untamed frontier as vast as the stars themselves. We extended a hand to those who needed friends... and thwarted the schemes of an implacable enemy. By the end of our first year, the SGC had established a foothold in the galaxy.

It was a good beginning – just enough to let us know how much further we had to go.

Fantastic Frontiers is the Season One sourcebook for the *Stargate SG-1* role-playing game, containing all the information on the first year of the Stargate Program's existence. In order to use it, you'll need a copy of the *Stargate SG-1* core rulebook, though the information in the first few chapters is accessible to anyone who's a fan of the series. The book is divided into three chapters:

Chapter 1: Mission Logs is an episode-by-episode breakdown of the first season, from the series premiere to the cliffhanger finale. Each episode listing includes a complete synopsis of SG-1's mission, as well as background materials covering new species, new planets, and new dangers which might challenge other Stargate teams. This material is designed to expand upon previously revealed information, letting you pick up where the TV series left off.

Chapter 2: NPCs details the myriad and colorful characters which SG-1 encountered during their first year. Some are staunch allies, like Master Bra'tac, while others are dangerous foes, like the System Lord Apophis or the Machiavellian Colonel Maybourne. All of the principle figures from the first season are included, and all of them contain full stats, as well as details on their past and personality.

Chapter 3: New Rules explores new mechanics for the material covered in Season One: new species traits for the Nox, the Unity, the Ohnes and others, new skill uses, new equipment and SGC protocols, new classes (both for players and NPCs), and new feats. It also includes a few miscellaneous rules, such as how to force a Stargate to open on a secondary location, and statistics for the terrifying "Touched" disease from the Land of Light.

The first year of *Stargate SG-1* held surprises undreamed of, and lay the groundwork for the exciting missions to follow. Turn the page and find out how it all began.

CHAPTER ONE

MISSION LOGS

1-01: CHILDREN OF THE GODS

World Visited: Abydos.

Thermosphere: Hot (CR 0; orbits at the inner edge of its sun's habitable zone; 3d20+50° F).

Atmosphere: Normal (CR 0; 1.0 atmospheres).

Hydrosphere: Arid (CR 1; daily weather 1-89: none, 90: flood 1d10 MPH, 91-93: rain 1 in., 94-95: dust storm, 96-100: wind 1d10 MPH).

Geosphere: Very Unstable tectonic activity (daily earthquakes– 1-90: none, 91-95: minor, 96-99: moderate, 100: major; no volcanoes within 1d10 miles of the Stargate).

Seasons: Severe (1-25: spring, unchanged; 26-50: summer, +4d12° F; 51-75: autumn, unchanged; 76-100 winter, -4d12° F).

Anthrosphere: 5,000 natives; Bronze Age (3 picks, 1 RP); Feudalism; Suspicious (-1 with disposition checks); Aggressive (300 soldiers, squad size 2d4 soldiers); Very Poor civil rights.

Origin: Indeterminate.

Stargate Location (desert region): Hundreds of miles of desert, as well as some of the oldest rock formations on the planet.

Abydos is described at greater length on pages 66-69 of the *Stargate SG-1* core rulebook.

World Visited: Chulak.

Thermosphere: Warm (CR 0; orbits around common point in binary system; 2d20+25° F).

Atmosphere: Normal (CR 0; 0.9 atmospheres).

Hydrosphere: Semi-arid (CR 1; daily weather 1-88: none, 89: flood 1d10 MPH, 90-92: rain 1d3-1 in., 93: thunderstorm, 94: dust storm, 95: hurricane, 96-97: wind 1d10 MPH, 98: wind 1d10+10 MPH, 99: wind 1d10+20 MPH, 100: wind 1d20+30 MPH).

Geosphere: Very Stable.

Seasons: Mild (1-17: spring, unchanged; 18-50: summer, +2d10° F; 51-83: autumn, unchanged; 84-100: winter -2d10° F).

Anthrosphere: 3,000,000 natives; Early Medieval* (4 picks, 2 RP); Feudalism; Suspicious (-1 with disposition checks); Aggressive (300 soldiers, squad size 2d4 soldiers); Very Poor civil rights.

Origin: Indeterminate.

Stargate Location (scrub region): Rocky terrain, surrounded by elevated and lush forests, swamps and jungles to the west.

* With significant exceptions due to the presence of Goa'uld System Lords, who provide the Jaffa with more advanced technology while in their direct service.

An overview of Chulak's planetary features, society, and culture can be found on pages 69-72 of the *Stargate SG-1* core rulebook.

Episode Summary

Deep inside Cheyenne Mountain, five soldiers are playing cards in a unused storage room where a large circular object lies beneath a tarp. Suddenly, they hear a sound from the object, causing the tarp to fall away, revealing a large metallic ring which is now spinning and emitting light. Soon, a field of energy — looking like a great burst of water — appears within the ring and figures dressed in snake-headed helmets emerge through the center. One of these figures grabs a female soldier and subdues her. Soon, a new figure, one dressed in a golden snake helmet appears and uses a strange device to immobilize the soldier. When her companions attempt to rescue her, the snake-headed guards open fire with their staff weapons and eliminate them; they then step back through the ring and disappear. Base commander General George Hammond and another group of soldiers can only watch helplessly as they arrive on the scene.

Soon thereafter, Major Samuels visits Colonel Jack O'Neill, who is living in retirement and practicing amateur astronomy. Samuels asks O'Neill to accompany him to Cheyenne Mountain to meet with General Hammond. When the Colonel shows reluctance, Samuels explains that Hammond wishes to see him about the Stargate, which quickly changes his mind. Upon arriving at Cheyenne Mountain, O'Neill is grilled about his previous exploits through the Stargate. He recounts his adventures on Abydos, including the destruction of the alien who assumed the identity of the ancient Egyptian sun god Ra. Hammond shows O'Neill the body of one of the alien guards that came through the gate previously. He has a kangaroo-like pouch in his abdomen. O'Neill claims never to have seen any aliens like this on Abydos and reiterates that Ra is dead and so could not be responsible for this latest attack.

Hammond is skeptical of O'Neill's claims and interrogates him further about his mission. When the General reveals that he intends to send a bomb through the gate to eliminate any further threat, O'Neill admits that the Abydos gate was not buried as ordered and that Dr. Daniel Jackson—his colleague during the original mission — is still alive and living among the Abydonians. However, he continues to insist that Ra is dead and that Abydos poses no threat to Earth. A furious Hammond tells O'Neill he intends to follow through with his orders and has the Colonel confined to a holding cell.

While interred, O'Neill is visited by Major Charles Kawalsky, an Air Force officer who also traveled with him to Abydos. The two men reminisce about their experiences, including meeting a young Abydonian named Skaara, who reminded O'Neill of his son, Charlie, who died just before the first Stargate mission. Hammond eventually joins them and admits to reconsidering his plan to send a bomb through the gate. O'Neill recommends sending a team through to investigate, a plan whose wisdom Hammond questions. The Colonel says he knows a way to test the safety of going to Abydos. He sends a box of tissues through the gate (Jackson suffers from allergies and would understand the box to be a message from a friend rather than the military). After a few hours, the empty box reappears through the Stargate with the message, "Thanks, send more," proving that Jackson is still alive and in control of the Abydos gate.

With the president's permission, a new team is authorized to go through the Stargate to investigate the origin of the aliens and to retrieve Jackson. To O'Neill's consternation, Hammond adds Captain Samantha Carter, a theoretical astrophysicist, to the team. The team makes it through the Stargate with little difficulty, but quickly find themselves surrounded by young Abydonians armed with rifles. Skaara, who greets O'Neill fondly with a salute and a hug, is among them, as is Jackson, who asks why they have come. O'Neill explains the circumstances, and Jackson assures them that no hostile life forms could have come from Abydos, since the Stargate is under constant guard.

Jackson leads O'Neill, Carter, and Kawalsky to a large room near the former Temple of Ra covered with strange hieroglyphic markings. He believes they are coordinates for using the Stargate. Despite Earth's assumptions, the Stargate need not go to only a single locale — Abydos — but can open portals to other worlds as well. Jackson therefore suspects that the aliens came from some other world that also possesses a Stargate. Together with Carter, he hypothesizes that millennia of planetary drift has rendered the coordinates somewhat inaccurate, but they could be corrected and used once again, thereby opening up countless new worlds for exploration and discovery.

Back in the Temple, the Stargate activates again, with more snake-helmeted guards coming through. They seize Skaara, who is in the room at the time, as well as Sha're, Jackson's Abydonian wife. Many Abydonians and several members of O'Neill's team are wounded in the fight. When Jackson learns of the attack, he blames himself. O'Neill tells him to return to Earth with the team, where perhaps they can unravel the mystery of the Stargate and rescue Skaara and Sha're. One of O'Neill's men Major Louis Ferretti, saw the coordinates where the snake-helmeted guards took their captives before he was injured. Jackson reluctantly agrees to join O'Neill, then tells the Abydonians to cover the Stargate for one year. They should then remove the cover. If he has found Skaara and Sha're, he will return on that day. If he does not return, they should bury the Stargate forever.

Skaara and Sha're find themselves on the planet Chulak, where the alien leader, Apophis, has placed all his prisoners. His snake-helmeted guards, called Jaffa, enter a holding area and select several women, including the kidnapped female airman and Sha're. These are then taken to determine if they find favor with Apophis' queen, Amaunet. It is revealed that the aliens are in fact worm-like symbiotes, called the *Goa'uld,* that live for thousands of years within human hosts. Amaunet is a newly-matured queen, in need of her first host, thus prompting Apophis' kidnapping excursions. She rejects the female airman, who is killed by Apophis, but approves of Sha're, whom she takes as her new host body.

Upon returning to Earth, the team finds that General Hammond has had a titanium iris installed on the Stargate as a safeguard against further incursions. Once Ferretti awakens, he conveys the coordinates of Chulak Hammond orders two teams, called SG-1 and SG-2, to enter the Stargate. O'Neill leads the first team and Kawalsky leads the second. Thanks to his protests, Jackson is assigned to SG-1 in order to find Sha're and Skaara. Hammond gives the teams 24 hours to achieve their goal, after which their transmission codes will be locked out and they will be unable to return to Earth via the gate. Once on Chulak, SG-1 heads off in search of the prisoners, while SG-2 remains behind to secure the Stargate.

With the help of the local inhabitants, SG-1 makes its way to a large city. There they see Apophis, who presents his queen to the people. He commands them to bow before her. When Jackson realizes that Amaunet is really Sha're, he attempts to speak with her. Apophis uses his ribbon device to fling him across the room. The other members of SG-1 — O'Neill and Carter — are also captured, and thrown in with the other prisoners. The leader of the Jaffa, Teal'c, approaches O'Neill and asks him where he is from. Jackson makes the Egyptian symbol for Earth in the sand, but Teal'c does not seem to understand it.

Later, Apophis and Amaunet, along with their followers, return. They say they have come to determine who among the humans there will become the children of the gods. They systematically examine the captives, taking some, and rejecting others. Skaara is claimed by Apophis himself, despite O'Neill's attempts to prevent it. Once this process is completed, Apophis orders Teal'c and the other Jaffa to kill the remaining humans. O'Neill appeals to Teal'c to help him. He believes the Jaffa is not interested in killing any longer; he is right. Teal'c turns on his fellow Jaffa, allowing the humans to escape, and abandons his position to follow the humans. Along the way to the Stargate, Teal'c explains that all Jaffa carry a larval Goa'uld within their abdominal pouch, where it grows until maturity, during which time it grants long life and excellent health. Should the larva ever be removed, the Jaffa will die.

When SG-1 and Teal'c reach the Stargate, they find Apophis, Amaunet, and Skaara leaving for an unknown locale. O'Neill calls out to Skaara, who responds by sending the Colonel flying across the ground with his ribbon device. He looks back and his eyes glow – a sure sign that he too has been possessed by a Goa'uld. O'Neill cannot dwell on this

terrible turn of events for long. He needs to get the other escaped prisoners back through the Stargate before Hammond's deadline passes. With the help of SG-2, he fends off an attack by more Jaffa, during which Teal'c proves his effectiveness. Jackson dials the Stargate and opens a wormhole to Earth. As the teams retreat, Kawalsky rushes over to an injured comrade to assist him; a larval Goa'uld from a nearby body leaps out and into Kawalsky's neck.

On the other side, the many refugees that O'Neill has brought with him amaze Hammond. Teal'c hands over his weapon and O'Neill introduces him to the General, asking that he be assigned to SG-1 as its fourth member. As everyone's thoughts are elsewhere, Kawalsky's eyes glow, indicating that the Goa'uld within him has taken control.

BACKGROUND

The Map Room located by Dr. Jackson not far from the former Temple of Ra is, in fact, only one part of a much larger structure, which, for lack of a better name, has been deemed the Map Building. It is a narrow but deep structure that broadly resembles an ancient Roman basilica. Of course, its exterior decoration and architectural style are not Roman at all but Egyptian, like all the structures on Abydos. The interior implies a great many things about Ra, the Goa'uld who originally ruled Abydos, and the nature of the universe in general. For one, its decoration is eclectic: some of it looks Egyptian, while some of it does not. The non-Egyptian decoration is of indeterminate origin, being seemingly non-representational in appearance. Instead, geometric and abstract designs are most common, vying with the hieratic and stolid decorations favored during the rule of Ra. In addition, there are many rooms and corridors within the building that have no decoration at all.

Preliminary examination of the Map Building suggests that it may predate the arrival of the Goa'uld some 15,000 years ago. Naturally, this hypothesis is controversial, because there is very little evidence of any life on Abydos prior to the arrival of the Goa'uld. There are no other buildings from before that time, nor is there any other archeological support for the notion. However, SGC researchers have nevertheless shown that the rock from which the Building were constructed cannot be found on Abydos. Neither can it be found on Earth. This unknown compound exhibits certain similarities to naquadah in non-metallic form, suggesting that it has an otherworldly origin. No other Goa'uld world has ever shown evidence of this mysterious rock, which further supports the claims that the Map Building predates Ra's arrival.

The other difficulty regarding the Building is its cartouche room. As Dr. Jackson understood it, the room was intended as a pictographic catalog of all the worlds reachable by the Stargate, along with their coordinates. There is a definite logic to this theory, although it has many problems as well. Why would Ra need an entire room covered with hieroglyphs to store his catalog of Stargate coordinates? The Goa'uld are an advanced species. They possess more compact and efficient means of data storage. What purpose does the room then serve? A more baffling question is why does the Map Room contain coordinates for worlds that, even given millennia of planetary shift, still would have been inaccessible during Ra's time. That is, just as some of the coordinates were outdated when Jackson found them, so too would some of them have been during Ra's reign. This suggests that the coordinates are very old indeed, perhaps as old as 30,000 years or more. With the death of Ra, there is no one on Abydos who could possibly have any definitive insight into this matter. Other Goa'uld have offered no further evidence that might clarify the issue. Among the Abydonians, legends persist of how it was their ancestors who build the Map Building and not Ra. These stories are unlikely to be true, since humans were not extant on the planet until the Goa'uld brought them there. However, it does suggest that those who seek a non-Goa'uld origin for the Map Building may not necessarily be wrong. At the very least, the structure bears further examination and study.

THE MAP BUILDING ON ABYDOS

The Map Building is located several miles away from the city of Nagada, in a small valley surrounded by low-lying mountains. The surrounding terrain is arid desert, just like the rest of the planet. However, it is somewhat more rocky than other areas, partially due to the mineral deposits found in the mountains, some of which periodically break off and roll down the slopes. These rocks have slowly wrought damage on the Map Building, although none is so significant that it threatens the overall structure.

The Building is usually uninhabited. By special permission, SGC researchers and SG teams may be allowed to visit. Abydonian desert fighters keep a constant eye on the place, just in case uninvited guests should decide to take an interest in the place. Thus far, there has been no evidence of outside incursions into the area, but the Abydonians aren't willing to take any chances.

PERISTYLE COURT

The outermost area of the Map Building is a large courtyard supported by columns decorated to look like Ra and other mythological figures as. Many of these figures have been defaced in the time since the discovery of the Building, so great is the hatred (and fear) of the deceased System Lord among the Abydonians. Three sets of stairs can be found here as well, allowing entry into the Map Building proper. During duststorms (which are not uncommon in this part of the desert), the court often fills with sand, preventing entrance – or exit – into the Map Building.

PORTICO

This area is a covered walkway that leads deeper into the Map Building. Like the Peristyle Court, it is covered with Egyptian-style artwork, this time mostly hieroglyphics. The portico is well constructed and nicely protects anyone under its roof from the worst effects of sandstorms. It is also connected to five different rooms, two of which are significant and described below.

GEOMETRIC CHAMBERS

These two rooms are mirror images of one another. Located at opposite ends of the Portico, they contain no artifacts or furnishings of any sort. However, their walls and ceilings are covered with impressive bas-reliefs drawn in complex geometric designs. What is most significant about these chambers is that the designs are not only wholly unlike the designs seen elsewhere, but they are also wholly unlike one another: the bas-reliefs use fractal geometry as their basis. Although the Goa'uld possess the knowledge of such geometry, there is no evidence of its use in artwork elsewhere.

HYPOSTYLE HALL

The hypostyle hall stands directly opposite the stairway leading to the Peristyle Court. It is supported by multiple carved columns, each of which bear the image of an Egyptian-looking individuals or (in some cases) individuals who cannot be definitely identified with any Egyptian deity or historical personage, nor with any Goa'uld formerly associated with Ra. Consequently, they may not actually represent such personages but may be simply decorative. This thesis is somewhat controversial among SGC researchers, however, since it runs counter to what's been observed of Goa'uld artwork elsewhere.

CARTOUCHE ROOM

The cartouche room is the single most important room in the Map Building and, some would argue, on all of Abydos. Its walls are covered with thousands of hieroglyphic symbols representing Stargate coordinates for worlds throughout the galaxy. By means of these coordinates, the SGC was able to begin its exploration program in earnest; without them it would be nearly impossible to guarantee dialing the address of a world with a functioning Stargate. As noted above, the cartouche room's original purpose is unknown. The SGC has many theories, of course, but none fully explain the enigmatic nature of the place. The information contained in this room is more than enough to keep them busy for many years to come.

SIDE ALTARS

These rooms flank the cartouche room, and are adorned with the same geometric designs as the chambers elsewhere in the Map Building. Unlike those chambers, however, the so-called side altars show evidence of those designs being partially effaced and replaced with Egyptian-style art and hieroglyphs that laud the glory of Ra and his dominion. In the center of each room are two large square "altars" that stand about four feet tall and have a flat, polished surface. Made of stone not native to Abydos, it's believed they were brought here when the former System Lord conquered the planet millennia ago. More than likely, the structures are not altars at all, but rather truncated supports for some larger piece of architecture that once dominated each room.

STATUE OF RA

This narrow room, accessible from the far end of the cartouche room, once contained a large state of Ra. However, since the fall of the Goa'uld tyrant, the statue has been defaced and many of its limbs hacked off. There is now just a trunk and legs remaining. The native Abydonians avoid the place if at all possible and there is little reason to visit it, except perhaps to look upon the shattered ruins of the glory of Ra

"OKAY, WE'RE GODS. NOW WHAT?"

– COL. JACK O'NEILL

CHULAK

As described in the core rulebook, Chulak is noteworthy for several reasons. First and foremost, it is the homeworld of the Jaffa, for it was there that the Goa'uld first brought humans from Earth to create their loyal race of servants. Jaffa make up the bulk of Chulak's population, making it a vital world for many System Lords. Consequently, Chulak is jointly held by multiple System Lords, although there is usually only a handful of preeminent Goa'uld who can claim any degree of control. As of Season One, the serpent god Apophis holds the balance of power on Chulak, although there are at least a dozen other System Lords of varying power (chief among them Anhur) who overtly or covertly challenge his claim. Unsurprisingly, Chulak is rife with intrigue, as System Lords and their allies vie with one another to seize the Jaffa homeworld for themselves.

Equally significant is the fact that Chulak also possesses a large minority of near-humans brought from countless worlds across the galaxy. The Goa'uld abducted them for a variety of purposes – simple slavery, blood sports, and as hosts for larval Goa'uld – but their presence makes Chulak a crossroads of Goa'uld space. Near-humans from almost any worlds could be found here and indeed probably have been. Apophis is very fond of a wide selection of potential hosts, as evidenced by the displaced persons held within the Temple of Gods. Players and GMs alike will find this fact a convenient way to bring disparate near-humans together in a single place should the need of a mission or campaign demand it.

ANHUR, WARMASTER OF RA

Anhur is a Goa'uld warmaster who once served the defeated System Lord Ra. Indeed, he was Ra's chief general and often led the former Sun God's armies into battle on innumerable worlds. His strategy and tactics were second to none, and Ra rewarded him greatly for his efforts. This greatly pleased the warmaster, since it allowed him to draw upon Ra's vast resources to settle his own private scores with other Goa'uld. The Sun God never disapproved of Anhur's private activities and in fact subtly encouraged them. He believed that they kept his general's instincts sharp and ensured that he would never have the time to consider overthrowing him.

Anhur was engaged in such a vendetta during the time of the original Stargate mission led by Colonel Jack O'Neill. Rather than being present on Abydos, Anhur was waging war against the Goa'uld Amurru on the planet Tuat (designated PY9-623). He was close to final victory when an urgent message was sent through the Stargate by Ra: return to Abydos at once to deal with an uprising among the Tauri. Anhur did not believe the message to be genuine, however, – or at least that is what he later claimed. In any event, the warmaster refused his lord's call and remained on Tuat, hoping to end his long feud with Amurru once and for all. Meanwhile, O'Neill and the original Stargate team succeeded in killing Ra and ending his tyranny on Abydos.

Some of Ra's Jaffa managed to escape to Tuat, where they informed Anhur of the terrible events there. At first, Anhur did not believe they could be true, but the Jaffa assured him otherwise. Realizing that his own inaction had brought about the death of his master, Anhur immediately left Tuat, allowing Amurru to survive. He visited several other worlds, never once returning to Abydos, despite the best efforts of Ra's surviving Jaffa to convince him otherwise. Anhur believed that he could never again set foot on that world, for it had been consecrated by Ra's spilled blood and he, as his betrayer, was unfit to walk upon it. In time, he made his way to Chulak, where he ensconced himself among the Goa'uld who rule that world.

On Chulak, Anhur initially took a low-key role, serving primarily as a military counterbalance against the schemes of Apophis and his allies. In time, though, it became clear that Apophis' might was waxing precisely because Ra had fallen, an act for which Anhur believed himself responsible. He has since been egged on by other System Lords on Chulak to oppose Apophis at every turn. Not nearly as powerful as his enemy, Anhur is uncertain he shall succeed. Nevertheless, he continues his somewhat quixotic quest, considering a means of atoning for his past misdeeds. Whether he lives or dies is unimportant to Anhur. All that matters is that he makes the effort to stand defiant before the Snake God just as his deceased master would have wished.

More information on Anhur can be found in Chapter Two.

1-02: The Enemy Within

World Visited: Earth.

Episode Summary

Warning claxons sound as the SGC detects an unrecognized traveler attempting to come through the Stargate – most likely Jaffa in the service of Apophis, who did not take kindly to SG-1's interference on Chulak. Thanks to the iris, however, the would-be invaders are unable to reach Earth and abandon the attempt in relatively short order. Shortly afterward, Colonel O'Neill notices Major Kawalsky rubbing the back of his neck and asks what is wrong. Kawalsky claims to have a very bad headache, which leads O'Neill to order him to the infirmary and have it checked out.

Soon, O'Neill is summoned to Hammond's office, where the general informs him that his request to have Teal'c join SG-1 has been denied. Hammond explains that it was not his decision and that someone from the Pentagon – Colonel Kennedy – is already en route to take custody of the renegade Jaffa. Kennedy has many questions to ask Teal'c, whose loyalty is considered suspect both because of his alien nature and the fact that he proved himself willing to change loyalties when it suited him. O'Neill is disappointed and angered by this turn of events, but can do nothing to prevent it.

Colonel O'Neill immediately visits Teal'c in his cell to explain the situation to him. He explains that some humans fear him and question his motives for betraying Apophis. The Jaffa understands and offers to prove his loyalty to Earth and its people through his actions. O'Neill says that he hopes Teal'c gets the chance to do just that, but is worried that Kennedy and the Pentagon may have other ideas.

In the infirmary, Dr. Nimzicki examines Kawalsky and initially finds nothing wrong with him. In fact, he believes that the headache may simply be a bad physiological reaction to gate travel. He quickly reassesses his diagnosis when he notices a strange lump at the back of Kawalsky's neck. Suddenly, the lump slithers into his head and Kawalsky screams in agony as Nimzicki looks on in horror. Then Kawalsky's eyes glow and he grabs the doctor by the throat, snapping his neck and killing him.

Later, in the briefing room, Daniel Jackson and Captain Carter are briefing other SGC personnel on the DHD. While Jackson is speaking, he looks out the window and sees Major Kawalsky walking up the ramp toward the Stargate. Carter quickly alerts General Hammond and O'Neill. Both arrive in short order and confront Kawalsky about his actions. The Major claims he does not remember coming into the embarkment room. His last memory is of being in the infirmary. O'Neill personally takes him back there to be checked out, this time by Dr. Warner, who plans to perform an MRI to determine the cause of Kawalsky's blackout.

Meanwhile, Colonel Kennedy sits in Hammond's office, interrogating Teal'c. O'Neill barges into the meeting and attempts to act as Teal'c's advocate, something Kennedy assures him is unnecessary. Kennedy asks the Jaffa many questions about the Goa'uld, their technology, and their past. From his answers, they surmise that Earth is the so-called "First World," the home of the Tauri people, whom Teal'c names as the origin of all the Goa'uld hosts, Jaffa, and slave races.

Trying to get some sleep, Jackson stumbles across the bloody arm of Dr. Nimzicki. Simultaneously, Dr. Warner examines Kawalsky's MRI and realizes that the Major is possessed by a Goa'uld. Kawalsky flees the infirmary and heads for the control room, where Carter sees him trying to dial the Stargate. When she attempts to stop him, he takes her captive, but when confronted by O'Neill and security guards, Kawalsky again claims to have no recollection of his actions.

Hammond confines Kawalsky to the infirmary, where Dr. Warner works on a way to remove the Goa'uld larva from his body. Kawalsky has no idea how the alien parasite entered his body, but, upon questioning, recalls a sharp pain in his neck shortly before leaving Chulak on his last mission. He appears genuinely distressed by the thought of having done any harm while under the Goa'uld's influence and O'Neill assures him that it is not his fault.

Despite the protests of Colonel Kennedy, an operation begins to remove the Goa'uld from Kawalsky. Kennedy believes that, since the chance of success is so low, it would be better to keep the Goa'uld alive so that it can be interrogated later. Teal'c confirms that Goa'uld possess genetic racial memory, which Kennedy argues would justify keeping Kawalsky alive as a host. Hammond overrules Kennedy, who leaves the meeting threatening to take up the matter with his superiors.

The operation apparently goes well, with Kawalsky making a full recovery. Because Teal'c is now the only host of a living Goa'uld, Kennedy plans to take him back to Langley, Virginia for study. Nevertheless, Kawalsky asks to see him before he goes, to thank the man whose knowledge of the Goa'uld may have saved his life. When the two men are alone in the infirmary, Kawalsky's eyes glow and he reveals that the Goa'uld had already taken full control of the Major by the time of the operation. He commands Teal'c to serve him. When Teal'c resists, Kawalsky knocks the Jaffa unconscious and heads for the Stargate control room. He dials Chulak and sets the Stargate for self-destruction. However, by the time he reaches the ramp, Teal'c has regained consciousness and blocks his path.

The two struggle on the ramp before the active Stargate. When Teal'c partially pushes the Major's head passed the event horizon of the gate, O'Neill orders it shut down. This severs the top of Kawalsky's head and kills the Goa'uld possessing him, which falls smoking to the ground. O'Neill mourns the loss of his friend, but Jackson finds some hope in the fact that at least some of Kawalsky's memories (such as the Stargate auto-destruct codes) survived possession. Perhaps there is hope for Sha're and Skaara as well.

General Hammond later speaks directly with the president, who countermands Kennedy's orders, allowing Teal'c to remain with the SGC as the fourth member of SG-1. Together, the new team head off into the Stargate on their next mission, to P3A-577.

Prakiti is the local name for planet P3-575, the original destination of SG-2 under Major Kawalsky. However, the unfortunate events surrounding Kawalsky's return from Chulak delayed the team's exploration of this world. Prakiti is an arid planet whose predominant terrain is rocky and barren. The native population, who number slightly more than 100,000 eke out a primitive existence whose technological level mimics Earth's High Middle Ages.

The survival of Prakiti's population is due to an extensive – and sophisticated – irrigation system that brings water from underground reservoirs and transports them over long distances. They were constructed under the direction of Indra when he first brought humans to this world. The system is a remarkable achievement, especially considering the comparatively low level of local technology. Because Indra took so little personal interest in the planet's growth and development, it was left to his Jaffa and human servants to bring water to the parched communities that dotted the habitable regions of Prakiti. The end result has lasted for several hundred years with only a minimum of upkeep.

Originally, the planet was unified under the rule of the Goa'uld Indra. The central city, Saravad, held the majority of the population, as well as being the locale of the Palace of the Thunder God, where Indra stayed on those occasions when he visited the planet. This impressive structure held a large audience chamber, dozens of apartments (for Jaffa and advisors), research labs, and other rooms. Those who wished to petition Indra would make their way here, where a senior Jaffa or human advisor would meet them. In principle at least, the petition was then relayed to Indra himself, but more often than not, his local servants would make the decision.

The society of Prakiti is a comparatively simple one. Despite its Hindu origins, there was never a caste system on the planet. Instead, honor and social importance were determined by proximity to Indra and his servants. Those who directly served the Goa'uld were considered of a higher standing than those who did not (or whose service was mediated in some way). The people lived simple lives as farmers, craftsman, and herders of animals (such as the kadaiva), in addition to providing hosts for the larval Goa'uld that Indra brought to the planet from time to time. Becoming a host was considered a singular honor and carried with it much prestige.

The people of Prakiti led comparatively good lives, largely left to their own devices thanks to Indra's preoccupation elsewhere. They worshiped the Goa'uld as a god, of course, but their worship was lively and colorful. Numerous festivals were held in Indra's honor, although most had very little religious content, being primarily raucous gatherings to mark the turning of the seasons and other events. If anything, Indra was himself a fairly minor component of Prakiti culture. The people had an almost "agnostic" approach to their lord; they never outright denied his existence or his divinity, but their affirmation of both was lackluster and reserved – certainly not the religion of oppressed slaves.

PRAKITI

World: Prakiti.

Thermosphere: Warm (CR 0; median orbit; 2d20+25° F).

Atmosphere: Normal (CR 0; 1.1 atmospheres).

Hydrosphere: Arid (CR 2; daily weather 1-89: none, 90: flood 1d10 MPH, 91-93: rain 1 in., 94-95: dust storm, 96-100: wind 1d10 MPH).

Geosphere: Very Stable tectonic activity.

Seasons: Normal (1-25: spring, unchanged; 26-50: summer, unchanged; 51-75: autumn, unchanged; 76-100: winter unchanged).

Anthrosphere: 100,000 natives; Early Medieval (4 picks, 2 RP); Theocracy; Suspicious (-1 with disposition checks); Aggressive (10 soldiers, squad size 2d4 soldiers); Moderate civil rights.

Origin: Hindu.

Stargate Location (wasteland terrain): Rocky terrain in semi-arid desert, scrublands dotted with small lakes.

All that changed with the invasion of Vritra, a rival System Lord who routed Indra's forces on the planet. He then immediately set about changing Prakiti's society to serve his own needs. He enlisted a significant portion of the population to serve as miners, boring deep into the planet's crust in quest to find a mysterious cache of "treasure," and enforced his will through the use of his Jaffa, the asuras.

Within a few months of Vritra's takeover, however, an insurrection began, led by the Maruts, humans who'd taken up the mantle of Indra's no longer present Jaffa. They began a lengthy war, one which continues to this day. Unfortunately, despite their valiant efforts, their skills are no match for the superior firepower and numbers of the asuras. Nevertheless, they carry on the fight in the belief that Indra will one day return from the stars and free his people. How likely this outcome is remains unknown. Indra's reputation has gone up considerably since he disappeared from the planet. Most do not remember that he is a Goa'uld like any other, however light his rule might have appeared. Should he return, it is unlikely that he would come to save "his people" so much as to displace Vritra.

Life on Prakiti is quite unpleasant at present. The mines that Vritra first established grow larger and deeper with each year. More and more humans are pressed into service, leaving fewer behind to tend to the people's basic needs. The asuras act as enforcers and wander local communities looking for any signs of rebellion. Anyone who aids the Maruts is killed on the spot, while those suspected of sympathizing with these would-be Jaffa are often assassinated in the night. The situation on Prakiti is quite grim. It is perhaps a blessing that SG-2 did not visit this world as scheduled, for it poses many dangers that are not easily resolved.

INDRA

Indra is the System Lord who formerly ruled Prakiti. Although far from a pleasant master, Indra was at least a distant ruler who rarely became involved in the day-to-day governance of Prakiti. Instead, he left that to his most trusted servants, the Maruts, These Jaffa were drawn from the native population rather than being imported from another world like Chulak. Consequently, they had familial connections within the local communities, which made them somewhat more effective as governors than many Jaffa might have been. Moreover, being selected as a Marut was deemed a great honor on Prakiti and families whose sons and daughters were so favored received great respect.

Indra's interests were primarily focused off-world. His lack of involvement in Prakiti had more to do with distraction than any kind of theory of governance. He warred continually against his neighbors and coveted the wealth and dominions of more powerful System Lords. Unfortunately, he could be timid and even cowardly when faced with an intractable foe. His brilliant stratagems often came to naught when he showed a lack of follow-through if opposition stiffened. Not surprisingly, his wars were primarily against weaker System Lords.

Eventually, other Goa'ulds grew tired of Indra's incessant attacks and formed an alliance against him. Slowly but surely, they beat him back, world by world, until his own domains were reduced to only a handful of planets. Though never as mighty as others of his station, the losses he suffered were still considerable, enough to make him value the worlds he did possess all the more highly. One such world was Prakiti. When Vritra's forces landed on the planet, Indra was torn as to the best strategy. Initially, he ordered his Jaffa to fight fiercely against the invaders. He even enlisted the aid of many of his human slaves, offering them a chance to better their position by showing their loyalty to him. Surprisingly, far more humans rallied to Indra's cause than he had expected. Though the populace did not love Indra, they feared Vritra even more.

In the end, though, Indra's old instincts proved to be the strongest. Against the desires of his advisors, Indra decided to withdraw from Prakiti and seek safety on another world, one that had fewer things to attract the envy of his fellow System Lords. He removed his Jaffa along with him - or at least he intended to do so. A handful of Maruts asked to stay behind and fight against Vritra in their lord's name. Indra consented to this and promised that he would one day return in glory to defeat his enemy and reward the successes of his most loyal servants. Needless to say, Indra has not yet reappeared on Prakiti.

At present, Indra's whereabouts are unknown. He is not believed to have been defeated by any other System Lord, and certainly, no System Lord claims his few remaining worlds. His Jaffa say that they receive communications from him, who is currently undertaking some project that will allow him to defeat his enemies once and for all. What this project is they cannot say for only Indra's most trusted advisors (most of whom are also unseen) have any knowledge of it. Naturally, all sorts of rumors can be heard on Prakiti.

VRITRA

Vritra is a vicious and sadistic System Lord who revels more in destruction than in stewardship. Consequently, he often raids worlds as if for sport, wreaking great damage and then moving on. He has little interest in taking permanent control of a world. More often than not, the simple idea of bringing down another System Lord and terrorizing its native population is sufficient to give him pleasure. Consequently, Vritra has become an outcast among the Goa'uld. Few do more than tolerate his behavior and then only when his wrath is directed toward their enemies rather than themselves. From time to time, coalitions of System Lords have formed to destroy Vritra once and for all, but none have succeeded. The fact that he and his forces are constantly on the move, usually by means of starships, makes it difficult to wipe them out permanently. Likewise, Vritra is a paranoid sort who does not believe in overstaying his welcome on any one world... that is, until he found Prakiti.

Vritra's methods may appear to stem from sadism and a desire to wreak random chaos, but there is in fact a method to his madness. Long ago he studied ancient Goa'uld texts stipulating that the Stargate network had been constructed by some other race – far older than the serpents – referred to as the Ancients. Vritra reasoned that if the Ancients possessed the technology to build the Stargates, they undoubtedly had knowledge and technology far beyond that of other beings. Likewise, if they scattered their Stargates throughout the galaxy (and beyond), perhaps they also scattered other pieces of technology as well – such as weapons and defenses. If so, Vritra believed it was his duty to find them and use them to impose his will on all other races, including his fellow System Lords.

Vritra realized that finding such Ancient technology – should it in fact exist – would require careful planning. Simply scouring the galaxy for worlds where the Ancients might have been would prove fruitless. Instead, he devoted himself and his considerable scientific resources to finding clues that might aid him in his quest. He followed up every lead he could, from old texts to hieroglyphic carvings to legends and myths. It took many years and many expeditions to far-flung worlds before Vritra found what he sought: a set of coordinates that led him to Prakiti: a planet which his research suggested had once been a stronghold of the Ancients.

Vritra invaded with the intent of using the human population and the rest of his resources to find the Ancient cache and use it for himself. After nearly a decade on Prakiti, he has yet to find it, but not for lack of trying. As the failures mount, Vritra is becoming more and more obsessed with his quixotic quest. He has ordered more and deeper shafts to be dug into the planet's surface, convinced that the conclusion of his ambitions can be found somewhere far underground. Likewise, the System Lord grows more and more paranoid and instructs his asuras to crack down on any sign of insurrection. Although Vritra has total control of Prakiti now, none can say how long it will last. His actions encourage active insurrection, and his decisions grow less and less rational by the day. Should things degenerate on Prakiti, who can say what Vritra will do to maintain control?

THE TRUTH

Though Vritra does not know it, there is no Ancient cache on Prakiti; there never was. After centuries of seeking such a cache, the System Lord has slowly lost his mind. He interpreted the "clues" he found in an overly generous way. They do not point to anything other than the planet's Stargate, which is of course an actual artifact of the Ancients. Beyond that, though, there is nothing else left of the days when the Ancients visited Prakiti. Some of Vritra's Jaffa and scientists suspect this to be the case, but they dare not contradict their lord lest they be killed for such "insubordination" and "lack of faith." The same fate awaits anyone else who dares to speak the truth in Vritra's presence.

1-03: EMANCIPATION

World Visited: P3X-593 (Simarka).
Thermosphere: Warm (CR 0; standard orbit; 2d20+25° F).
Atmosphere: Normal (CR 0; 1 atmosphere; Auto: None; Exp. Inc: None; SV None; Dmg None; Recup None).
Hydrosphere: Semi-arid (CR 1; daily weather 1-88: none, 89: flood, 90-92: rain/snow, 93: thunderstorm or snowstorm, 94: dust storm, 95: hurricane, 96-97: wind 1d10 MPH, 98: wind 1d10+10 MPH, 99: wind 1d10+20 MPH, 100: wind 1d10+30 MPH).
Geosphere: Stable tectonic activity (daily earthquakes 1-99: none, 100: minor; 0 volcanoes within 1d10 miles of Stargate).
Seasons: Normal (1-25: spring, unchanged; 26-50: summer +2d20° F; 51-75: autumn, unchanged; 76-100: winter -2d20° F).
Anthrosphere: 5,000 natives; Iron Age (3 picks, 1 RP); Tribal; Neutral (+0 with disposition checks); Moderate (100 soldiers, squad size 1d4 soldiers); Poor civil rights.
Origin: Mongolian.
Stargate Location (semi-arid region): Rolling terrain in grasslands, shattered ruins of stone temple.

EPISODE SUMMARY

The Stargate opens on P3X-593 depositing the members of SG-1, step on the world of Simarka. Finding little more than ruins of a stone temple near the gate, the team heads away from the gate, looking for any signs of inhabitants or civilization. Before long the sounds of dogs barking echoes over the grassy hills. The sounds grow steadily louder, and within moments, the team spots a young man running through the tall grass towards them, dogs close on his heals.

Gunshots from O'Neill's sidearm frighten the dogs off as the young man comes face to face with SG-1. He introduces himself as Abu. Before he can explain further, however, he and SG-1 are joined by warriors on horseback who have come in search of Abu. Things take a turn for the disastrous when Carter speaks to Abu and the warriors. They respond by raising weapons against her. She has unknowingly violated the ancient tribal laws forbidding women to speak in such a manner. Moments later, Moughal, the chief of the Shavadai, arrives and orders Carter's death, but when he learns that Carter helped save Abu, he changes his mind and orders the warriors to lower their weapons. Because she has saved a life, hers cannot be taken.

Moughal and his warriors lead SG-1 to the Shavadai village; once inside Moughal's tent, the team discovers that though Moughal enforces the ancient laws oppressing women, he doesn't believe in them, and in fact wishes to one day rid their tribe of such outdated practices.

Moughal's wife and daughter escort Carter from the tent and dress her as a Shavadai woman, while O'Neill, Daniel, and Teal'c learn about the powerful medicines used by the villagers, including a strong local anesthetic. Upon her return to the tent, Carter learns that while the men will attend a party celebrating Abu's return to the village, she has to remain in their tent for the evening. As Carter sleeps, Abu abducts her, and takes her from the village in the forest. He explains that women are considered property on Simarka, and that he intends to trade Carter to a rival chieftain. When SG-1 awakens, they find Carter missing; together with Moughal, they set out in search of her and Abu.

Abu and Carter arrive at a Toughai village, and enter the tent of the chieftain Turghan, where Abu offers Carter in exchange for Nya, Turghan's daughter, with whom he is in love. Turghan refuses – Nya is betrothed to Chimakka, chieftain of the People of the Desert – leaving Abu instead with 300 weights of gold.

Meanwhile, SG-1 and Moughal track Abu and Carter through the forest; the Shavadai chieftain quickly realizes where Abu has gone. To help them better understand the situation, he explains the ancient laws. Women were once the equals of men, but when the people were brought to Simarka (presumably by the Goa'uld), the ancient laws were written to protect the women from the "demons."

From the edges of the nearby forest, Abu keeps a watch on Turghan's camp until he spots Nya. He quietly approaches and urges Nya to run away with him. Meanwhile Carter joins the other Toughai women in daily chores. When no one is watching her, she attempts to escape on horseback, but is quickly captured by Turghan's warriors inside the forest. Turghan is furious with Carter, explaining that Nya's mother and the other women responsible for her are to be punished for allowing her to escape.

Before this punishment can be meted out, SG-1 arrives. Carter sets a part of the camp on fire to create a distraction, which allows Nya to run off to meet Abu. Moughal and SG-1 meet with Turghan and attempt to trade for Carter, but Turghan is not interested in trading, at least not for money. Only when O'Neill offers his sidearm does Turghan agree to the trade.

Camping in the forest on their way back to the Shavadai village, SG-1 and Moughal encounter Abu, who informs them that Nya was caught by Turghan's guards, and is to be stoned to death for attempting to escape. Abu pleads with SG-1 to help; when O'Neill refuses, Carter insists that they at least try, since Nya's capture is partially her fault. Moughal warns that doing so could cause a war between the two tribes, but Carter and Abu insist they do something. Realizing that Turghan's strict adherence to the law might be used against him, Moughal searches his memory for any ancient tenets that could prevent Nya's stoning.

Arriving at the Toughai camp moments before the execution, Moughal invokes his right as a chieftain to challenge Turghan's ruling. Turghan refuses to fight Moughal, who is crippled, but Carter steps up to challenge Turghan in Moughal's place. As Carter prepares to battle Turghan, she and SG-1 learn that it is a battle to the death. Unable to stop the challenge, she faces off against Turghan and defeats him, earning both a reprieve for Nya and permission for the girl to marry Abu.

Moughal plans a grand celebration for the wedding to be held in a few days time. Just as SG-1 leaves the Shavadai village to return to the Stargate, Moughal renounces the ancients laws, announcing that "All Shavadai be Free!"

BACKGROUND
THE TRIBES OF SIMARKA

The world of Simarka is home to many disparate tribes of natives descended from ancient Mongols of Earth, brought to this world by the Goa'uld centuries ago. Initially the tribesmen remained near the Stargate, but over time they have spread across an area of more than 10,000 square miles, stretching from the corner of a vast desert nearly 175 miles to the north and west.

As the people of Simarka explored their world, they separated themselves into four broad groups of tribes: the Shavadai, the People of the Steppe; the Toughai, the People of the Forest; the Linghai, the People of the River; and the Dalghai, the People of the Desert. Each grouping comprises anywhere from as few as ten to as many as thirty loosely-allied tribes, which share resources and help to defend one another from enemy tribes.

Individual Simarkan tribes typically range from thirty to sixty people, with a slightly larger percentage of men than women. Tribes subsist primarily on hunting local animals, birds, and fish (where possible), and gathering edible plant life. Simarkan tribes live in tents and, in some tribal groups, thatched huts. Being nomadic by nature, most Simarkan tribes move around as needed, usually ranging within an area of up to roughly twenty miles in diameter.

Contact between tribal groupings is not frequent, and the few instances of interaction often entail armed conflict over either territory or goods. All able-bodied men over the age of fifteen serve as warriors for their tribe when needed, and many continue to serve until the time of their deaths.

Trade between tribal groups, particularly between the Shavadai and the Linghai has become more common in recent years. In addition to barter, exchanges based on silver and gold currency also grows more popular, with many goods priced in terms of "weights of silver" (ws) and "weights of gold" (wg). 20ws generally equals 1wg, though bartering is often quite heavy. Each of the groupings of tribes has commodities unique to them, a fact that encourages trade among the differing tribes.

Though the tribal groupings of Simarka consider themselves separate peoples, they all share a common bond in their adherence to their laws. The Ancient Laws that rule the tribes were written long ago, when the demons (*sholmoses* in the Mongol tongue) that brought the people to this world still appeared seeking slaves. Many of these laws confine and restrict the role of women in Simarkan society, and were first written to protect the women of the tribes from the "demons." Primary among these is the Law prohibiting women from showing their face or speaking in public, a crime punishable by death. Some laws also address the ways in which the tribes are ruled and governed. One example of this is the rite of Challenge, whereby a tribal chieftain can challenge a ruling made by another chieftain by defeating him in a duel to the death.

THE SHAVADAI — THE PEOPLE OF THE STEPPE

The Shavadai, or People of the Steppe, number twelve tribes, and live in the northwestern corner of the settled region of Simarka. Shavadai territory is primarily grasslands, with areas of light forest between them and the lands controlled by the Toughai. The Shavadai are a peaceful people at heart, but the constant threat of attack from enemy tribes keeps them ready to defend themselves at all times.

Moughal, an aging and crippled man of great wisdom and courage leads the Shavadai. Tired of the old ways and the Ancient Laws, Moughal looks forward to the day when trade replaces war among the people of Simarka forever. Unlike chieftains of other tribal groups, Moughal has only one wife, whom he treats with honor and respect. As a means of making progress in his goals, he recently reached a trade agreement between the Shavadai and the Linghai, a practice that grows with each passing year.

The Shavadai breed the fastest horses and camels in all of Simarka; each specimen can bring as much as 100wg in trade. The Shavadai also boast some of the finest foods in the land, including smoked and cured antelope and gazelle meats, and dried fruits and berries. Also, the Shavadai brew several powerful medicines sought after by other tribal groups, including pain-relieving and healing salves, as well as cures for diseases such as yellow fever. These medicines often fetch prices as high as 50wg per 10 doses.

After SG-1's departure from Simarka, the Shavadai abandoned the old laws restricting women's rights, and now all Shavadai are free people – theoretically at least. This change has drawn harsh words from the other tribal chieftains, who don't wish their tribes to follow suit, but it is likely only a matter of time before other tribes begin to soften their adherence to the ancient laws.

Concerning relations with the other tribal groups, the Shavadai are on friendliest terms with the Linghai, with whom they've traded for the past few years. The sheer distance between the lands of the Shavadai and the Dalghai keeps contact between them infrequent. Relations with the Toughai are strained at best, and often teeter on the brink of war. The recent marriage between Abu, son of Moughal, and Nya, daughter of Toughai Chieftain Turghan has eased some tension between the two groups, but the war-like ways of the Toughai are not easily subdued.

THE TOUGHAI — THE PEOPLE OF THE FOREST

The Toughai, or People of the Forest, live in the southwest corner of the settled region of Simarka. The Toughai live on the forested foothills of nearby mountains, with lighter forests to the north and west, and heavier forests to the south and east. The Toughai are the most war-like of all the tribal groups, taking what they desire from others.

The Toughai leader is Turghan, a fierce but honorable warrior who commands the loyalty of twenty-two tribes (his own being the largest and most powerful). Unlike his Shavadai counterpart Moughal, Turghan has no desire for change in the old ways; they continue to serve him well. Though war is his preferred method of acquiring goods, Turghan also understands the usefulness of trade with his neighbors, especially where such trade can spare his warriors for more worthwhile battles.

The Toughai boast the best metal craftsmen in the settled areas of Simarka, and Turghan's own tribe has the best craftsmen of all the Toughai tribes. Toughai craftsmen forge the strongest tools and deadliest weapons, with workmanship that commands top value in trade. The secret of the Toughai's metal craftsmen is the metal ores they use in their wares, mined from the nearby mountains. No other tribal lands offer such rich mineral deposits, and Turghan viciously defends his claim on the mountain mines. In addition to craft metals, the mountains controlled by the Toughai are also a source of silver ore used for currency, and gold, mined from the rivers that flow through the mountains.

Until recently the Toughai were most closely allied with the Dalghai, the People of the Desert. Turghan had arranged for his daughter Nya to wed the desert warlord Chimakka, chieftain of the Dalghai. After his defeat at the hands of Samantha Carter, Turghan allowed Nya to wed Abu of the Shavadai instead of Chimakka, and has since sent peace offerings to appease the desert chieftain. The Toughai have little contact with the Linghai, though an enmity exists between the tribal groups that borders on outright hostility at times. Relations between the Toughai and the Shavadai are uneasy, even given the recent marriage between Nya and Abu. Turghan's recent defeat at the hands of Captain Carter caused him to lose face among some of his lieutenants, for which he holds Moughal and the Shavadai tribe responsible. For now Turghan maintains an uneasy peace with the Shavadai, but even the slightest provocation could push him to war.

THE LINGHAI — THE PEOPLE OF THE RIVER

The People of the River, the Linghai, live to slightly south and east of the lands of the Shavadai, on the other side of the Stargate from the People of the Steppe. They make their homes along the shores of the Simark River and in the nearby forests to the east. The lands of the People of the River are the closest to the Stargate and the now ruined Temple of the Sholmoses. Like the Shavadai, the Linghai are a peaceful people by nature but are quick to defend themselves when attacked or provoked.

Abu'an, an aging warrior leads the People of the River. His caution and wisdom have earned the loyalty of fifteen tribes. Abu'an shares many of Moughal's beliefs about the future of their people, and like his Shavadai counterpart, seeks to replace war with trade among the tribal groups of Simarka. More scholar than warrior, Abu'an recently learned how the tribes united against the demons and destroyed the Temple of the Sholmoses. The legend came from ancient scrolls passed down to the leaders of the Linghai, the discovery of which led explorers of the People of the River to study the Stargate and the ruins of the temple. This in turn allowed the gate to be activated once again (*see Raiden and the Temple of the Sholmoses, page 17*). The Linghai tried to activate the gate using the DHD, but all their attempts met with failure. The explorers took several pieces of the temple ruins back to their villages for further study, but have since made no further progress in deciphering the ancient writings.

The Linghai are the best hunters and fishermen of all the tribes of Simarka, and use the fruits of their efforts as trade goods. Dried and cured fish from the Simark River fetches a good price in trade, due to its excellent taste and resistance to spoiling. The Linghai have standing trade arrangements with all three of the other tribal groups for their fish, and make monthly merchant excursions to the lands of the other tribes. The Linghai also mine gold from the river, and use the precious metal for both monetary and decorative purposes.

They enjoy stable, if not always good, relations with all the other tribal groups. Their strongest ties are with the Shavadai, as the two tribes have traded goods for several years. The borderline hostility between the Linghai and the Toughai make relations tense at best, but since contact between the two is infrequent, the danger remains minor for now. Relations between the Linghai and the Dalghai are for the most part unremarkable, though slightly strained by the tension that exists between the People of the River and the Toughai. Though less frequent in recent years, raids by Dalghai warriors on Linghai villagers were once a common occurrence.

THE DALGHAI — THE PEOPLE OF THE DESERT

The Dalghai, or People of the Desert, live in the south east corner of the settled region of Simarka. Numbering sixteen tribes strong, they are second in size and strength only to the Toughai. Dalghai lands stretch along the northernmost edge of a vast desert, an area that gives way to grasslands and forests to the north and west. Aggressive and seemingly eager for war, the Dalghai stand ready to strike at any who would challenge them.

The Dalghai are led by Chimakka, a warlord of great cunning and skill. Descendent of a long line of desert warlords, he strives to strike a balance between maintaining the traditions of his people while at the same time accepting the changes overtaking Simarkan society. And while he prefers tradition over change, Chimakka understands that continued war among the people of Simarka would likely lead to extinction for him and his tribe. Likewise, he has come to realize that the reasons for the old laws, especially as they pertain to women, are gone and largely forgotten, and that perhaps it is time to reconsider the old ways. Unfortunately, war and tradition are all he has known, and changing the laws of his people and basing relations with other tribes on trade make him very uneasy.

The Dalghai have few trade goods as valuable as those of the other tribal groups. Among their most valued commodity are powerful anti-venoms, used to counter the effects of scorpion stings and snakebites. These salves are the basis for Dalghai trade, which they supplement with dried fruits and nuts, and armor created from lizard skin.

Of the other tribal groups, the Dalghai's relations with the Toughai are the strongest, followed by the Shavadai and the Linghai. Despite Turghan's breaking a marriage arrangement between his daughter Nya and himself, Chimakka chose to remain allies of the Toughai and accepted Turghan's peace offerings, but demanded additional trade concessions in the form of weapons and tools.

RAIDEN AND THE TEMPLE OF THE SHOLMOSES

The Simarkan Stargate once stood within a large stone temple, built by the Goa'uld who transplanted the people of Simarka from Earth. Inscribed on its walls are legends of the ancient days, when the "demons" known as Sholmoses came through the Stargate and took the people as slaves. It was during these dark days that many of the ancient laws were first written, including those restricting women's freedom in Simarkan society and were originally intended to protect women from the Goa'uld.

The temple stood for centuries, collapsing only in the last two hundred years. Legends told by the People of the River (the Linghai) tell that the temple's collapse was the result of an uprising against the Goa'uld in which all the tribes of Simarka bonded together to combat their common enemy. Combining their numbers, the tribes broke through the temple walls, destroying the entire structure, and disabling the Stargate in the process. Portions of the crumbled walls and ceiling came to rest within the Stargate, preventing a wormhole from establishing, and remained there for many years, until Linghai explorers moved the stones and rubble from the gate while studying it and the DHD.

Some of the ruins near the Stargate still bear worn and weathered writing in an obscure Goa'uld dialect. While most refer to the Sholmoses, some of the writings speak of the Thunder God Raiden, how he defended the land of Nihon from Mongol raiders, and how as punishment for their attack, he took the Mongols from their lands and brought them to Simarka to serve him for eternity.

In addition to these legends, the temple writings also contain a number of Stargate addresses to worlds within Raiden's domain. Though most of these are only partial addresses (missing the 5th and sometimes 6th symbols), one address remains visible. It dials in to the planet Kyoto, home of the warlord Ashikaga, although it only functions when Raiden's flagship is in orbit about Kyoto *(see Raiden, below, for more information)*.

Also buried among the temple ruins are tablets describing the tribal alliance and how the combined tribes destroyed the temple and freed themselves form the sholmoses. Should these tables be uncovered and their writings deciphered, it could contribute to eventually unity and peace among the currently warring tribes.

RAIDEN, THE THUNDER GOD

Raiden takes his name from the Japanese God of Thunder and Lightning who, according to Mongol myths, prevented the Mongols from invading Japan by sending a shower of lighting arrows upon their invading fleet. Raiden enslaved the people of Simarka for centuries, using them as slaves and hosts as he expanded his empire, but has not been seen on Simarka for the past century.

Raiden styles himself in the manner of a Japanese Emperor, and while not as powerful as any of the System Lords, retains a moderate power base in a remote area of Goa'uld space. He structures his empire in a manner similar to the shogunate of feudal Japan, with himself as the Supreme Overlord. Beneath him, his Shogun and daimyo (warlords) control individual planets and territories within his domain.

Raiden's empire currently comprises twelve worlds, and is patrolled and defended by a fleet of 7 ha'tak warships and nearly two dozen al-kesh bombers. Each world is ruled by one of Raiden's shogun, who in turn rules over several daimyo that each control a region of the planet. Raiden's domain borders space controlled by Yu, the Jade Emperor, who battles Raiden continually over the planets residing between their domains. These battles are evenly matched, and each Goa'uld claims victory in one battle only to lose another shortly after. The border between them shifts frequently during these skirmishes.

The worlds of Raiden's domain are populated by people of Asian descent – primarily Japanese, but a few ethnic Chinese live on a number of worlds, particularly those taken in battle from Yu. The culture and society of these worlds is akin to Japan of the early 14th century, with corresponding levels of technological and economic development. Only four of these worlds – Akita, Mito, Naha, and Tosa – have Stargates on them. All other planets under Raiden's control can be accessed only by ship.

The best-defended world within Raiden's domain is Kyoto, ruled by the most powerful of Raiden's warlords, Ashikaga. Kyoto is home to most of Raiden's Jaffa, and its capital city serves as a training ground for all warriors who serve the Thunder God. In addition to its centers of learning, Kyoto also houses several Goa'uld laboratories where warriors and scientists seek to advance the technology that empowers their Supreme Overlord. Whereas most Goa'uld are content to use ancient and plundered technology, Raiden seeks to boost his technological advantage however possible. Among the advances born from Raiden's laboratories are the Thunder Staves and Lightning Staves used by his personal guard and the enhanced capabilities of Raiden's kara kesh (see Chapter Three).

Raiden's home and base of operations is the *Katana*, the flagship of his ha'tak fleet, which constantly roams from world to world within his domain. Use of a mobile base of operations has made him a difficult target, an advantage that more than compensates for his relatively minor seat of power. The *Katana* also carries the Stargate that was once on Kyoto onboard; it can be used for outgoing travel whenever the ship is in orbit of a planet with a Stargate of its own, but can only be reached from other Stargates when the *Katana* orbits Kyoto.

Raiden has two distinct groups of Jaffa who serve him directly, the Thunder Guards and Lightning Guards. Trained in a remote monastery in the mountains near Kyoto's capital city, these units are unquestionably loyal to Raiden, and would sooner die that betray their master. They use specialized versions of staff weapons that can mimic the abilities for which their god is known. Thunder Staves can fire a thunderous sonic-based attack (in addition to the staff's normal blast) that deafen victims for up to one minute. Lightning Staves can fire an electrical blast similar to a lightning bolt that stuns victims for up to one minute. In keeping with the deity he personifies, Raiden has modified his kara kesh such that it can also mimic thunder and lightning when used to attack. More details about these weapons can be found in Chapter Three.

Raiden's shoguns and daimyo are also served by standard Jaffa.

KYOTO

Kyoto is the best-defended world within Raiden's domain, and ruled by Ashikaga, the most powerful of Raiden's warlords. The people of Kyoto are Near-Humans (see page 151 in the Stargate SG-1 core rulebook), whose society mirrors that of feudal Japan during the era of the shogunate. Kyoto does not have a Stargate, and is accessible only via ship.

World: Kyoto.

Thermosphere: Warm (CR 0; standard orbit; 2d20+25° F).

Atmosphere: Normal (CR 0; 1 atmosphere; Auto: None; Exp. Inc: None; SV None; Dmg None; Recup None).

Hydrosphere: Sub-humid (CR 1; daily weather 1-85: none, 86-87: flood, 88-93: rain/snow, 94-95: thunderstorm or snowstorm, 96 hurricane or blizzard, 97-98: wind 1d10 MPH, 99: wind 1d10+10 MPH, 100: wind 1d10+20 MPH).

Geosphere: Stable tectonic activity (daily earthquakes 1-99: none, 100: minor; 0 volcanoes within 1d10 miles of Kyoto city).

Seasons: Normal (1-25: spring, unchanged; 26-50: summer +2d20° F; 51-75: autumn, unchanged; 76-100: winter -2d20° F).

Anthrosphere: 5,000,000 natives; Early Medieval (4 picks, 4 RP); Feudalism; Suspicious (-1 with disposition checks); Extremely Sensitive (1,000 soldiers, squad size 1d4 soldiers); Poor civil rights.

Origin: Japanese.

Stargate Location: N/A.

1-04: THE BROCA DIVIDE

World Visited: P3X-797 (Land of Light/Land of the Dark).

Thermosphere: Warm (CR 0; close orbit; 2d20+25° F).

Atmosphere: Normal (CR 0; 0.8 atmospheres; Auto None; Exp. Inc: None; SV None; Dmg None; Recup None).

Hydrosphere: Sub-humid (CR 0; daily weather 1-85: none, 86-87: flood, 88-93: rain/snow, 94-95: thunderstorm or snowstorm, 96: hurricane or blizzard, 97-98: light wind, 99: moderate wind, 100: strong wind).

Geosphere: Stable tectonic activity (daily earthquakes 1-99: none, 100: minor; 0 volcanoes within 10 miles of Stargate).

Seasons: Mild (1-17: spring unchanged; 43-50: summer +2d6° F; 51-92: autumn unchanged; 93-100: winter -2d6° F).

Anthrosphere: 250,000 natives; Bronze Age (3 picks, 1 RP); Oligarchy; Extremely Open (+3 with Disposition checks); Moderate (150 soldiers, squad size 1d4 soldiers); Moderate civil rights.

Origin: Minoan.

Stargate Location (equatorial region): Rocky terrain in forest, permanent dark side near the terminator.

Episode Summary

At the briefing room table, SG-1 stands beside a solid unit of elite Marines: SG-3, under Col. Makepeace. One marine, Lt. Johnson, eyes Teal'c suspiciously while Gen. Hammond outlines the joint mission to P3X-797, the first possible match for the planet to which the Goa'uld dialed from Chulak. *(See Children of the Gods, p. 6.)* There's just one hitch: The location of the Stargate appears to be very dark, and the MALP's lights were evidently damaged in transit.

Arriving on P3X-797, the SG teams have just enough time to take a look at the battered MALP before a band of primitive humanoids attack, engaging both teams in a brief hand-to-hand scuffle until the noise of firearms frightens them off. SG-1 and SG-3 then track the primitives to their camp. Observing them from a concealed vantage, Jackson notes superficial traits in common with early human species, while Carter spots a young female – who looks more human than the rest of the group – cowering and shrieking as one of the males grabs her. Despite O'Neill's order to stay put and Jackson's observation that sex among early humans may always have been forcible, Carter insists they should help the girl. Before they can act, someone else does it for them: a rescue party, swathed in gauze veils, scatters the primitives with rocks flung from slings. SG-1 steps forward to make contact and – after correcting the assumption that the visitors are gods – follows them to a sun-drenched city in a style reminiscent of the Minoan culture of ancient Crete. Their hosts' leader, High Councilor Tuplo, explains that they are the Untouched, and that the primitives have been "Touched" by the *heelksha*, gods of the underworld. Because of their savage nature, the Untouched must be driven out of the Land of Light for the protection of the populace. The rescued girl, Tuplo's daughter Melosha, is placed in isolation to wait and see whether the curse will take hold of her.

Fascinating as the culture is, it quickly becomes clear that the Goa'uld have not visited this world for some time, and O'Neill orders the team home over Jackson's protests. During the debriefing, Hammond – as soon as Jackson allows him to get a word in edgewise – informs them that the President has decided SG teams will now be called upon to assess the scientific as well as strategic value of each world they visit. The debriefing is interrupted when Lt. Johnson's distrust of Teal'c erupts into full-blown rage; he assaults the renegade Jaffa and must be forcibly restrained before relenting. Hammond orders him to the infirmary, but soon two more members of SG-3 succumb to the Touched "curse;" their reckless fight sends them crashing through the briefing room window to land in the gate room two stories below. Carter is next, ambushing O'Neill in the locker room with a sexual advance that rapidly devolves from inappropriate to savage; and O'Neill in turn attacks Jackson in a jealous fury when the anthropologist expresses concern for her.

The contagion spreads rapidly through the base, and Hammond orders the mountain sealed off as Dr. Fraiser and her medical staff struggle to handle infected personnel. Fraiser identifies the cause as a "parasitic virus" that feeds on chemical transmitters, disrupting higher brain function and stimulating primitive areas of the mind that normally lie dormant in modern man. Only Teal'c – protected by his larval symbiote – and the bewildered Jackson seem immune, forced to watch their colleagues lose the capacity for reason and speech. As the syndrome progresses, patients develop swollen brow ridges and new hair growth, giving them a primitive appearance to match their brutish behavior. Analysis of Jackson's and Teal'c's blood shows that the organism is present in both, but Fraiser needs more data to explain their resistance. Someone must return to the planet to obtain a blood sample from one of the Untouched, a task that falls to Teal'c and Jackson.

In their absence, conditions at the SGC continue to worsen, as all available isolation quarters are occupied, forcing Fraiser to double them up and keeping the harried remnants of the medical and security staffs running. O'Neill, who has been more violent than others, surprises Fraiser with a few laboriously produced words. The conversation is all too brief, but leaves the doctor with hope that her patients' faculties can be restored.

On P3X-797, Teal'c and Jackson are again set upon by the Touched, some of whom drag Jackson away while Teal'c is occupied. Pressed for time and unlikely to rescue Jackson without harming his captors, Teal'c continues to the Land of Light, where he tells the Councilors that there is hope of a cure for the Touched if one of them will allow him to take a blood sample. Offended by the request, they inform him that he is no longer welcome, ordering the guards to make sure he leaves before they hasten from the room. Teal'c makes short work of both guards, apologizing to one unconscious man before drawing the needed sample from him.

He returns to the SGC and hands over the sample to Fraiser. Analysis shows an extremely low level of histamine, one of the body chemicals upon which the virus feeds. The results lead her to the theory that the virus has been starved out by natural antihistamine properties of something in the diet of the Untouched. Like Jackson, she remains unaffected, and she now realizes that it is likely because both take strong antihistamines for allergies.

Fraiser injects O'Neill with a hefty dose of the antihistamine chlorpheniramine maleate, hoping that it will eradicate the virus in his body. The cure is a success, and the base is soon up and running again. SG-1 returns to P3X-797 armed with tranquilizer dart guns loaded with the antihistamine, to rescue their captured team member and restore the Touched to their families in the Land of Light.

Background
The Land of Light

P3X-797 has a permanent, fixed terminator, dividing the land between daylight sides and night sides. The terminator falls on the equator, with the planet revolving around the fixed axis pointing at the sun. Whether this is a result of some massive planetary engineering or merely an extraordinary natural phenomenon that attracted the gate-builder's attention is not known. Habitation is possible only in a thin band stretching approximately 100 miles in either direction of the equator. The poles do precess at an accelerated rate, causing the 'fixed terminator' to actually fluctuate up to a mile in either direction over the course of a 78 year cycle. This rapid pace is thought to be evidence of the terraforming of the equatorial zone to make it habitable. Once capable of supporting life, the planet became a natural laboratory on the effects of perpetual day or night cycles, and caused the locals transplanted there to adapt to their non-standard sleep patterns. The Touched virus itself may have been a failed attempt by the Goa'uld to correct the side effects of this adaptation in the hopes of developing servants who literally never needed sleep.

The prosperous land on the light side of P3X-797 opens a window on a chapter of Earth's history known only in fragments. Its people offer a gracious welcome that brings to life the frescoes of the palace at Knossos on Crete, home of the long-vanished civilization we call Minoan.

"DANIEL, YOU DOG. KEEP THIS UP AND YOU'LL HAVE A GIRL ON EVERY PLANET."

– COL. JACK O'NEILL

To its inhabitants, who call themselves the Untouched, the Land of Light is a gift of the benevolent gods. Though these gods have not visited in more than a generation, the people remain ever-prepared to welcome them, maintaining the herd that produces sacred bulls and holding annual games, culminating in the Bull Dance, in which young people demonstrate their strength and agility. In times past, exceptional champions of the Bull Dance have been chosen by the gods to accompany them to their celestial home – a clue, to the ears of SGC personnel, that the competition is a means of selecting superior Goa'uld hosts. The Untouched believe that the gods have names, but that mortals are not permitted to know them; visiting gods were addressed simply as "Lord" or "Lady."

While the primary motif of sacred art is the bull, the City also boasts numerous representations resembling the famous Minoan "Snake Goddess," a smiling lady with a serpent in each hand. When asked, the Untouched explain that she is the Mother of the Gods, and the serpents her children. How these children take the human-like form of the gods is, like their names, a mystery... though the SGC has some suspicions.

The Untouched draw a sharp distinction between the benevolent gods and the unseen *heelksha* whose touch is a curse. They have responded with courteous confusion to attempts to explain the true cause of the Touched Syndrome. Understanding – and believing – that their powerful new friends are not gods is challenge enough for the moment.

More on the Land of Light can be found on pages 84-85 of the *Stargate SG-1* core rulebook.

A NEW PLAGUE

After the near-disaster of the histaminolytic virus outbreak, experts from across the armed services were brought in to evaluate the SGC's protocols guarding against future contamination. Initially the base was outfitted only with basic isolation rooms, such as those found in a prison or psychiatric ward, but following this inspection changes were made in both the facility and post-mission proce-

dures. The main improvements involved the construction of true isolation labs that could be outfitted to handle Level 4 biohazard materials with minimal effort, as well as expanded examinations and blood work upon return through the Stargate, with on-base quarantine until the CMO signs off on the results. The standard protocol is sufficient for Level 2 or 3 bioagents – those that are deadly, but treatable – on a routine basis.

Samples of the parasitic virus from the Land of Light were sent to the Army Medical Research Institute of Infectious Disease (USAMRIID) for continued study. Though precautions were taken to mask the true source of the pathogen, the team working on sequencing the genetic code of the virus at Fort Detrick, Maryland discovered enough to fill in the blanks and realize the virus was neither terrestrial (which the SGC already knew) nor naturally occurring (which was only suspected). When they reported these suspicions to their superiors, the team was initially ordered to abandon that line of inquiry and focus on what could be learned from the virus, regardless of its origin.

Meanwhile, elements within the government saw the Touched virus as a potential weapon. The combination of its highly communicable nature and obscure but easily-implemented cure made it a promising way to subdue a selected population. Though Dr. Fraiser pointed out that such a use would be ineffective against the Goa'uld or their Jaffa troops, it was deemed that the non-lethal nature of the infection would allow it to be used on support staff not protected by symbiotes. This could allow them to foment chaos and confusion even among the stolid troops of a System Lord.

To do this, the virus would have to be studied, the transmission vectors measured precisely, and the complete pathology documented. The very same team that cracked the virus' genetic code was recruited for just that purpose. Officially on an open-ended assignment to track the virus in the wild, the USAMRIID team was transferred to the SGC and assisted in the redesign of the facilities for bio-isolation in the mountain before taking their place off-world on the dark side of P3X-797.

The decision to set up shop off-world was not taken lightly, and in the end Gen. Hammond was only persuaded because of the legal responsibilities international treaties forced on the military. As long as the development and deployment remained on another planet, it was outside the jurisdiction of existing agreements. So with the permission of the Untouched, a semi-permanent research center was set up in a defensible location on the dark side, not far from the Stargate.

Consisting of a single prefab warehouse and a mobile biological containment unit that the Army personnel brought with them, the base was set up on a hilltop cleared of trees and surrounded with floodlights to make the area navigable and easy to locate from the Stargate. This necessitated frequent fuel shipments from Earth to sustain the generators, but was thought to be a safer arrangement for those in the Land of Light, and allowed the virus' natural environment to be restored with the flip of a switch. If a long-term presence is required, it is hoped that the Untouched will help locate alternative sources of fuel locally. Their hospitality has already reduced the logistics of resupplying, as they insist on providing food and lodging to all who stay.

The staff is comprised of four Army researchers, two civilian academics and four SGC Marines (in case the "gods" return). The commanding officer is Col. Douglas Russo, a senior USAMRIID investigator. Under existing protocols, only he and his fellow Army personnel are permitted to work in the "Mini-Sub," a trailer housing the portable Level 4 containment rooms inside an airlock. As such, only these four have the blue Centurion space suits designed for long-term work at that level of risk. Besides the blue suits, the base maintains a dozen of the more portable orange Racal suits, which can be used in the field if a "hot spot" is located.

The base's mission is threefold: one, to research the virus itself; two, to discover its origins, if possible; three, to monitor the population and ensure that they remain free of infection. To those ends, while the base is continuously operated by at least four persons, there are explorations farther into the dark side to recover samples and search for signs of past Goa'uld activity that could lead to determining where the virus was developed.

THE MINOTAUR

Within a month of the establishment of the medical research base, a team scouting farther into the dark side was attacked by what appeared to be some sort of man-beast. The creature was killed and brought back for analysis. The results indicated that the beast was a man, who had been infected with a mutant strain of the Touched virus. Fortunately tests have shown that this variant is not as contagious, and could only be contracted by blood or fluid exchange with a victim. The secondary effects are more pronounced than in the normal form of the Touched Syndrome. The entire upper body is covered in a heavy coat of hair, and the brow deformation is extreme, giving the appearance of horns if viewed from a distance. With such severe alterations, it is possible that the damage to the mind and physiology of the victim could be permanent. Even more disturbing is the fact that the normal course of treatment, the application of antihistamines, has had no effect on this variant pathogen in laboratory trials.

High Councilor Tuplo, when shown the beast, indicated that legends existed about creatures of this description being used by the *heelksha* as guardians and for sport. Though they were said to roam the Land of the Dark, no one had seen one for many generations. This reappearance has been taken as a sign by some of the Untouched that the gods will return soon. Others, including the Councilor, take it as a sign that they have made a wise alliance with these friends from another world.

1-05: THE FIRST COMMANDMENT

World Visited: P3X-513 (Avnil).

Thermosphere: Hot (CR 0; tidally locked to its sun; 3d20+50° F).

Atmosphere: Thin (CR 1; 0.4 atmospheres; Exp. Inc: 10 minutes; SV Fort (DC20); Dmg 1d6 subdual; Recup 2 rounds).

Hydrosphere: Humid (CR 2; daily weather 1-79: none, 80-81: flood 1d10 MPH, 82: flood 1d10+10 MPH, 83-91: rain 1d6 in., 92-96: thunderstorm, 97-98: hurricane, 99: wind 1d10 MPH, 100: wind 1d10+10 MPH).

Geosphere: Stable tectonic activity (daily earthquakes 1-99: none, 100: minor).

Seasons: Severe (1-25: spring unchanged; 26-50: summer +4d12° F; 51-75: autumn unchanged; 76-100: winter -4d12° F).

Anthrosphere: 5,000 natives; Iron Age (3 picks, 1 RP); Oligarchy; Suspicious (-1 with disposition checks); Extremely Sensitive (1 soldier, squad size 1d4 soldiers); Moderate civil rights.

Origin: Indeterminate.

Stargate Location (jungle region): Thick forest with high canopy, tall trees and low-lying plants, rolling hills and gullies.

EPISODE SUMMARY

SG-1 is dispatched to P3X-513 to determine the current whereabouts of SG-9, which is long overdue. The world has intense ultraviolet radiation but significant plant life as well. Teal'c explains that this is probably the result of Goa'uld terraforming efforts centuries ago, in order to make the world more habitable to humanoid lifeforms. Despite the explanation, Captain Carter notices that the forest where the Stargate is located is devoid of birds.

Daniel Jackson wanders off alone and is surprised by a man, who grabs his pistol and points it at his neck. Colonel O'Neill defuses the situation when he recognizes Lieutenant Conner of SG-9. He asks Conner why his team sent a signal through to SGC six hours ago and never came through. Conner at explains that SG-9's leader, Captain Jonas Hanson, has gone mad with power. The natives believed Hanson to be a god because he came through the Stargate, and in short order Hanson set himself up to rule P3X-513.

O'Neill decides that Hanson needs to be captured for court martial. He orders Carter and Conner to go back to SGC and inform them of the situation. Carter refuses, saying that, since she was once engaged to Hanson, she knows how he thinks better than anyone. Conner likewise refuses, saying that he knows the local situation and could be of help. Perturbed, O'Neill acquiesces and the team heads off to find Hanson in the cave system where the natives live to escape the planet's UV rays.

After they set up camp, Conner explains how Hanson hoped to use the natives' belief in his divinity as a way to inspire them to retake their world and advance their society. The captain solidified his hold over the natives when he spent two days seeking out a child who wandered out of the caves. He returned with the child alive, but his sanity was shattered by the ordeal. His belief in his own divinity grew as more of the natives worshiped him. Now Hanson mercilessly punishes anyone who opposes him, tying them to a stake beneath the unforgiving sun until they die. In addition, he forces the natives to labor in the sun to build a temple that he claims will save them all.

Later that night, natives attack the team's camp and capture Conner. O'Neill decides to travel to Hanson's base of power to find out what is really going on, as well as to rescue Conner. While O'Neill reconnoiters, Carter sees one of Hanson's men beating a young native. She goes down to rescue him and is captured – just as she intended. She believes she can reach Hanson and convince him to come back to Earth with SG-1.

Carter is indeed taken to Hanson, who proclaims his divinity to her and explains that he is only helping the natives. He denies that he is not "posing" as a god, since the natives' beliefs are sincere. He is their only hope for a better life. Without his guidance, they would remain in their caves forever and never advance. Realizing that he is insane, Carter threatens to shoot Hanson. He eggs her on, daring her to do it. When she cannot, her pistol is taken away and she is once again a prisoner.

The rest of the team follows the young native Carter rescued from beating. His name is Jamala and claims that SG-1 are all devils, especially Teal'c, whom recognizes from old tales as a Jaffa, a "servant of the old gods." O'Neill attempts to convince Jamala that Hanson is not a god, but the youth is not easily swayed. He says that Hanson has promised to make the sky orange when the natives finish building his temple. The sickness caused by the sun will then end and the people can leave the caves for good. Teal'c soon says that he may know what Jamala is describing – a Goa'uld solar shield that would block the UV rays and turn the sky orange in the process. Jamala says that cave paintings corroborate what Teal'c has said.

Meanwhile, Hanson shows Carter the very device of which Teal'c speaks. He asks her to get the device working again; at first, she refuses, but Hanson says that without her help even more natives will die. Rather than face that prospect, Carter reluctantly agrees to assist him.

Meanwhile, O'Neill trades clothing with Jamala and sneaks into Hanson's base to rescue Conner. At the same time, Teal'c attempts to convince Jamala that Hanson is not a god any more than the Goa'uld are. Jackson adds that the solar shield, if activated, could actually help them undermine Hanson's power. However, Teal'c says that the shield requires two devices to work properly. If Hanson has only one, it will not work. Therefore, they must find the second one.

While Teal'c, Jackson, and Jamala search for the second device, O'Neill rescues Conner, but is himself captured and taken before Hanson. He orders their immediate execution. Carter, however, bargains for their lives in exchange for getting the solar shield operational. Jamala, who has returned to the caves, learns of this and comes to warn Teal'c and Jackson. He says that Hanson has gathered the people at the "circle of the gods" (the Stargate), which he has tilted on its side like a pool of water. He intends to send

O'Neill and Conner through the "gate to the underworld," even though it will kill them if they do not first send a signal to open the iris.

Before Hanson can do this, Jackson and Jamala arrive. Jackson claims that Hanson is not a god and that the device is not magic but a machine anyone can use. Hanson attempts to disprove his claim by activating the device, but is unsuccessful because he does not control the second machine. Then, Jamala fires Teal'c's staff weapon into the air, alerting the Jaffa to activate the second device. Together, the two devices form a solar shield. Infuriated, the natives attack Hanson and toss him into the Stargate's event horizon, killing him.

With the solar shield now operational, the natives can leave their caves and begin a new life on the surface. Carter questions whether they should tell the natives to bury the Stargate, since she thinks they had already done enough damage on this world. Jackson disagrees and thinks they should check in on them again to see how they are progressing. The matter is left unresolved as SG-1 steps through the gate and returns home.

BACKGROUND
AVNIL (D3X-513)

Nearly 1,000 years ago, a minor System Lord name Afa visited the planet known locally as Avnil for its geological wealth. There, they found rich veins of naquadah and other valuable minerals. Afa immediately recognized that Avnil would add much to his dominion, in addition to providing him with bargaining chips against his enemies. He brought several thousand humans with him and set up a mining colony on the planet. Because the world's atmosphere was thin, deadly UV radiation was insufficiently filtered which proved hazardous to humans and Goa'uld alike. To combat it, he ordered a radiation shield set up around the mining colony and had underground facilities constructed to process the ores.

Unfortunately for Afa, Avnil's mineral wealth played out after about 500 years of constant mining – a good run by any standards but not as much as the System Lord had hoped. He abandoned the planet and chose to leave his slaves behind – he no longer had any need of them – but left the radiation shield running so that they might survive on their own. A handful of the now-abandoned slaves knew how to operate and repair the radiation shield. They became prominent members of their communities, acting as priests and lore keepers, and their actions ensured the continued survival of the people as well as keeping the memories of the Goa'uld – the "old gods" – alive.

Like many primitive societies, though, the Avnilians soon forgot how to maintain the radiation shield. When it ceased to function, the deadly UV radiation returned and they retreated to the caves on a permanent basis. They abandoned their few surface dwellings and made the mines their homes. Though the caves were dark and cramped, they possessed an ample supply of water (via subterranean springs) and food in the form of fungi and blind cave fish. This was supplemented by limited game from the surface. After all, the UV radiation harmed most other living things on Avnil as well. The few creatures that continued to survive were very hardy and generally nocturnal in nature.

The society in the caves soon grew superstitious and fearful. Legends of the Goa'uld and their Jaffa servants became the bogeymen of Avnilian society, stories used to frighten. The Stargate was viewed with equal fear, as it was the means by which the old gods entered the world. When the first SG team came through the gate on their mission, the Avnilians at first feared them. However, it soon became obvious that the SG team members were not Goa'uld and, as they themselves explained, had fought the System Lords. To the Avnilians, this meant that humans could only be good gods, a belief adopted wholeheartedly by Captain Hanson.

Avnilian society is very communal in nature. Most items are held in common possession and labor is divided as equally as possible. Of course, those with natural aptitudes in certain areas are expected to use them for the good of the community. Consequently, there is comparatively little freedom in choosing one's vocation. The survival of the entire community depends on everyone doing their part, no matter how unpleasant it might be. There is no acknowledged leader of the Avnilians. Most decisions are made through consensus, enforced through violence if necessary. Again, there is little room for dissent. Anyone whose beliefs or actions make them a threat to the survival of the community is dealt with harshly. Exile is the typical sentence... which often means death since, outside the caves, there is little chance of long-term survival.

Avnilian family life is also quite communal. Children are raised together by all adults, and polygamy and polyandry are the norms. The concept of monogamous marriage does not exist among these near-humans, since it would be impractical and even detrimental to the health of the community. Children learn to respect and obey all adults, although special reverence is reserved for one's parents.

Captain Hanson found the society to be quite conducive to his own goals. Being superstitious, communal, well ordered and occasionally violent, it was all too easy to rework these tendencies to serve his megalomania. For many Avnilians, Hanson really was a god. After all, he had begun to improve their lives and he seemed to understand and respect their ways, as any god would. Of course, he also imposed strange orders on them, such as his quest to build a temple on the surface. Most Avnilians have nothing but utter fear for the surface world and it was only through a combination of charisma and force that Hanson convinced them to work as they did.

Now that Hanson is dead and SG-1 has put the planet on a better footing by restoring the operation of the radiation shield, Avnil's future is in flux. The initial survey of the planet suggested that there may yet be valuable minerals deep beneath its surface. The Avnilians know the mines better than anyone and would be of great assistance to any-

one attempting to access them. The SGC was interested in establishing peaceful trade with the Avnilians, progress is slow after the disaster of SG-9. General Hammond believes that it is best to let the cave dwellers find their own way and learn once again to accept SG teams as ordinary men not gods. Therefore, contact with the Avnilians is sporadic and short-term at best. However, many cave dwellers, such as Jamala and those like him, love receiving visits from other SG teams. After hiding beneath the surface for so long, they are ready to explore their world and would be grateful for any help. Clearly, Avnil offers many opportunities for SG teams in the future.

SG-9

SG-9 was a diplomatic ops team, meaning that it was charged primarily with making contact and negotiating with alien races (*see page 41 of the Stargate SG-1 core rulebook*). In the case of Avnil, the team was sent because the initial survey of the planet (made by SG-4) indicated that it possessed rich mineral deposits that would be invaluable to the SGC. In order to avoid the problems that might arise if extraction teams were sent in without warning, SG-9, under Captain Jonas Hanson, was supposed to make peaceful contact with the local inhabitants. As explained above, this did not happen and one of the worst disasters of the early SG program was averted only through the efforts of SG-1.

The original SG-9 team consisted of four members, like most SG teams. Its leader, Captain Jonas Hanson, was a career Air Force officer who'd spent most of his tours doing black ops for the United States government. Needless to say, these missions slowly ate away at his conscience. By the time he ended his work, he had lost many of his inhibitions — and morals. Nevertheless, Hanson remained a charming personality and his successes in black ops won him many patrons within the Air Force, as well as opportunities to expand his career. He eventually landed the position as leader of SG-9, because his patrons felt he possessed the perfect combination of ruthlessness and diplomatic skill.

Hanson's right hand man was Lieutenant Matthew Baker. Like Hanson, he'd spent most of his career in black ops. When Hanson took his new post, he chose Baker because he saw in him a man of unquestionable ability who shared a similar outlook on the world. Not surprisingly, it was Baker who became Hanson's primary supporter and enforcer on P3X-513.

The third member of SG-9 was Lieutenant Thomas Frakes. Frakes was an anthropologist before he joined the Air Force, and had lived among many tribal peoples in remote parts of the world. He brought these experiences with him to the SGC, which is why Hanson wanted him on his team. If SG-9 were to be a diplomatic unit, he'd need someone like Frakes to help him.

The final member of SG-9 was Lieutenant Michael Conner, a disciplined officer who'd spent a lot of time working as an attaché to various ambassadorial staffs. Nevertheless, he trained himself very hard, believing that his fellow officers didn't consider him a "real airman." Hanson understood what drove Conner and respected him for it. He also knew that Conner's time as an attaché made him an ideal addition to his diplomatic team.

Under Hanson, SG-9 undertook successful missions on numerous worlds. While not as glamorous as those undertaken by teams like SG-1 or SG-2, they were vital to the early success of the SGC. SG-9 quickly gained the respect of their peers for their ability to enter into peaceful negotiations with newly contacted near-human and alien cultures. These successes owed a lot to Hanson, whose years as a black operative had taught him how to produce "innovative" solutions to seemingly intractable problems. He gave his men a lot of leeway in deciding the best course of action and they thanked him for that.

What no one realized at the time was that Hanson had falsified many of his reports. Several of the "successful missions" he'd described were fabricated. For example, P2B-011 was a seemingly idyllic world whose near-human inhabitants had provided Hanson with intelligence about the Goa'uld that later proved vital to other SG teams. What Hanson did not reveal was that he had provided the natives automatic weapons in exchange for this information, a gift that allowed one faction to gain the upper hand in their intermittent civil war. It was only months after Hanson's death on P3X-513 that SG-7 learned the truth. As a result, General Hammond has reopened every one of SG-9's mission reports and dispatched a SG team to re-visit those worlds. It may be months – even years – before the full extent of Hanson's deception (and its effects for the SGC) will be known.

Since SG-1's visit to P3X-513, SG-9 has been reconstituted with an entirely new team. The sole surviving member of the original team, Michael Conner, is now on detached duty at SGC, filling in for missing or busy members on other SG teams. The new SG-9 has a difficult job ahead of it. For one, some military officers are superstitious and believed that the SG-9 designator is "cursed." The failure of the original team was so spectacular that there were calls to expunge it from the roster entirely. General Hammond disagreed, however, and the buck stopped with him. Now, the new SG-9 must find a way to overcome the stigma attached to their team and undo some of the damage wrought by the madman who once led it.

1-06: BRIEF CANDLE

World Visited: P3X-8596 (Argos).

Thermosphere: Warm (CR 0; standard orbit; 2d20+25° F).

Atmosphere: Normal (CR 0; 1.10 atmospheres; Auto None; Exp. Inc: None; SV None; Dmg None; Recup None).

Hydrosphere: Sub-humid (CR 1; daily weather 1-85: none, 86-87: flood, 88-93: rain/snow, 94-95: thunderstorm or snowstorm, 96: hurricane or blizzard, 97-98: wind 1d10 MPH, 99: wind 1d10+10 MPH, 100: wind 1d10+20 MPH).

Geosphere: Stable tectonic activity (daily earthquakes 1-99: none, 100: minor; 1 volcano within 1d10 miles of Stargate).

Seasons: Mild (1-17: spring Unchanged; 18-50: summer +2d10° F; 51-83: autumn unchanged; 84-100: winter -2d10° F).

Anthrosphere: 350 natives; Bronze Age (3 picks, 1 RP); Theocracy/Democracy Friendly (+1 with disposition checks); Absolute Pacifistic (N/A, N/A); Poor civil rights.

Origin: Greek.

Stargate Location (Mediterranean region): Rocky terrain in Grassland, inside the Temple of Pelops near the Argosian village.

EPISODE SUMMARY

SG-1 steps through the gate to the planet designated P3X-8596, only to find themselves in a temple in the style of ancient Greece. Moving down the stairs in front of the Stargate, the team approaches the back of a statue depicting a figure riding a chariot throwing lightning bolts when they hear a woman screaming. They quickly spot a frantic man and his very pregnant wife Thetys, in active labor. Having once delivered a baby on an expedition in the Yucatan, Daniel Jackson helps the couple, and within minutes the woman gives birth to a healthy baby boy.

Astonished by the mother's quick recovery, SG-1 accompanies the couple and their newborn son Danel to the nearby village courtyard, where a celebration is under way. The villagers are all young, vital, and attractive, and refer to themselves as the Chosen (and their world as Argos). They are enjoying the gifts of their gods for "one hundred blissful days." Moments later a stunning woman named Kynthia approaches O'Neill, and offers him a piece of a decorative cake, which O'Neill accepts. Kynthia's friends then seat O'Neill in a chair set off from the courtyard, where Kynthia begins to dance for him. His vision blurred and feeling light-headed, O'Neill follows Kynthia into a nearby house, where he joins her in bed. A few minutes later, other villagers enter the house and both they and Kynthia suddenly fall fast asleep. O'Neill rises from the bed as the rest of SG-1 enters the house, hoping to understand this rapid series of events. But before they can determine anything, O'Neill suddenly grows tired and falls asleep just as Kynthia and villagers had moments before.

The next morning, O'Neill and the rest of the village awaken as the sun rises, and he and SG-1 try to discover what caused the populace to fall asleep at the same time.

Daniel and Teal'c return to the temple, while Carter begins taking soil samples. Deciphering a series of Goa'uld glyphs on the base of the statue, Daniel and Teal'c find a Goa'uld writing device, and the two begin to try to translate the writing. Meanwhile, while speaking to Thetys, Carter discovers that the baby born only the previous day has aged several years overnight. The people of this world measure their age with mayfly brevity: each lives only one hundred days.

O'Neill and Carter join Daniel and Teal'c, who have learned a few things about their hosts. Apparently, the Goa'uld Pelops brought the people to this planet to study human evolution, and created a virus that ages the population at an extremely accelerated rate. As the sun sets, the villagers and O'Neill fall asleep again, leaving the rest of SG-1 with the knowledge that O'Neill has somehow contracted the aging virus.

Back at the SGC, Carter and Dr. Fraiser examine blood samples of both the Argosians and O'Neill and discover an unknown organism in both, one that O'Neill has considerably more of than the Argosians. When they return to Argos, SG-1 finds that O'Neill has aged significantly overnight. SG-1 plans to set up a lab to study the organisms, but O'Neill orders them to return to Earth and solve the problem from there. Further study of the organism reveals that it is in fact a *nanocyte,* a microscopic device that rearranges matter at the sub-atomic level. Hordes of them infest O'Neill's body, as well as those of the natives.

On Argos, O'Neill learns from Kynthia that they are considered married because he accepted the Marriage Cake and joined Kynthia in her bed. As O'Neill begins to come to grips with growing old much sooner that he expected, Kynthia tries to convince him to accept his fate and enjoy what remains of his life on Argos with her.

On Earth, the nanocytes almost escape their containment vessel as Carter and Dr. Fraiser study them. Realizing the potential risk they pose, General Hammond orders them destroyed and all work on the Argos project stopped. SG-1 sends a recorded message to O'Neill explaining their progress, as they are prohibited from returning to Argos.

A day later, Argosians from the village arrive in the temple, bringing food as an offering to Pelops to hopefully persuade their god to return to help O'Neill. O'Neill convinces the people that Pelops is not a god to be worshiped, but an alien Goa'uld who manipulated them for his own ends. Angered at this revelation, the Argosians topple the statue of Pelops. When Pelops does not strike them down, they realize the truth in O'Neill's words and celebrate their new found freedom.

As O'Neill and Kynthia walk along a nearby beach, Kynthia expresses her fear of traveling too far: remaining in the village is the first of Pelops' Laws. O'Neill persuades her to continue walking with him, and the two spend the

evening together in a nearby forest, remaining awake long after sunset. When they return to the village, O'Neill and Kynthia find the rest of the villagers still asleep. O'Neill realizes that these two events must somehow be related; he returns to the temple and finds an electronic device in the base of the temple – damaged when the Argosians toppled the statue of Pelops. Guessing that it relates somehow to the changes in the villagers' sleeping patterns, O'Neill contacts the SGC, and the rest of SG-1 returns. Study of the damaged device reveals it is a transmitter, designed to emit signals to the nanocytes in two frequencies: one to activate them (putting the Argosians to sleep and aging them), the

other to deactivate them (waking the Argosians from their sleep). These two frequencies were referenced in the Goa'uld writing device. SG-1 uses Earth technology to broadcast the "wake up" frequency, and within moments the entire village is awake. SG-1 then disables the Goa'uld transmitter entirely, disabling the nanocytes within the Argosians and O'Neill. With the nanocytes gone, the Argosians will age normally, and within days O'Neill reverts to his normal age.

BACKGROUND
THE WORLD OF ARGOS

The world of Argos changed considerably as a result of SG-1's visit. Besides persuading the Argosians that Pelops was not a true god and eliminating the nanocytes from their physiology, SG-1 also set in motion a number of other changes, which are detailed below.

THE ARGOSIANS

The most drastic change occurred within the people of Argos themselves, when they went from living only one hundred days and aging rapidly to living normal life spans and aging as normal humans. No longer able to simply enjoy "one hundred blissful days," the Argosians must now adjust to a far lengthier lifespan.

This adjustment, while still ongoing, was at first difficult for many. They were used to noticeably aging nearly every day of their lives, which made waking up unchanged day after day quite unsettling. It was months before they altered their lifestyles in any way. Slowly the people of Argos came to the realization that in order to survive, they would have to adopt a slightly less frivolous attitude towards life. They could no longer simply eat, drink, and be merry. Instead they would have to work and support themselves and their families in a way previously unknown to them. Ironically, their former lifestyle helped prepare them for this in ways they had not anticipated.

Having lived with such short life spans for so many generations, the Argosians are extremely efficient and productive. Now with longer life spans, this efficiency serves them well in their efforts to make the necessary adjustments in their lives. For instance, buildings that might take offworlders several months to build take the Argosians only a few weeks. The Argosians put this efficiency to work in the development and expansion of their village itself.

SPARTA

Sparta is Pelops' stronghold, and home to nearly all of his military forces. Fifty barracks, each housing a hundred Jaffa, ring the perimeter of the capital city. Interspersed among them are six hangars, each capable of housing two al-kesh bombers. All of the military installations on Sparta are heavily guarded, with up to a dozen squads of 1d4 Jaffa patrolling the perimeter of each. Similar forces guard Pelops' research facilities, which also feature Blast doors equipped with an Electronic Keyboard lock. A successful Electronics check (DC 25) unlocks the door. Even more Jaffa guard Pelops' fortress, with squads of 1d6 patrolling both the perimeter and interior.

World: Sparta.

Thermosphere: Warm (CR 0; standard orbit; 2d20+25° F).

Atmosphere: Normal (CR 0; 1.10 atmospheres; Auto None; Exp. Inc: None; SV None; Dmg None; Recup None).

Hydrosphere: Sub-humid (CR 1; daily weather 1-85: none, 86-87: flood, 88-93: rain/snow, 94-95: thunderstorm or snowstorm, 96: hurricane or blizzard, 97-98: wind 1d10 MPH, 99: wind 1d10+10 MPH, 100: wind 1d10+20 MPH).

Geosphere: Stable tectonic activity (daily earthquakes 1-99: none, 100: minor; 1 volcano within 1d10 miles of Stargate).

Seasons: Mild (1-17: spring Unchanged; 18-50: summer +2d10° F; 51-83: autumn, Unchanged; 84-100: winter -2d10° F).

Anthrosphere: 100,000 natives; Bronze Age (3 picks, 1 RP); Theocracy Hostile (-2 with disposition checks); Extremely Cautious (5,000 soldiers, squad size 1d4 soldiers); poor civil rights.

Origin: Greek.

Stargate Location (Mediterranean region): Urban terrain, just outside Pelops' fortress near the capital city.

Shortly after SG-1's departure, the Argosians began to expand the borders of their settlement and explore and settle the nearby region. Though their population was still small (just over 350 residents), the Argosians soon learned that they needed more room to sustain their now longer lived population. Their efforts resulted not only in new buildings and homes, but also in additional and expanded farmlands. Where once the entire village shared in daily chores and duties, the people soon began to divide their efforts, leaving some to tend to the farms, while others worked on constructing new buildings, while yet others taught others new skills and knowledge. Where the people once idled away each day savoring in the "gift" of the hundred days, now their devote themselves to work and productivity, resulting in a thriving village where the people help each other learn and succeed.

As the people began to pursue individual efforts, rudimentary trade and barter soon followed. They trade between themselves for necessities such as food and clothing as well as luxury items such as scrolls and jewelry, and a standard of currency is beginning to form. While trade has not yet grown into true commerce, the beginnings of an economy are emerging, as some villagers plan and prepare for trade with others rather than simply produce enough for themselves as they once might have.

In addition as the villagers move away from their monolithic lifestyle to more individual concerns, they recognize a need for rules beyond the now defunct Laws of Pelops. Towards this end the Argosians have adopted a form of representative government where one person in twenty-five is elected to govern the village. Thus far this group has had to do little in terms of true governing, but they have drafted a number of laws and statutes related to trade and commerce.

Once free of Pelops' Laws, many Argosians sought to learn more about the world beyond their village. Several groups set out and formed their own smaller communities in the nearby area, ranging from one to up to five days walk away. These communities average twenty-five to fifty people each, with one as large as sixty. Most conduct regular trade with the emerging merchants in the village, preferring to remain in contact with their former neighbors.

In addition to settling new communities, a number of Argosians have traveled even further, seeking to explore and discover the wonders of their world that for so long were denied them by Pelops' Laws. These explorers, usually in groups of four to eight, set out for anywhere from ten days to two months, only to return to the village with tales of wondrous sights, captivating the imaginations of all who listen. Some tell of a tunnel at the bottom of cliff overlooking the sea that holds a strange doorway made of metal, covered with writings similar to those on the statue of Pelops that once stood in the temple. This doorway is in fact the entrance to a laboratory Pelops used when he first brought the Argosians to this world (see Pelops' Lab on page 27). Several groups have tried to open the door, but none have succeeded thus far.

While most explorers travel the land, one such group built a rudimentary ship and set sail on the open sea, traveling along the coast. Months after their departure, the ship and its crew have yet to return.

THE TEMPLE OF PELOPS

Prior to SG-1's arrival, the Temple of Pelops was a place of worship for the Argosians, who tended to it while they awaited the return of their god. Since that time, however, the temple has undergone significant change. It is now known as the Temple of Freedom and Learning, in celebration of the Argosians' release from their false god. The statue of Pelops that once dominated the temple was removed entirely and destroyed, as was the transmitter device that lay below it. The Argosians painted over most of the walls in the temple, and inscribed upon them the tale of their liberation from Pelops at the hands of SG-1. These writings celebrate O'Neill in particular, as he lived among the people for a time and was instrumental in their learning the truth about their former god. Portions of the walls that tell the story of their arrival Argos and early life remain in place as a reminder of how the people were led astray.

The temple is also used as a school. Prior to SG-1's arrival the people passed on some knowledge from generation to generation (such as how to grow and harvest crops and how to care for children), knowledge for the sake of knowledge was unheard of. Time was simply too precious for such things. With their lengthened life spans, many Argosians now seek to expand their understanding of their world and the greater universe around them. Using materials and equipment provided by the SGC, interest in learning among the Argosians grew at exponential rate, filling the temple with students both young and old.

The SGC maintains regular (though infrequent) contact with the people of Argos. On a recent visit, SG-17 taught the Argosians how to use the Dial Home Device in the temple to activate the Stargate if they need to contact Earth, and gave the Argosians a simple transmitter they can use to contact the SGC if necessary.

PELOPS' LAB

When Pelops first brought humans to Argos, he built a lab in which he could properly prepare his subjects for his experiments. He placed it inside a cliff wall overlooking the ocean roughly three hours walk (ten miles) from the village. Though much of his research was conducted on his home world of Sparta (see Pelops, the Giver of Days, page 28), it was in this lab that Pelops created the nanocytes that he would later inject into his unknowing subjects.

After perfecting his technology, Pelops brought each of the original inhabitants of Argos into the lab and injected them with nanocytes, returning them to their village with no memory of what had transpired. No records of the lab's existence ever appeared, and Pelops even removed references to the lab from the tablet he left within the base of his statue. After implanting the Argosians, Pelops sealed the lab, leaving it intact should he have need of its equipment in the future. Since that time the lab remains untouched (Pelops remained in the village during his infrequent visits), arriving and departing via the Stargate.

The lab is located deep inside a seaside cliff roughly ten miles from the village. A successful Spot check (DC 12) within 30 feet of the base of the cliff reveals the tunnel that leads to the entrance of the lab. Note: All doors within the lab (except the Entrance and the Specimen Study Room) are equivalent to a Blast door, but with no locks.

ENTRANCE

The entrance is at the end of a thirty foot long tunnel leading from the base of a large cliff that overlooks the ocean. The door is the equivalent of a Blast door (Hardness 18, wp 840), and is equipped with an Electronic Keyboard lock and an advanced fingerprint Sensor. A successful Electronics check (DC 25) unlocks the door. A successful Electronics check (DC 30) disables the sensor. Opening the door without disabling the sensor activates a device that sends a long-range signal into space that will reach Pelops' home world of Sparta within three months. Failure to disable the motion sensor is obvious to the characters, as a loud claxon goes off for two minutes after opening the door (though no signal is sent off-world).

PELOPS' CHAMBERS

Pelops' chambers served as his personal quarters while he introduced the nanocytes into the Argosians. This room contains personal sleeping quarters, transportation rings, and a computer console. The personal quarters are little more than a bed and wardrobe. The transport rings are to the far right of the entrance, and their controls are on the computer console. A successful Computers check (DC 20) allows a character to retrieve data concerning Pelops and his research, including:

· Information about Tiryns (including its Stargate address), and the nature of the experiment on that planet (see Tiryns on page 29).

· The Stargate address for "Aegis," which appears to be an important world in Pelops' domain (see The System Lords sourcebook for more information on Aegis).

· Records that name Pelops' home world as "Sparta," though there is naturally no record of the gate address for such a sensitive location (see Sparta on the previous page).

· Records of other types of experiments performed using nanocytes, including extending the life span of humans, enhancements to natural abilities, and torturous stress tests on the human body in which the nanocytes attacked major organs from the inside (see Pelops' Nanotechnology on page 28).

NANOCYTE LAB

This is the room where Pelops produced the nanocytes used on the Argosians. Containers used to store them line the wall opposite the entrance. These metallic cylindrical containers measure four inches long by two inches in diameter. Within each container lies a tiny capsule containing an injection of nanocytes. Most containers are empty, but a Search check (DC 20) uncovers five with dormant nanocytes still inside. The rest of the room is taken up by now-inoperable devices that once produced the nanocytes.

SPECIMEN STUDY AND AUTOPSY ROOM

Here, Pelops injected the first inhabitants of Argos with nanocytes. The door to this room can be hermetically sealed and locked (DC 25 to unlock). A large autopsy table fills the center, while robotic instruments (which Pelops used to inject his subjects) line the walls. This room also contains a transmitter – similar to the one O'Neill removed from the statue of Pelops – used to activate the nanocytes once properly injected into a subject.

OBSERVATION ROOM

This small room is provides a view of the Specimen Study and Autopsy room through a large window. Pelops used this room to monitor his subjects during his first stress tests on human subjects. This room also contains a control console used to operate the robotic instruments in the Specimen Study room, as well as a portal used to load nanite containers *(see Nanocyte Lab, page 27)* into the instruments used to inject nanocytes into Pelops' subjects.

POWER GENERATOR

This room contains the generator that powers the lab. A successful Computers check (DC 15) on the control console here reveals the power grid of the entire lab.

PELOPS, THE GIVER OF DAYS

Named for the son of Tantalus from Greek mythology, Pelops is the Goa'uld who brought the humans to the world of Argos and used them as lab rats in experiments in evolution. Though not seen or heard from on Argos for several decades, Pelops is still alive and active, and may return to trouble them someday. He currently controls only a handful of worlds and a small fleet of ships, and doesn't represent a threat to the other System Lords, who largely ignore him. This has allowed Pelops to slowly expand his domain, attacking other minor Goa'uld, capturing slaves, and recruiting restless Jaffa. His most recent attack against the Goa'uld Raiden *(see Raiden and the Temple of the Sholmoses, page 17)* ended with Pelops' forces retreating in the face of a superior enemy.

Though he shares the trademark arrogance common to nearly all Goa'uld, Pelops doesn't exhibit the same wicked and tyrannical bent. He only rarely resorts to torture or death as forms of punishment, and doesn't engage in the wholesale slaughter of slaves and captives. Compared to other Goa'uld, Pelops seems almost compassionate or beneficent, but this is merely a facade that hides a far darker truth. He shows his true Goa'uld nature in his experiments applying nanotechnology to human physiology.

Pelops considers humans ideal subjects for his experiments, just as Earth scientists might view lab rats. His has no moral qualms about slaughtering his subjects; it simply wastes valuable resources. He shows them no regard in terms of subjecting them to all manner of tests and experiments. The case on Argos in which he shortened the lifespan of the populace to one hundred days so as to study human evolution at an advanced pace is just one of many experiments (some far more insidious) applying nanotechnology to humans. *(See Pelops' Nanotechnology and Tiryns – Home of the Cursed for more about these experiments.)*

Of the planets under Pelops' control, two – Argos and Tiryns – were home to long-term experiments in human evolution. The Argos experiment ended after SG-1's intervention (of which Pelops thus far remains unaware), but the experiment on Tiryns remains in place *(see Tiryns – Home of the Cursed on page 29)*. Another two of his worlds, Pilos and Tripolis serve as little more than breeding grounds for human subjects. The people of these worlds remain largely ignorant of their purpose as potential lab rats, and consider themselves subjects of a more or less neutral despot. They don't think to question the rationale when people are taken through the Stargate (they supposedly go to Pelops' home world of Sparta to serve closer to their god). Ruled by contingents of Jaffa, these worlds are for the most part peaceful, but rumors of an underground resistance on Pilos recently reached the Goa'uld ruler, who has yet to decide on a course of action.

The best defended of Pelops' planets is his home world of Sparta. While weak in comparison to the military outposts of other System Lords, Sparta is still well defended, with more than 5,000 Jaffa and human soldiers at Pelops' command plus another 5,000 in reserve on the homeworld of his Jaffa, Aegis. The two ha'tak and twelve al-kesh that comprise his fleet remain either in orbit or on the surface of Sparta when not engaged in battle elsewhere. The bulk of Sparta's population lives in a sprawling city that surrounds their god's vast fortress. Military stations including Jaffa barracks, training facilities, and hangars for Pelops' al-kesh lie just beyond the edges of the city. Sparta is also home to several research facilities that Pelops uses in his on-going nanotechnology experiments. These are among the most well guarded buildings on Sparta, second in defenses only to Pelops' castle itself.

PELOPS' NANOTECHNOLOGY

One of the rare true scientists among the Goa'uld, Pelops' focus (more an all-consuming passion really) is the development of nanotechnology and its application to human physiology. This focus is the drive behind nearly all of his experiments, including those on Argos and Tiryns, and continues to drive Pelops, as he sees the fruits of his labors as a key to gaining power among the Goa'uld.

Pelops' study of nanotechnology began before the creation of the first Jaffa, 10,000 years ago as a series of experiments designed to determine the effects of nanocytes on human subjects. These initial tests and experiments proved largely unsuccessful as the subjects' bodies either rejected the nanocytes (killing the subject), or their immune systems rendered the nanocytes useless. Hundreds upon hundreds of subjects died painful and gruesome deaths as Pelops perfected his nanite technology. It was only after a long series of failures that he at last successfully implanted his subjects with nanocytes without the subject's body rejecting or destroying them. It was during this period of failure that Pelops stumbled on possible applications for his nanotechnology, including accelerated aging, reversed aging, enhanced abilities (including strength, coordination, and endurance), and healing and curing the body of injury and disease.

TIRYNS

Tiryns' toxic atmosphere affects off-worlders within moments of their arrival. Upon breathing the atmosphere (which permeates the interiors of all the buildings in the village), a character must make a Fortitude save (DC 15) or suffer 1d3 points of subdual damage, as well as extreme nausea that imposes a -2 penalty to all checks for the next hour. In addition, each hour a character remains exposed to Tiryns' atmosphere he must make Fortitude save (DC 15) or suffer an additional 1d3 points of subdual damage and continued nausea for the next hour. After six hours of exposure, the DC for the Fortitude save drops by one for each hour, and failing the save no longer causes subdual damage, but the other effects continue for an additional six hours. After twelve hours of breathing Tiryns' atmosphere, the character must make a Fortitude save (DC 20) or suffer a -2 loss to his Constitution, after which point the nausea ceases. This loss remains until the character is able to breathe normal (i.e. non-toxic) air for at least one day. If the character breathes Tiryns' atmosphere for more than one month, the Constitution loss is permanent.

One of the walls in the Temple of Pelops conceals a stairway that leads to a basement where Pelops stores the storage tanks and ventilation ducts used to emit toxic gases. This door is the equivalent of a Blast door (Hardness 18, wp 840), and is equipped with an Electronic Keyboard lock, and an advanced fingerprint Sensor. A successful Electronics check (DC 25) unlocks the door. A successful Electronics check (DC 30) disables the sensor. Opening the door without disabling the sensor activates a device that sends a long-range signal into space that will reach Sparta within three months. Failure to disable the motion sensor triggers a loud claxon that goes off for two minutes after opening the door; the claxon's range is limited to the base itself.

> **World**: Tiryns.
> **Thermosphere**: Hot (CR 0; standard orbit; 3d20+50° F).
> **Atmosphere**: Normal (CR 0; 1.0 atmosphere; Auto 1d3 subdual plus special; Exp. Inc: 1 hour; SV Fort (DC15); Dmg 1d3 subdual plus special; Recup 1 day).
> **Hydrosphere**: Semi-arid (CR 1; daily weather 1-88: none, 89: flood, 90-92: rain/snow, 93: thunderstorm or snowstorm, 94: dust storm, 95: hurricane, 96-97: wind 1d10 MPH, 98: wind 1d10+10 MPH, 99: wind 1d10+20 MPH, 100: wind 1d10+30 MPH).
> **Geosphere**: Unstable tectonic activity (daily earthquakes 1-98: none, 99: minor, 100: moderate 2 small volcanoes within 1d10 miles of Stargate).
> **Seasons**: Normal (1-25: spring unchanged; 26-50: summer +2d20° F; 51-75: autumn unchanged; 76-100: winter -2d20° F).
> **Anthrosphere**: 350 natives; Bronze Age (3 picks, 1 RP); Theocracy/Democracy Suspicious (-1 with disposition checks); Defensibly Pacifistic (30 soldiers, N/A); poor civil rights.
> **Origin**: Greek.
> **Stargate Location (Mediterranean region)**: Inside the Temple of Pelops near the Tirynsian village.

Pelops conducted experiments in all of these areas, eventually perfecting the technology to produce the effects he desired. He began his latest experiments on the worlds of Argos and Tiryns *(see Tiryns, left)*, hoping to observe the evolution of the human body via rapidly accelerated aging. Experiments on reversed aging resulted in human test subjects living hundreds of years without the use of outside aids or other technology. Pelops has since applied this use of his nanocytes to himself and his Jaffa — greatly reducing the need for his sarcophagus in the past few centuries, and granting his Jaffa even longer life than most. Pelops' experiments into the healing and curative capabilities of nanotechnology also led to a gruesome realization: any damage the nanocytes could heal or cure, they could also cause. In testing this unintended capability, Pelops caused the nanocytes to mimic various diseases and injuries that would slowly kill his subjects.

More on Pelops can be found on page 115, and in the upcoming *System Lords* sourcebook.

TIRYNS — HOME OF THE CURSED

Shortly after Pelops relocated the Argosians and began his experiment there, he set up a similar experiment on the world of Tiryns. The Tirynsians have the same shortened life spans as the Argosians, but where Argos was an idyllic world whose climate and topography supported the inhabitants, Tiryns is a small planet with a mildly toxic atmosphere, and a local climate and topography that makes growing any sort of food difficult. Just as Pelops intended the Argos experiment to allow him to study human evolution under ideal circumstances, Tiryns allow him to study it under adverse circumstances, and to see the effects of prolonged exposure to a toxic environment have in his test subjects. He eventually intends to directly compare specimens from each world, but that day is still far off (and will likely never happen after SG-1's intervention on Argos).

Tiryns has a nitrogen-oxygen atmosphere similar to Earth's, but with higher concentrations of argon and xenon. While scouring Tiryns for a suitable location for his experiment, Pelops found a region where a handful of small, mostly dormant volcanoes spewed gases into the local atmosphere. He moved the Stargate on Tiryns to this location, and established the Tirynsian village and his Temple nearby. In addition to these natural toxins, Pelops also built a series of ducts beneath the Temple that continually emit other chemicals from underground storage tanks into the local atmosphere. Sophisticated sensors in the Temple monitor the atmosphere and adjust the levels of the gases, slowly increasing the toxicity every few dozen years. Having lived on this world for centuries, the Tirynsians adapted to the poison atmosphere over time, but off-world visitors suffer from nausea and coughing fits when exposed to the air for even a few moments.

The Temple of Pelops on Tiryns is located in the center of the village, and is an almost exact duplicate of the temple on Argos, including the statue of Pelops in its center, (which also conceals the transmitter device that controls the nanocytes responsible for the Tirynsians accelerated aging and a Goa'uld tablet containing the details of his experiment on this world). Inscriptions on the walls of the temple tell the story of how the Tirynsians were brought to this world and how the people, known as the Cursed, must endure one hundred days of suffering and torment as punishment for some unspecified crime of their ancestors.

The Cursed are aptly named, as life on Tiryns is harsh indeed. Sunshine rarely penetrates the thick layers of clouds and gases in the atmosphere, and the land is dry and poorly suited for agriculture. The few crops are largely tasteless, and offer only marginal levels of nutrition. The village itself consists of dozens of drab stone and plaster buildings of ancient Grecian architecture, much like the village on Argos, but lacking in decorations. Every few years Pelops sends Jaffa and other servants through the Stargate to ensure that the people are still "paying for the crimes of their ancestors." This also provides him the opportunity to check on the conditions of the atmosphere and to ensure the stores of artificial toxins remain sufficiently stocked.

1-07: COLD LAZARUS

World Visited: P3X-562 (Hot World).

Thermosphere: Hot (CR 0; normal orbit; 3d20+50° F).

Atmosphere: Normal (CR 0; 1.0 atmospheres).

Hydrosphere: Desert (daily weather 1-92: none, 93: rain (less than 1 inch), 94-95: sulfur dust storm, 96-100: wind 1d10 MPH).

Geosphere: Stable tectonic activity (daily earthquakes 1-99 none, 100 minor).

Seasons: Normal (1-25: spring unchanged; 26-50: summer +1d10° F; 51-75: autumn unchanged; 76-100: winter -2d10° F).

Anthrosphere: Less than 100 natives; Exotic; Pantisocracy; Neutral; Defensively pacifistic (no formal military); very progressive civil rights.

Origin: Exotic Life Forms.

Stargate Location (sulfuric desert): Sulfuric sand dunes within 200 feet of clusters of native life form.

EPISODE SUMMARY

SG-1 arrives on an alien world unlike any they have seen before, with bright blue skies, an intense sun, and sand made up of some sulfurous mineral that extends for miles. Near the Stargate the team makes an interesting discovery. Several thousand blue crystals, each one as large as a human forearm, are scattered around a bowl-shaped pit carved out of a nearby dune. Most of the crystals are broken and shattered, but a few remain fully intact.

As O'Neill orders Captain Carter to collect any samples she needs, he wanders off over a nearby dune only to discover another grove of these crystals that appears to be mostly intact. Briefly fascinated, he bends down and extends a hand out toward one of the larger crystals when a bolt of energy hurls him several feet back and knocks him to the ground, unconscious. There is another flash of ener-

gy, and a perfect copy of the unconscious O'Neill appears seemingly out of nowhere. When the rest of the team calls out, the faux O'Neill turns and rejoins them. The four of them head through the Stargate back to Earth, leaving the real Colonel O'Neill behind.

Back at Stargate command, the members of SG-1 begin noticing a significant change in the Colonel's behavior. Seeming lethargic and disoriented, the impostor is granted leave by General Hammond, while Carter begins her investigation into the strange crystals gathered from P3X-562. She is startled when the crystals begin to shift their form. After a few moments, a face eerily similar to hers forms within the crystal and a haunting voice begs "Help me." Within seconds the image and voice are gone, but Carter and Jackson have already begun to investigate the strange life form.

Meanwhile, the duplicate O'Neill has gone to the home of his estranged wife, Sara. After a few tense moments and some strange encounters, Sara finally invites him inside where they reminisce about their deceased son, Charlie. The duplicate seems obsessed with finding Charlie, even though he died many years ago, and continues to have flashbacks straight from the Colonel's memories. Sara realizes that there is something wrong with her ex-husband, but does not understand that he is merely an imposter despite frequently making mention of the Stargate. The two of them move to a nearby park to continue their discussion, but after only a few moments the duplicate falls to the ground, wracked with pain. As bolts of energy course through his body, Sara transports him to a nearby hospital.

At the SGC, the base is put on alert by an unscheduled off world activation of the Stargate. When SG-1's identification signal comes through, the iris is opened and the real Colonel O'Neill steps through, none too pleased at being left behind. Not realizing that the fake O'Neill came back with SG-1, Hammond has the Colonel taken into custody and examined by Dr. Fraiser. When she confirms that he is Colonel O'Neill (or a perfect impostor), Captain Carter reveals her discovery of the sentient energy life form in the crystals, which calls itself the Unity. Theorizing that the damaged crystals might have been the primitive forms of a more highly evolved species, the members of SG-1 deduce that a more advanced crystal must have duplicated Colonel O'Neill and come back to Earth. The search begins to find this alien life form before it can harm anyone.

At the hospital, the health of the impostor rapidly fades. The Unity cannot stand the intense electromagnetic field generated by the Earth and its degeneration carries dangerous side effects. As his body gives off electrical shocks and radiation, the doctors and patients evacuate the building. SG-1 arrives on the scene after receiving word that Sara O'Neill was at the hospital and, protected by radiation suits, they approach the dying duplicate. The Unity explains that a Goa'uld scout team came through the Stargate long ago, and that the crystals inadvertently killed one of the interlopers in a manner similar to the blast suffered by O'Neill. In retaliation, the Goa'uld wiped out most of his kind. When Colonel O'Neill was injured by touching the crystal, the Unity feared a similar reprisal from the new visitors and sought to make things right. Unable to heal the Colonel, the crystal mimicked him and came through the Stargate. Before the Unity can harm anyone else, SG-1 leads him out of the building in the guise of Charlie O'Neill and back through the Stargate to the safety of his own world.

BACKGROUND
THE UNITY

The encounter with the Unity introduced a new form of life to the scientists of Earth: energy-based beings. Each Unity crystal is a unique and separate sentient being and can function independently despite constant telepathic communication with its fellow s. The unique electromagnetic field on P3X-562 allowed the crystals to evolve into complex beings unlike any other in the galaxy. On first encountering the Unity, few would guess that the tall blue crystals were anything more than a natural geological formation. In truth, they are a vessel for the consciousness of a Unity, harnessing the electromagnetic energy that the planet generates and focusing it to produce sentient thought. Over time, the consciousness in these crystals learn to manipulate their surroundings and thus a Unity is born. The Unity do not reproduce normally but instead evolve as more crystals grow on the planet's surface. The best way that scientists have been able to classify the Unity is that they are sentient energy fields inhabiting and manipulating a crystal vessel.

Some Unity can only manipulate their physical forms a small amount; they can create images in the crystals themselves and manipulate the energy field around them for a few yards. Others, especially those that have been sentient for long periods of time, have mastered their abilities to the point that they can alter their crystal bodies to take almost any form and can deftly control energy fields whenever they choose. These evolved crystals can become mobile by taking on another form and are not limited to simply resting in one place like the less evolved members of the species. In fact, following the encounters with the Tauri on their homeworld the Unity has begun taking human (or occasionally other alien) forms at almost all times in order to better interact with the humans. Additionally, as a Unity evolves to a higher degree of sentience they begin to develop more consistent telepathy and can eventually learn to read the minds of biological life forms. This telepathy keeps them in constant touch with one another and serves as the source of their name. Though each Unity can function as an individual, when in telepathic contact with its brethren it shares something akin to a hive mind.

The Unity are affected by their planet's electromagnetic field, and as a result are limited to the planets they can safely visit. Earth, for example, has too strong of an electromagnetic field for them to survive for any length of time. In such an environment, a Unity will be wracked by pain and eventually lose control over its own energy. Conversely, a weak electromagnetic field will cause a Unity to become lethargic and sluggish, often resulting in unconsciousness or even the dissipation of the sentient mind of the Unity. Despite these limitations, many Unity (particularly those evolved enough to take on mobile forms) can survive for short periods of time on such worlds without having to worry about the side effects of their electromagnetic fields.

UNITY PACIFISTS

The sentient Unity were able to fully understand and comprehend the holocaust that befell them when the Goa'uld laid waste to their kind and have reacted in different ways to the event. They eventually divided into two factions: the pacifists and the vengeance seekers. While all were saddened and scared by the display of violence, many thought that they were themselves the cause of the whole event. The pacifists believe that they are somehow to blame for the death of the Goa'uld and that they originally started the entire conflict by inadvertently killing an outsider. These Unity claim that they were, in essence, the aggressors and now strive to make peace between themselves and any outsiders they may encounter. The Unity that impersonated Colonel O'Neill was one such pacifist, believing that further pain and violence could be avoided if he could only retrieve O'Neill's son from Earth. Other pacifists would rather destroy themselves than allow another being to be harmed by their energy, fearing similar reprisals even in the case of an accident. Entire groups of pacifists have destroyed each other to prevent harm to an outsider, while other pacifists consider them martyrs. For the most part, the pacifists are peace loving and will go to great lengths to keep other beings from harm.

One area in which these pacifists excel is in the healing arts. After a few encounters with other species, including the Tauri, the pacifists began studying ways to repair any damage done to another being. The Unity that impersonated Colonel O'Neill mentioned that he was unable to repair the damage that had been done, but other Unity have can perform miraculous feats of healing using their unique energy. Their telepathy improves these abilities even further, for it allows the healers to better understand how a certain being is put together (since the brains of most species controls the functions of the body), and thus repair any damage quickly and effectively.

UNITY VENGEANCE SEEKERS

Just as some among the Unity consider themselves responsible for the Goa'uld reprisals, others place the blame squarely on the outsiders, and demand justice and vengeance. These are the militant Unity, those that would use their powers to fight and destroy the Goa'uld. The vengeance seekers themselves are not inherently violent or filled with anger, but rather they do possess a cold need for revenge in order to send a message to the Goa'uld. These Unity are careful to ensure that other innocents are unharmed in their quests for revenge, but for the Goa'uld and their minions they show absolutely no mercy.

The unwavering focus of Unity vengeance seekers may seem strange to the Tauri at times because such unrelenting zeal is often seen as an excuse for brutality. It is also true that these Unity do not spare any agents of the Goa'uld nor are the encumbered by any sense of pity or mercy. Even the most driven vengeance seekers, however, frequently accept alternative means of achieving their goals when approached with a reasonable plan. The vengeance seekers are not zealots but are unafraid to use any means necessary of exacting their revenge. The ability to reason with them only partially offsets their dangerous nature.

The vengeance seekers are formidable combatants and use tactics and abilities that most beings in the galaxy have never encountered before. Their ability to fire powerful bolts of energy and exude radiation at will makes them both dangerous and subtle enemies. Carrying no visible weaponry, a vengeance seeking Unity can slip undeterred close to an enemy and attack without warning and then vanish. Their limited ability to shapeshift provides further advantage, though the process is clearly taxing, and has encouraged them to become stealthy assassins rather than straightforward warriors. These Unity can be both dangerous opponents or powerful allies, but most of them care for only one thing: bringing justice to the Goa'uld.

INHOSPITABLE WORLDS

One problem from which all Unity suffer is their limited ability to travel offworld. For example, the Unity cannot survive for long on Earth or any world with a strong electromagnetic field. Fortunately, each Unity has a short grace period during which it may discover whether or not the planet is hospitable. Most can survive for a few hours even in the most intense electromagnetic fields, and on worlds where the field is actually weaker than P3X-562 they merely become lethargic rather than experiencing intense pain. Despite this, many Unity that spend extensive periods of time away from their home world learn how to adapt to other electromagnetic fields and still maintain their health. These Unity can nearly double the amount of time they may spend on a world with a different electromagnetic field without succumbing to negative effects.

ALLIES OF THE SGC

Since the Tauri discovered P3X-562, relations between the Unity and the SGC have developed slowly to the point where they consider each other allies. Though the SGC does not always agree with or approve of the methods or actions of the vengeance seeking Unity, Stargate Command recog-

HEREVAH

Lord Kur operates from a hellish planet known as Herevah, using it as his throne world and seat of power. Herevah is an unstable world covered in mountain ranges and volcanoes with very little in the way of large bodies of water. The planet can sustain life, but has no indigenous sentient life forms. The System Lord transported all of his servants here long ago in order to serve him in a properly imposing environment. The inhospitable planet boasts an electromagnetic field that is surprisingly compatible with the Unity, allowing the faux Lord Kur to operate from the world without any difficulties. Since the replacement of the original Goa'uld, Lord Kur has rarely left the fortress of this world, relying on his underlings to take the battle to the other System Lords.

World: Herevah.

Thermosphere: Hot (CR 0; normal orbit; 3d20+50° F).

Atmosphere: Thick (CR 0; 1.6 atmospheres, -2 Int/Wis penalty, Fort Save DC 15, 1d3 subdual damage, recovery time 1 round).

Hydrosphere: Arid (daily weather 1-89: none, 90: wind 1d10 MPH, 91-93: rain 1 inch, 94-95: ash storm, 96-100 wind 1d10 MPH).

Geosphere: Very Unstable tectonic activity (daily earthquakes 1-90: none, 91-95: minor, 96-99: moderate, 100: major; volcanoes 1-98 none, 99 small (20%), 100: medium (20%)).

Seasons: Normal (1-25: spring unchanged; 26-50: summer +1d10° F; 51-75: autumn unchanged; 76-100: winter -2d10° F).

Anthrosphere: 400,000 natives; Goa'uld (7 picks, 6 RP); Autocracy; Hostile (-2 with disposition checks); Aggressive (1,000 soldiers, squad size 2d6 soldiers); Poor civil rights.

Origin: Sumerian.

Stargate Location (mountain region): Rocky terrain in mountainous region, near Jaffa city.

nizes the potential value of the Unity as allies (and conversely the associated danger of alienating them). Much like the alliances between Earth and other species, the alliance between the Unity and the Tauri has yielded many positive results. For one, the Unity have been eager to help assist on missions against the Goa'uld, either as healers or as combatants. Additionally, thanks to the cooperation of various Unity the scientists at Stargate command have learned a great deal about the way sentience develops within the Unity crystals. While no new weapons or technology have come from this research, it has allowed the SGC to determine why a Unity is able to fool most sensors and instruments when impersonating an individual (steps have been taken to discern whether or not a returning SG team member is in fact a Unity duplicate).

Since the Unity cannot survive for long on Earth, most interaction between them and the SGC takes place at the Alpha Site. The world chosen for the Alpha Site has an electromagnetic field that does not interfere with the energy of the Unity, meaning that Unity may travel freely there for extended periods of time. Additionally, in the cases where an SG team might have need of a Unity for a special task, they will operate from the Alpha Site as though it were the primary base of operations. All Unity use the Alpha Site as their primary location of interaction with the SGC.

In the rare case where a Unity might compromise the security of the SGC or the Alpha Site, the standard precautions are taken (such as GDO codes being changed) in the same manner as if another one of the SGC's allies was captured. Since the Unity display powerful telepathy that the Tauri simply cannot counteract, hiding any information from the Unity is a near impossibility. However, in order to encourage trust between the two groups the Unity promised not to use their telepathy against a member of the Tauri except in the most extreme circumstances (such as when a life depends on it). Though this has not eliminated all of the wariness associated with being around a telepathic being, it has certainly eased tensions between the two groups and fostered a healthy bond of trust.

tioned whether or not this was their god. Those doubts were silenced when the new Lord Kur displayed the ability to fire bolts of energy without a kara kesh and read the thoughts of his First Prime. The Unity, now impersonating the System Lord, seized the forces formerly under the real Kur's control and began using them for his own war against the other System Lords.

KUR

The original System Lord Kur was never a prominent figure in Earth's history. He appears in Sumerian (and occasionally Assyrian) mythology as a dragon or a dragon god, probably a reference to the snake-like appearance of the larval Goa'uld. Kur embraced this imagery as it made him an intimidating force and gave him a reputation for savagery and power. The helmets worn by Kur's Jaffa are modeled after dragons and the traditional draconic imagery associated with Kur is found in architecture throughout his realm. Kur was one of the few System Lords that truly embraced the uncomprehending imagery given to him by

"WE'D LOVE TO STICK AROUND, BUT SOME BRAIN-DEAD SYCOPHANT LEFT MY BUDDY OUT THERE TO DIE, SO WE'RE OUTTA HERE."

– COL. JACK O'NEILL

FALSE GOD

The Unity told the SGC that the mass grave found near the Stargate was the result of the accidental death of an outsider. Remnants of staff weapon fire in and around the pit confirm that a Goa'uld expedition slaughtered a large portion of the Unity, but the few Unity that survived were unable to discern which System Lord the expedition belonged to. The truth is that only one of the Unity ever discovered who it was, and when it did it shut off all telepathic communication in order to hide itself. Though the rest of the Unity thought it had died, the truth behind what happened to it is a far more dangerous story.

The Goa'uld scout team which massacred the Unity were servants of the System Lord Kur, who had been so anxious to seize some of these crystals himself (believing that they could be used to enhance his own technology) that he came along on the mission to personally oversee their collection. When he reached out and touched one of the highly advanced crystals, a powerful blast of energy lanced out of the crystal and killed him instantly. To the shock of all his loyal Jaffa, Lord Kur was dead beyond revival. Kur's First Prime ordered that the crystals be gathered in one place and destroyed, forever eliminating a threat to the System Lords and lashing out at the Unity for killing his master.

Though the scout team journeyed back through the Stargate the story does not end there, the crystal that Kur had touched manipulated its form and became an exact copy of the System Lord. When "Lord Kur," who had been presumed dead, appeared through the Stargate on his throne world of Herevah, even his most loyal Jaffa ques-

his followers and would go to great lengths to match their expectations of him. He was intimidating and imposing, even when dealing with his own Jaffa, and ruled through violence and fear. Even though Kur never rose to a significant position among the System Lords, many people of Earth knew him and feared his might.

When Kur was killed by the Unity and replaced, most saw the switch as a display of his true divinity. Their god had been killed and resurrected without the help of a sarcophagus, emerging with the power to throw lightning from his hands and to read the very thoughts of follower and enemy alike. Combined with his already formidable reputation, the new Lord Kur quickly began a new war against the System Lords. Such attacks were seen as the normal struggle for power, and none suspected that the god they now served was an impostor taking over for the System Lord it had killed. Raids on other Goa'uld were incredible successes, and his forces, now instilled with an unsurpassed zeal, saw nothing but victory on every front.

The other System Lords were baffled by his success; they always considered Kur to be little more than a minor figure in their pantheon. A few of his rivals took him seriously enough to send an ashrak to eliminate him, but when the assassin failed to return, they decided not to waste any more resources until more System Lords could be rallied against him. Since Kur did not possess a significant space fleet or enough Jaffa to challenge one of the major System Lords, he was allowed his petty victories.

After a few initial successes, Kur (as the Unity now thought of itself) became more conservative in his tactics. With his initial thirst for revenge sated, he realized that too much aggression would call down the might of the more powerful System Lords before he was ready. Lord Kur has only one goal in mind – the total eradication of the Goa'uld – and it wouldn't do to overextend himself too early. His drive for justice has made him as dangerous as any true System Lord, and unlike other vengeance seekers, he has no compunctions about harming the innocent in order to slay another Goa'uld. His quiet war has lasted for centuries with no one – not even his fellow Unity – the wiser.

DRAGON GUARDS

Lord Kur's dragon imagery extends to his Jaffa, the dragon guards. Each is trained to be a vicious warrior that will fight to the end, never surrendering even in the most dire circumstances. Additionally, Jaffa lore describes the dragon guards as both cunning and deceitful warriors that will not hesitate to use any advantage given to them in battle. Some see them as dishonorable, but the dragon guards are too dedicated to victory to give up an advantage. They have been known to fight their way out of seeming impossible odds by using unadulterated savagery in combat.

Dragon guards are outfitted with standard Jaffa armor and staff weapons, while some carry zat'nik'tel. Additionally, they wear special helmets bearing the visages of fierce dragons, that are used for both practical and intimidation purposes. Additionally, all dragon guards are equipped with a special weapon unique to the forces of Kur: twin blades known as dragon talons, which strap to the forearm and extend over the back of the hand roughly 8 inches in front of a closed fist. The blades curve slightly downward roughly two inches from the tip, giving the weapons the appearance of talons. These weapons are used in close combat and allow the dragon guards a means of lashing out at an enemy that is too close for a staff weapon or a zat gun.

GOA'ULD SCOUT TEAMS

The forces of Kur that came to P3X-562 originally belonged to what is known as a Goa'uld scout team. Each scout team is tasked with investigating new worlds in the Stargate system and reporting their findings back to the System Lords. Even though the System Lords have used the Stargate system for millennia, the sheer number of hospitable and valuable planets on the network means that exploration takes time. Since most System Lords have more important things to do than hop between planets searching for anything that might be of use, a scout team is dispatched to locate resources or report on possible threats. In many ways, the Goa'uld scout teams are like the System Lords' version of Stargate Command, traveling across the gate network in search of new worlds, new weapons, and new resources.

Though Kur himself happened to be with the scout team on the mission where he was killed, most teams consist of several Jaffa and perhaps a Goa'uld underlord to oversee them. A scout team is not heavily armed and frequently carries little more than staff weapons and survival gear.

Though occasionally the underlord leading the scout team will bring along a zat'nik'tel or some other advanced weaponry, the Goa'uld recognize the risk associated with sending a scout team onto unknown worlds carrying Goa'uld technology. Team members are trained to operate with a bare minimum of support (and frequently with no support at all) and can spend extended periods of time on a world without ever having to return to their System Lord's forces to gather supplies.

Since the scout teams are mostly concerned with investigation of worlds on the Stargate network, they have little time for posing as gods (or even the agents of gods) to other civilizations. Most team members forgo the traditional helmet of their System Lord and instead opt to wear only the chain shirt and armored plates used by standard Jaffa troops. Others, particularly those who were in the service of Ra, did not even bother with the protective armor and opted to wear lightweight clothing that permitted rapid movement and easy camouflage. Many System Lords do not brand their insignias into the foreheads of scout team members, allowing them to blend in with local populations or avoid implicating that System Lord if captured by a rival Goa'uld. Goa'uld scouts use the spy specialty found on page 415 of the *Stargate SG-1* core rulebook.

1-08: THOR'S HAMMER

World Visited: P3X-974 (Cimmeria).
Thermosphere: Cool (CR 0; normal orbit; 2d20° F).
Atmosphere: Normal (CR 0; 0.9 atmospheres).
Hydrosphere: Moist Sub-Humid (daily weather 1-85: none, 86-87: flood, 88-93: rain 1d4 inches/snow 1d6 inches, 96-100: tornado or blizzard).
Geosphere: Stable tectonic activity (daily earthquakes 1-99 none, 100 minor).
Seasons: Normal (1-25: spring unchanged; 26-50: summer +1d10° F; 51-75: autumn unchanged; 76-100: winter -2d10° F).
Anthrosphere: 10,000 natives; Bronze Age (3 picks, 1 RP); Feudalism; Friendly (+1 with disposition checks); Aggressive (500 soldiers, squad size 2d4 soldiers); Poor civil rights.
Origin: Norse.
Stargate Location (mountain region): Forest terrain in mountainous region, near native villages.

Cimmeria is described at greater length on pages 72-74 of the *Stargate SG-1* core rulebook.

EPISODE SUMMARY

Having encountered multiple examples of the Goa'uld impersonating Earth deities, Daniel Jackson reasons that other alien species may have done the same thing. Looking to Norse mythology, he points to the god Thor as an example of a benevolent deity that protected his people rather than oppressed them. When Teal'c chimes in with the knowledge of Stargate coordinates of a forbidden planet, taught to all Jaffa so that no Goa'uld might accidentally go there, SG-1 is given a green light to seek out signs of benevolent aliens and potential weapons against the Goa'uld.

Arriving on P3X-974, SG-1 receives a startlingly unexpected reception: the natives double over in uproarious laughter, pointing at the team and apparently mocking them. In front of the Stargate stands a massive stone structure, vaguely shaped like a hammer and covered in runes. As the local inhabitants begin chanting the name of Thor, the hum of energy begins to emanate from the device. Colonel O'Neill orders Daniel to begin dialing home, but it is too late; the monolith scans each member of the team with a ray of blue energy and teleports Teal'c and O'Neill, who dives to knock the Jaffa out of the beam, away from the Stargate. Dr. Jackson and Captain Carter are left alone with Gairwyn, a local woman, who explains that Thor relocated the inhabitants many generations ago, bringing them from Earth ("Midgard") to this new world of Cimmeria. Her fellow natives thought SG-1 to be ettins (the Cimmerian nickname for the Goa'uld), explaining the strange reception they received.

Meanwhile, O'Neill and Teal'c awaken inside a mysterious cave to a holographic recording from Thor – a Viking human complete with hammer and helm. It addresses them as Goa'uld and identifies himself as the Supreme Commander of the Asgard fleet. Under a provision of the Protected Planets Treaty, Cimmeria is off-limits to all Goa'uld under pain of death according to the hologram. The recording instructs them to go through the Labyrinth to the Hall of Mjolnir where the host will be freed and the parasitic Goa'uld destroyed. Additionally, it is noted that Goa'uld weaponry will not work in these caves, though human weapons still seem to. Seeing no other alternative, O'Neill and Teal'c set off to find a way out without harming Teal'c's symbiote.

Gairwyn introduces Sam and Daniel to a woman named Kendra, who was once host to a Goa'uld. Kendra originally served as a priestess on a world known as Jebanna, but was taken from her home by Marduk and given to another Goa'uld as her host. During her possession, she was forced to endure the pain which the parasite inflicted on countless beings and watched helplessly as she committed horrible atrocities. Despite this, she was able to fight back and, thanks to her temple training, began planting thoughts of ambition into the mind of her Goa'uld. As the crowning act of rebellion, she convinced her symbiote to go to Cimmeria and tricked her into being destroyed by Thor's Hammer. Dr. Jackson is heartened by this news, seeing a chance to free Sha'uri and Skaara from their symbiotes, and implores Kendra to take them to the caves where Thor's Hammer was. After much personal struggle, Kendra agrees.

Inside the labyrinth, O'Neill and Teal'c make little headway in their search for an alternate exit. Soon, however, their presence awakens a massive and powerful beast that Teal'c identifies as an Unas, among the first hosts of the Goa'uld. The Unas is incredibly tall, monstrous, and cov-

ered in chitin and bone. This Unas, still host to a Goa'uld, tries to convince Teal'c to betray Jack; Teal'c responds by reiterating his rejection of the false gods. Enraged, the Unas attacks the pair but is seemingly defeated. Teal'c is only partially convinced that the Unas is dead, but the pair continues on toward the Hall of Mjolnir.

Kendra continues to lead Sam and Daniel through a mountain path, but has difficulty recalling where exactly the entrance to the caves is. Captain Carter believes that Kendra is trying to trick them, either still under Goa'uld influence or for some other reason, but Daniel's desperation to find hope for freeing Sha'uri drives them to continue. Eventually the trio discovers the hidden entrance to the caves, only to arrive just in time for another battle against the Unas.

The creature soon revives and pursues O'Neill and Teal'c through the maze to the Hall of Mjolnir. Teal'c hurls himself against the beast and encourages his friend to flee. He is initially overwhelmed by the fearsome Unas, but eventually manages to force the creature between the archway that makes up Thor's Hammer, killing the Goa'uld and its Unas host using the painful energy generated by the weapon. In order to save their friend, the rest of SG-1 steps outside of the Hall of Mjolnir through the archway unharmed, and Daniel fires Teal'c's now-functional staff weapon at Thor's Hammer. The device is destroyed – along with the hopes of using it to free Daniel's wife – and Teal'c is freed. SG-1 returns to Earth no closer to meeting Thor but secure in the knowledge that he possesses great weapons against the Goa'uld.

BACKGROUND
AGAINST THE ETTINS

As one of the most advanced species in the galaxy, the Asgard have developed numerous means of fighting the Goa'uld. Unfortunately for the System Lords, they possess superior technology and have designated many planets as off-limits to the Goa'uld. In order to enforce these bans and prevent the Goa'uld from expanding beyond into Asgard territory, the Asgard use a number of technological advances that specifically target the Goa'uld without causing any collateral damage to other protected species (such as the humans on Cimmeria). Some of the most prominent are described below. More information on the Asgard can be found in the *Stargate SG-1* core rulebook.

GOA'ULD WEAPON DISABLER

One of the major advantages that the Goa'uld have over the species they subjugate is their highly advanced technology. With weapons and armor far superior to that of primitive cultures, the Goa'uld are capable of imposing their will quickly and decisively. In order to counteract this, the Asgard developed technology to strip invading Goa'uld of their weapons without having to overpower them. The result is the *ramir*, a device that renders all Goa'uld weapons completely useless. The ramir is a small disc that projects a spherical field out from its center; any Goa'uld technology within that radius simply will not function. It interrupts the energy transmitted by the naquadah in Goa'uld technology and can also be used to disrupt weapons and devices of non-Goa'uld origin that use naquadah as the primary element for power generation. These discs are small and require little energy to operate, meaning that the power cells the Asgard installed in them last for a considerable amount of time.

The Labyrinth on Cimmeria has a number of ramir installed in the walls, floors, and ceilings such that the energy fields they generate overlap and create a seamless bubble inside which Goa'uld technology ceases to function. Within the Labyrinth, the ramir prevent Goa'uld from using staff weapons or other devices to escape their prison without going through the Hall of Mjolnir. Additionally, the ramir are powered independently and unconnected to the Goa'uld-killing Thor's Hammer. As a result, when SG-1 disabled Thor's Hammer with a staff weapon blast, the ramir inside the Labyrinth continued to function.

MJOLNIR PENDANTS

Before the construction of the Labyrinth and the installation of Thor's Hammer, the Asgard tried several methods of protecting humans from enslavement at the hands of the Goa'uld. One device that came out of these weapons is an ornamental piece of jewelry known as a *mjolnir*, named after the chosen weapon of Thor. The mjolnir is a small pendant shaped roughly like a hammer that many humans wore as a good luck charm. Each pendant is made from a metal alloy designed to repel Goa'uld larvae. The pendant produces an odor that the Goa'uld cannot stand (and that humans cannot smell) and the metals disrupt the naquadah in the blood of the symbiote, causing them extreme discomfort and pain. The Asgard distributed these pendants to the people at first to protect them from being taken as hosts by the Goa'uld. However, as the humans became more fruitful and populations began to grow, the Asgard could no longer produce the pendants in such abundance to protect all of them and sought out new ways to protect their charges. The result was the development of Thor's Hammer.

Though the Asgard ceased the distribution of the mjolnir pendants some time ago, many remained in the hands of humans on planets like Cimmeria, and Vanaheim. Additionally, human craftsmen began making their own pendants, though they never possessed the same Goa'uld-repelling powers of the ones distributed by the Asgard. So many of these powerless charms were produced that eventually all of the true mjolnir pendants were lost in the jumble of human creations and sank into obscurity. Many are thought to reside in the museums of the Tauri, while others remain as family heirlooms and good luck charms. Though there is no way for anyone but the Asgard themselves to identify the true mjolnir pendants, those that have them are always safe from infestation by a Goa'uld and most of the remaining pendants are highly valued for their protective powers.

THOR'S HAMMER

When the Asgard could no longer protect the humans of Cimmeria on an individual basis, Thor deemed it time to try something new. Since most of the fiercest fighting between the Asgard and the System Lords was long over, the Asgard could focus their attention on the protection of Cimmeria and other threatened worlds. The result of their research was a complex device dubbed Thor's Hammer, actually an amalgamation of several pieces of Asgard technology into a single functional system. First, a monolith designed to imitate the Norse architectural was placed at the base of the Cimmeria Stargate, featuring both sophisticated sensors and a miniaturized version of the Asgard teleportation technology. A cave in the mountains was hollowed out and filled with ramir in order to disable Goa'uld weaponry; additionally, the designers of the cave made sure that suitable food was available for a Goa'uld to scratch out a meager existence for an extended period of time. At the end of the cave system, the Hall of Mjolnir holds the actual Thor's Hammer device. Built into an archway leading to the cave's exit, the device targets and kills Goa'uld symbiotes by delivering a high-intensity energy stream to the Goa'uld inside the host. The process is excruciating for both the Goa'uld and its hosts, but in the end the host survives while the symbiote dies and is broken down by the host's immune system. Once the entire structure was complete, a holographic recording of Thor—in the human form he used to appear to humans—was added to explain the design (and legal validity) of the caves to any trapped Jaffa or Goa'uld.

VANAHEIM

Tyr chose the world of Vanaheim as the new home for his people for its similarity to the terrain on Earth. Though much of Vanaheim is locked in a permanent winter, there are enough temperate zones to sustain wildlife and provide the land and food the people needed. Massive glaciers cover a large portion of the planet, and the oceans remain relatively cold even close to the equator. The flora and fauna of the world resemble that of the American northwest, with trees and plant life that can survive cold winters and animals covered in thick coats of fur that hibernate through most of the harshest conditions.

Vanaheim was one of the few worlds that did not have its own Stargate and was, at the time, unreachable except by starship. Tyr chose this world because it lay outside of Goa'uld knowledge and transported his people there, leaving behind a Stargate brought from a world made uninhabitable by natural disaster. Untamed at the time of the arrival of the humans, Vanaheim itself quickly became the first test of the durability of humanity. A harsh winter wiped out large chunks of the population, and many feared that each day would be their last. When spring finally came, the people of Vanaheim were so toughened by the experience that they were able to endure almost any weather conditions. Over time, their society evolved and expanded. New luxuries gave rise to cities, and eventually the world evolved from an agrarian society into a scientific revolution (aided by the discovery of naquadah deposits underneath some of the thinner glaciers); at present day they share a technology level similar to that of Earth during the 1960's.

Vanaheim has three major cities, the most prominent of which is called New Midgard. The Stargate resides in this city and is guarded around the clock by soldiers with shock spears, awaiting the inevitable return of the Goa'uld. Vanaheim has its own system of roads and automobiles and has developed basic jet engine technology. Though the use of naquadah in their primary power source, their technology is capable of greater energy output that comparable technology on Earth. Each member of the Vanaheim military (which also doubles as the world's police force) carries a shock spear, though there have been no recorded wars in the history of the world.

Most citizens of Vanaheim accept the military control of their world as a matter of course, and believe that the return of the ettins is inevitable. Almost every person living on the world still considers Tyr to be an active part of their lives, and as such they are devoutly religious. Additionally, any characters emerging from the Stargate are immediately treated as hostiles (and probably as ettins) by the gate guards. As of yet, the people of Vanaheim have not mastered the use of the Stargate, considering it to be little more than the means of Goa'uld invasion to be kept under guard at all times.

World: Vanaheim.

Thermosphere: Cold (CR 0; normal orbit; -(1d%° F).

Atmosphere: Normal (CR 0; 0.8 atmospheres).

Hydrosphere: Humid (daily weather 1-79: none, 80-81: flood 1d10 MPH, 82: flood 1d10+10 MPH, 83-91: 1d6 inches of rain/1d10 inches of snow, 92-96: thunderstorm or snowstorm, 97-98: hurricane or blizzard, 99: wind 1d10 MPH, 100: wind 1d10+10 MPH).

Geosphere: Stable tectonic activity (daily earthquakes 1-99: none, 100: minor).

Seasons: Very Mild (1-42: spring unchanged; 43-50: summer +2d6° F; 51-92: autumn unchanged; 93-100 winter -2d6° F).

Anthrosphere: 2.1 million natives; Electronic Age (6 picks, 4 RP); Stratocracy; Suspicious (-1 with disposition checks); Sensitive (4,600 soldiers, squad size 2d4 soldiers); Progressive civil rights.

Origin: Norse.

Stargate Location (mountain region): Interior of a building in an urban region, inside the city of New Midgard.

The device was first built and tested on Cimmeria but has since been placed on a handful of other planets shielded by the Protected Planets Treaty. Additionally, a few other Fleet Commanders implemented similar designs and renamed them according to their own places in the Norse pantheon. Since the Goa'uld still rely on Stargate exploration as a primary means of travel, these devices remain one of the best defense systems in use on otherwise unprotected worlds.

VALKYRIES

Though most of the Asgard are capable of using their technology to defeat their enemies, few are as capable warriors as the Valkyries: a group of Asgard soldiers (and officers in the fleet) that have taken it upon themselves to be prepared for close, personal combat when necessary. Unlike the other members of their species, the Valkyries train in personal weaponry and individual or small group combat in order to be more effective in the fight against their enemies. The Valkyries were formed to combat the Goa'uld – rooting out fugitive System Lords, searching out hidden Goa'uld bases, and the like – making them one of the most unusual branches of Asgard society.

The Valkyries appeared to humans first as warrior women in order to distinguish themselves from the other Asgard. Over time, this image stuck with the Norse people and the organization became as legendary as the gods themselves. Eventually, the Valkyries could no longer focus their efforts on protecting humans from the Goa'uld and were forced to move on to other battlefields; notably to combat the Replicators. Over time, they vanished from the minds of humans and sank into the annals of mythology.

The Valkyries use the shock spears developed by Tyr (who commanded the Valkyries for a time before the Protected Planets Treaty) as their primary weapons and are as adept with the weapons as the soldiers of any other species. Valkyries also train in small-squad tactics and act as the Asgard equivalent of "Special Forces" teams in combat. They develop advanced tactics for dealing with particular enemies by studying their opponents' combat methodology, and are particularly lethal in groups. While most modern Valkyries primarily focus on fighting Replicators, others still train to combat the Goa'uld, Reetou terrorist squads, and the like. Additionally, some Valkyries have been placed on protected planets to safeguard a particular group against an expected invasion, though this guard duty is rare. A surprising number of cultures have integrated the Valkyries (or their equivalent divine protectors) into their religion and history, however, indicating that these Asgard once defended far more than a few scattered planets.

WARDS OF TYR

Thor was not the only member of the Asgard fleet to relocate a select group of humans for protection from the Goa'uld. Among those that aided in the preservation of humankind was Tyr, the one-time chief tactical officer and military strategist of the Asgard fleet. Unlike Thor, he did not think that sheltering his people from the Goa'uld would give them any incentive to grow stronger. He chose not to place one of the Thor's Hammer devices on the new world, which he called Vanaheim. When the Protected Planets Treaty was formed, Tyr designated Vanaheim as under his domain and relocated a select group of warriors and their families to populate the planet.

As a military officer, Tyr knew that the best way to protect his people from the Goa'uld was to let them protect themselves. Recognizing the significant technological advantage the Goa'uld have over more primitive species, he intervened in the natural evolution of mankind and gave his charges weapons with which to fight the Goa'uld. The people of Vanaheim were trained in the use of a weapon called the shock spear and were instructed to fire upon anyone that exited through the Stargate. Though there was a chance that a powerful System Lord and his or her associated forces might overwhelm the people of Vanaheim, he considered this an acceptable risk (and always kept a watchful eye on the world just in case) in order to promote the strength and capability of his chosen people.

Over the years, the people of Vanaheim became strong warriors and competent tacticians. Thanks to the technology placed in their hands, the curious among them began to promote scientific growth and the accumulation of knowledge. In time, the people of Vanaheim developed along two paths at the same time: the warriors evolved into a competent and well-organized military, while the citizens entered a scientific revolution similar to the Renaissance. Tyr was pleased with the way his people had developed, though many of the Asgard believed that his intervention prevented the humans from showing their true potential as a race. Thor, who was among the displeased, had Tyr removed from his position and relegated him to a secondary position as the captain of a single starship.

SHOCK SPEARS

Likely the most important contribution to the evolution of the society on Vanaheim, the shock spear is an Asgard weapon designed solely to combat the Goa'uld. Since most Asgard are unwilling to harm humans at any cost, the shock spears were engineered specifically to target Goa'uld physiology. As a result, a shock spear can only harm a character with naquadah in his or her blood, such as Goa'uld, and Jaffa. Unfortunately, this also means that they can harm Tok'ra and former hosts of the Goa'uld, but this is an acceptable risk given the need to protect the people of Vanaheim from invasion.

The shock spear is an energy weapon roughly 1.5 meters in length consisting of a long pole with a triangular nozzle at one end. The other end of the weapon has a square piece of metal with jagged teeth carved into it, designed to allow the bearer to brace the weapon against the ground without having it slide across a flat surface. The nozzle shoots forth a bolt of green energy that diffuses harmlessly against a target without naquadah in its bloodstream (occasionally causing one's hair to stand on end) but causing devastating damage to those that do. The energy bolt wracks a target with intense pain and can take down even the toughest Jaffa.

The people of Vanaheim were compelled to study the shock spears, which ignited the scientific revolution on their world. Thus far, their scientists have only been able to replicate the shock spears (providing enough for the military to make widespread use of) and have not been able to reverse-engineer the Asgard technology. The discovery of naquadah deposits on their world has prompted them to investigate the way the mysterious mineral is affected by the shock staff, and many of their scientists feel that they are on the verge of crafting energy weapons of their own without the limitations of the shock staff.

1-09: THE TORMENT OF TANTALUS

World Visited: PB2-908 (Heliopolis); originally designated as P3X-972.

Thermosphere: Hot (CR 0; Terran Orbit; 3d20 + 50° F).*

Atmosphere: Normal (CR 0; 1.0 Atmospheres).*

Hydrosphere: Humid (annual rainfall 60-80 in.; daily weather 1-79: none, 80-81: flood 1d10 mph, 82: flood 1d10+10 mph, 83-91: rain 1d6 in., 92-96: thunderstorm, 97-98: hurricane, 99: wind 1d10 mph, 100: wind 1d10+10 mph.*

Geosphere: Coast (Cliffs); Surrounding Terrain: Rolling; Very Stable Tectonic Activity (Daily Earthquakes N/A).*

Seasons: Mild (1-17: Spring unchanged; 18-50: Summer +2d10° F; 51-83: Autumn unchanged; 84-100: Winter -2d10° F). *

Anthrosphere: None.

Origin: Ancients.

Stargate Location (coastal region): Buried at the bottom of cliffs in a sea beneath the ruins of the Heliopolan castle.

See The Decaying Orbit of Heliopolis, page 154.

Dr. Daniel Jackson watches footage of a sepia-colored film dating from 1945 which reveals a group of army service men and scientists attempting to examine the Stargate. Even though the Pentagon has indicated the film footage contains the only information about these experiments, Dr. Jackson ponders the fact that he has found no notes or summaries and no apparent reason for the government's termination of the testing. Col. O'Neill enters the room just as the film shows a man being fitted into what appears to be a deep-diving suit as the Stargate is engaged by hand. Enraptured, the two watch as the man walks into the event horizon. Suddenly, the film ends abruptly when the Stargate disengages, cutting the air hose to the suit. Both are intrigued. Who had gone through the Stargate at this early date? As a follow up, Dr. Jackson decides to contact his old friend Dr. Catherine Langford, the originator of the Stargate program, to see if she can provide any information while Col. O'Neill remains behind to access SGC records for any explanation with reference to the scene they had witnessed.

Dr. Jackson confronts Dr. Langford with the question of why no one was told about the experiments the government conducted on the gate in 1945. Taken back, Dr. Langford recounts how President Roosevelt started the experiments on the Stargate to examine its potential as a weapon against the Nazis. He enlisted her father, Prof. Paul Langford, and his assistant, Dr. Ernest Littlefield, to lead the project. Dr. Langford remains steadfast in her claims the Stargate was never opened. In response, Dr. Jackson takes out the forgotten film footage and plays the scene he and Col. O'Neill had viewed earlier. With shock and dismay Catherine identifies the figure in the diving suit as Ernest, her father's assistant and her fiancé, whom her father claimed had been burned beyond recognition in an accidental fire.

Returning to SGC with Dr. Langford, Daniel attempts to convince Gen. Hammond to launch a mission using the coordinates in the film. After a bit of wrangling, Hammond agrees: if there is any possibility that Dr. Littlefield is alive, every effort should be made to find him. Arm-in-arm Dr. Jackson, Col. O'Neill, and Dr. Langford, together with the rest of SG-1, enter the Stargate.

The team emerges in a hot, dusty room falling into ruin. They hear thunder and lightening in the distance. Out of the shadows appears a wrinkled, stooped figure: a naked old man! In his bewilderment he stares at the visitors, thinking they must be a vision, for he is alone on this world and has been for over fifty years. Finally, the realization that the figures he sees are real sets in and runs hugging, laughing, and mumbling to each member of the team. When the old man is introduced to Catherine he scurries from the room in alarm. Running after the old man, Dr. Jackson finds him putting on clothes – a few pieces of an old diving suit. Ernest Littlefield is still alive! Samantha suggests Dr. Langford talk with Ernest, and she agrees to try.

Meanwhile Dr. Jackson attempts to engage Ernest on what he has learned about this world during the old man's exile. Ernest replies, "Heliopolis... repository... philosophy... astronomy". Excited with the possibilities, Dr. Jackson thinks this must be the remains of an ancient Egyptian city. People must have come from everywhere to gather here – scholars, community leaders, and scientists – since Heliopolis was also the central place of worship for Ra. Unfortunately, the strain of so many years alone has damaged Littlefield's psyche. He has spent fifty years imagining that Catherine has found him and they live together in a magnificent castle, their love growing with each day. The sight of the real Catherine – now as old as he – has proven too much for him.

Catherine enters the room and Ernest is confronted with reality. He and Catherine did not share a wonderful life together but, instead, she believed him dead. Seeing his entire life as a lie, Ernest stands in front of the love of his life with tears streaming down his face.

Meanwhile Col. O'Neill has discovered the instability of the structure and wishes to return the two doctors, Ernest and Catherine, to Earth then return with the SG-1 team for further study. Dr. Jackson implores the team not to leave because they might not be able to return. However, upon examination of the Dial Home Device, the team discovers it has been severely damaged and not functioning.

While Capt. Carter works on an alternate means of activating the Stargate, Dr. Littlefield takes Dr. Langford, Col. O'Neill, and Dr. Jackson back to his main room. He slowly uncovers a pedestal in the center of the room, causing four sets of writings to glow on the walls: one in runic (Asgardian); the others in languages of the Ancients, the

Nox, and the Furlings. The room is a meeting place for the four races to exchange information and converse – a United Nations of the Stars. Curious as ever Col. O'Neill investigates the pedestal in the center of the room. Lights shoot out forming into hundreds of elements: hydrogen, sodium, iron, silver, barium, xenon, and more, floating in the air with a total of 146 different elements. Catching on, Dr. Jackson realizes the images are, in fact, the most basic elements of the universe and they form the basis for a true universal language.

Walking to the pedestal, Dr. Littlefield touches the crystal again, and the lights rearrange into a new pattern. Dr. Jackson tries to record the images, but the recording will not allow for relative perspective. The pedestal contains some of the most important information known to man, including the collaboration of the knowledge of these four alien species, which could include some of the most profound secrets in the galaxy.

Meanwhile Capt. Carter and Teal'c manage to jury-rig the Stargate and DHD together. Once hooked together, the power-source from the DHD is wired directly to the Stargate. Even as the power is activated the lights dim and go off. The experiment fails. A section of the roof collapses, nearly taking Col. O'Neill and Capt. Carter to the bottom of the cliff, along with the DHD. Realizing that they need something with more kick to power the Stargate, Col. O'Neill suggests the "Ben Franklin" method of harnessing the lightning in the storm raging outside. Recovering the diving helmet from the rubble, Col. O'Neill and Teal'c use the brass helmet as a divining rod, placing it on one of the turrets outside the wrecked structure.

But, Dr. Jackson is not interested in helping. He is lost in obsession with the pedestal, but the secret lies just beyond his reach. Ernest tries to convince Daniel of the futility of his obsession, but Daniel will not budge. Suddenly, the lightning strikes the helmet on the tower roof. The power channels through a cable, charging the Stargate. Col. O'Neill orders Teal'c, Capt. Carter, and Dr. Langford through, while he searches for Dr. Jackson and Dr. Littlefield. Still, Daniel will not be deterred, refusing to abandon such a priceless find. Even as Ernest starts for the Stargate, Daniel stands in front of the pedestal as if made of stone. Jack physically wrests his friend away just as the building crumbles around them. The two make it back through the Stargate just before it disengages.

After a bit of rest, Jack, Daniel, Catherine, and Ernest look on in the control room as the SGC dials the coordinates to Heliopolis. As they fear, the seventh chevron will not engage, meaning the Stargate is now either buried or destroyed. All is not lost, however: Capt. Carter is working on a computer model of the pedestal room and the elemental book, much to Daniel's delight. And more importantly, Ernest and Catherine have been reunited, rekindling their love after so many long years of separation.

BACKGROUND
HELIOPOLIS AND THE ALLIANCE

Many millennia ago, four species – the Ancients, the Asgard, the Furlings, and the Nox – came together to form a great Alliance, based on mutual understanding, enlightenment, and the spread of knowledge to the betterment of the galaxy. Heliopolis became one of their primary meeting places, as evinced by Dr. Littlefield's amazing discovery. Here, they gathered the share their experiences, to debate matters of mutual interest, and to resolve disputes. For many millennia, their alliance prospered, but the departure of the Ancients symbolized a fragmenting of their union. The remaining three species went their own way, and while they maintained friendly relations, their active allegiance became a thing of the past.

Thousands of years later, the Goa'uld rose to prominence, spreading their parasitic tendrils across the galaxy. They made extensive use of Ancient technology – including the Stargate network – and often seized strongholds of the Ancients for their own use. One such place was Heliopolis, which the System Lord Ra claimed as his own. Though he could not entirely decipher the teachings that he found there (and had no interest in the lofty ideals most of it espoused), he refused to relinquish the planet, convinced that it held secrets better left in his hands than those of his foes.

So it remained until the Goa'uld encountered the Asgard, one of the four races of the original Alliance. The Asgard quickly recognized the Goa'uld for what they were, and responded to their aggression with force. Their conflict lasted for centuries and though the Asgard had the upper hand technologically, the Goa'uld proved a wily and tenacious foe. During this period, representatives from the Asgard visited the Nox and Furlings with the offer to renew their alliance – this time in opposition against the Goa'uld. The Nox wanted nothing to do with the Alliance – their pacifistic ways prevented them from taking violent action – but the Furlings agreed to join... on one condition. A single decisive strike had to be made against the Goa'uld, for the Furlings could not survive a long and protracted war of attrition. The Asgard agreed – they themselves wanted to avoid as much bloodshed as possible (particularly to the peoples subjugated by the Goa'uld, whom they viewed as unwitting accomplices and slaves) – and a plan was devised to strike a single devastating blow on one planet.

The planet to be chosen had to fulfill several criteria. The indigenous population must be minimal and also exist on other planets; no race could be completely wiped out by the attack. (This qualification ruled out the homeworld of the Goa'uld as this was the sole planet populated by the Unas.) Yet it also had to demonstrate the Alliance's strength and inflict a heavy blow on the Goa'uld. The planet could therefore not have naquadah as a natural resource (the Goa'uld could return to mine the planet), or possess some other advantage which the System Lords would seek to retake. Earth was not even considered as a target for two reasons. First, its destruction would not have caused the Goa'uld a significant enough set-back in their ability to wage war. Second, the Ancients, for reasons known only to them, forbade Earth from destruction, and the Asgard still honored the wishes of their long-gone allies.

While the Asgard and the Furlings deliberated, the Goa'uld continued their expansion, including territories controlled by the Allies... and the Nox. Several systems on the edge of Nox territory were wiped clean of sentient life by the Jaffa armies of the Goa'uld. Concerned that their philosophical beliefs had essentially painted them into a corner, the Nox chose to side with the Allies, sharing their cloaking technology, among others, on the condition that the chosen planet could not be completely destroyed. It must be allowed to continue its own existence. Even after the Nox joined the Alliance, they refused to take a hand direct hand in any attacks on the Goa'uld. Instead, they passively supported the other Allies in other means, materially, technologically, and morally.

The planet chosen was Heliopolis, which in the intervening centuries had become dedicated to the production of weapons, the building of vessels, and as a training ground for Ra's elite Jaffa warriors. Its loss would be devastating to the Goa'uld. Ra would lose a primary planet under his control, weakening his power enough for the other System Lords to take advantage of the situation. It also held symbolic power, as it had once been a great meeting place for the Alliance.

An immense fleet was dispatched to the planet. The Goa'uld had no chance at all. The allies wiped them out to a man, without suffering a single casualty in return. A weapon which had been designed specifically for this purpose was unleashed destroying all life on the planet and all artificial structures... all save a single fortress, in which Ra had held the gather knowledge of the Four Races. This they preserved, as a demonstration of their control and of the respect they held for their early unity. The attack had the desired effect. Ra fled for his life – eventually discovering the world of the Tauri – and the remaining System Lords sued for peace.

But the victory was short-lived. The Nox inspected the planet to ensure that it would survive, and discovered that the attack had altered its orbit in such a manner that life could not prosper there in any great abundance. Unfortunately, the Nox did not have the technology to fix this, neither did the Furlings, or the Asgard, at the time. The Ancients did have the capability, but they had long-since disappeared. So the planet was left abandoned and largely forgotten, the crumbling fortress the only remnant that anyone had been there at all.

THE STARGATE FROM 1928-1945

Nearly everyone in the SGC knows when and where the Stargate was discovered. A few even know who found it. But what happened to the Stargate after the discovery in 1928? Most believe it fell into the hands of the U.S. government, and indeed by 1945, the Americans were conducting secret tests on the device. But its route from Giza to Washington was more circuitous than most could imagine, and passed through a very dark and terrible place in the process.

The Stargate and all the artifacts found in the area were originally taken to the Egyptian Museum in Berlin. Prof. Paul Langford, who was in charge of the expedition, received permission to begin tests on the Stargate to discover its purpose. The research came to naught, though it had more to do with lack of funding (Germany was in precarious financial straits at the time) than any fault of Dr. Langford's.

This all changed once Adolf Hitler became Chancellor of Germany. Intrigued by the Stargate's occult possibilities, Hitler considered the device one of his "prized possessions" and authorize generous funding into its research. Langford

had fled Germany with his daughter to the United States when the Nazis took power, so the Führer assigned a military general as a replacement. Under his eye the Nazis soon uncovered a second device – the DHD – which made the their work considerably easier.

In 1939, just after the beginning of the war, a breakthrough took place: the Stargate opened. The address dialed was found by piecing together some of the stone fragments found at the dig site. Several explorers were sent through to investigate. Only one returned, with tales of a wondrous paradise... which was occupied by terrible "demons." According to his descriptions, the "Heaven" he discovered had apparently been overrun by Hell and was now populated by near-human looking beings, with horrendous powers of destruction. Not wanting to let the possibility of literally conquering Heaven slip through his fingers, Hitler ordered thousands of troops and tons of equipment to be sent through the Stargate. The battle was long and difficult, but in the end, the Germans prevailed. Approximately one year after the gate opened, Heaven was in the hands of the Nazis.

By this time, some of the senior members of the German high command were beginning to chafe under Hitler's heavy handedness and emotional instability. One of most senior, Field Marshall Erwin Rommel, was terrified of the Stargate's possibilities and unwilling to leave it in the Führer's hands. Heaven was rapidly becoming a thriving German colony, with thousands of "perfect" Aryan men and women passing through the Stargate to build a National Socialist Paradise. Rommel, however, had no intention of letting the colony give new resources to Hitler's cause... or of letting the Nazi leadership use the Stargate to escape should the Allies prevail. After allowing Heaven to develop to the point of self-sufficiency, he forged a set of requisitions ordering the Stargate to be transported to the town of Rostock (along with the coverstones that held it and other attendant artifacts). There, he would arrange for it to "disappear," never to be seen again. He deliberately left the DHD behind, so as to make operation of the Stargate impossible.

Meanwhile, the U.S. government had not lain silent. When they entered the war against Germany, Prof. Langford contacted the Roosevelt administration and shared what he knew about the Stargate. Discovering the location of the device became a top intelligence priority, and the OSS expended numerous resources in an effort to learn its location. Their big break came when Rommel's forged documents passed across the desk of an American mole at precisely the right time. The trucks never arrived in Rostock – they were seized by an elite commando unit on the shore of the Baltic Sea. The Stargate was hidden aboard a fishing vessel flying Swedish colors and surreptitiously transported to England, where it was flown by plane to the United States in early 1944.

President Roosevelt promptly ordered the gate to be researched as a possible weapon, and asked Prof. Langford to head the project. Though he disapproved of using the Stargate as a weapon, he reluctantly agreed to head up the project. Progress was slow without the DHD, but Langford and his team were very persistent. In January of 1945, as the war was winding down, they stumbled upon a second address.

Prof. Langford's assistant Dr. Ernest Littlefield was chosen to be the first through the Stargate. Not sure what was on the other side, the professor took every precaution. He allowed the explorer wear an underwater dive suit with an oxygen hose in case the planet on the other side proved inhospitable. Immediately after Ernest stepped through, the gate shut off severing the hose. When Ernest did not return, Prof. Langford feared the worst. All further attempts to use the Stargate were shut down and the project was mothballed. With the end of the war imminent, its use as a military weapon was no longer perceived as necessary. The Stargate was taken to a government warehouse, where it remained for several decades. Prof. Langford never mentioned what happened to Littlefield and discouraged his daughter Catherine from having anything to do with the artifacts. He was largely successful, until some unknown cause renewed her interest in the Stargate sometime around 1970. Her efforts since then led to the renewal of the Stargate program, which eventually resulted in the creation of the SGC.

Meanwhile, the Nazi colony on Heaven remains forgotten and undiscovered out among the stars. Cut off from the Fatherland and ignorant of Hitler's final defeat, their perverse ideology has flourished in the shadows of anonymity. Who knows what dark testament to the "Master Race" their civilization now embodies — and what will happen if the SGC ever finds them...

1-10: Bloodlines

World Visited: Chulak (*See Children of the Gods, page 6.*)

Episode Summary

In a nightmare vision, Teal'c watches powerless as a young Jaffa boy lies in a ceremonial tent, prepared to receive a larval Goa'uld. As a priest implants it, Teal'c finds himself in the boy's place. While the rest of SG-1 watches anxiously from the observation booth, Teal'c awakens to a very real disappointment: a drug that held out hope of replacing the immune function served by his symbiote has failed. Jackson asks about the word he cried out – "Rya'c" – but Teal'c claims it means nothing.

When he has recovered, SG-1 meets with Gen. Hammond and Dr. Fraiser to discuss the results of the experiment. More than Teal'c's hope for freedom from dependence on his symbiote has been dashed; the opportunity to study it could have proven invaluable. Teal'c points out that there are hundreds of Goa'uld larvae on his homeworld of Chulak, and that a daring team might be able to recover one. At the incredulous reaction of his team and the general — such a mission would be far too dangerous — Teal'c says he understands and will not speak of it again, but leaves abruptly without waiting for the briefing to be adjourned.

O'Neill follows him to his quarters and soon gets to the root of his uncharacteristic behavior: Rya'c is the name of Teal'c's son, who is about to come of age and receive his first symbiote in the "ceremony of implantation," called the *prim'ta.* Teal'c has kept his wife and son a secret from his

comrades, fearing that the liability they represent would prevent the SGC from accepting him. But now his overriding concern is to prevent his son from being enslaved by dependence on a Goa'uld larva.

In support of their teammate, SG-1 makes a case for a mission to Chulak, pointing out the potential advantage of recruiting other Jaffa to rebel against the Goa'uld. They make no mention of the primary reason, but O'Neill is forced to reveal Teal'c's worries in a private conference with Hammond. Meanwhile, Teal'c takes matters into his own hands: Donning his Serpent Guard armor, he is already dialing the Stargate before Hammond convinces him to stop, agreeing to approve SG-1's mission to retrieve the boy.

With Teal'c's helmet concealing his face and his teammates disguised in priestly robes, SG-1 bluffs their way past the priests and guards at the Stargate on Chulak. A grim surprise awaits them: the burned-out shell of Teal'c's former home, with a huge stylized dagger painted on one wall. Its meaning: "This was the home of *shol'va.*" Traitor. His friends point out that there is no reason to believe his family was present when the house was destroyed, but the distraught Jaffa pays little heed until they are surprised by a grizzled warrior, bearing the gold mark of First Prime of Apophis. Teal'c introduces his teacher, the Jaffa master Bra'tac, to his new comrades. Bra'tac's news is mixed: Teal'c's wife and son escaped safely, but are *kresh'taa,* outcasts, and could be living in any of several camps beyond the city boundaries. O'Neill orders Carter and Jackson to return to the Stargate and take up positions to cover the team's escape, while he accompanies Teal'c and Bra'tac.

Bra'tac takes charge, surmising that Teal'c's family has most likely gone to a camp in the south, nearest the city. They soon find what they are looking for: a graceful white tent set apart from one grubby shantytown. Rya'c's ceremony has already begun. The priest conducting it takes up a knife and attacks Teal'c, whose effort to defend himself is hampered when a hooded figure leaps on his back: his wife, Drey'auc. In the scuffle, the priest falls on his own knife and the glass vessel containing the Goa'uld larva is smashed, killing the fragile creature. While O'Neill and Bra'tac drag the priest's body away, Drey'auc rails at her husband, unable to understand why he has betrayed the gods and abandoned his family for strangers. Now he has returned only to condemn his son to death. Rya'c is gravely ill, the healing powers of the Goa'uld his only hope. O'Neill recognizes scarlet fever and offers medicine from his pack that will provide some relief, but any real chance lies in taking him to Earth for more effective treatment.

Meanwhile, Carter and Jackson encounter a formal religious procession of Jaffa, who unwittingly lead the humans to the temple sepulchre, where a tank holds Goa'uld larvae awaiting implantation. When the priests leave, Carter and Jackson come out of hiding to steal one, fulfilling the original mission objective. As they depart, Jackson opens fire on the tank and destroys it, despite Carter's assertion that killing these helpless young would make them no better than the Goa'uld.

Elsewhere in the forest, O'Neill's group reaches the clearing where they expected to meet Carter and Jackson, and Drey'auc realizes Rya'c has stopped breathing. O'Neill says they should try to make it to the Stargate, but Teal'c, fearing they are out of time, elects to give up his own symbiote – and with it his life – to save his son. Carter and Jackson arrive to find Rya'c recovering but Teal'c fading fast. Drey'auc and Bra'tac are momentarily shocked at the sacrilege of stealing a larva from the temple, but their surprise fades quickly next to the prospect of saving Teal'c.

The lifeline comes none too soon as a Jaffa patrol sounds the alarm. With guards hot on their trail, SG-1 and the others reach the Stargate, where Teal'c bids a painful farewell to his family. Finally understanding the cause for which he must leave them, Drey'auc assures him that they will be all right and urges him to go quickly, in order to return someday to free his people. Bra'tac, telling SG-1 their disguises will not work a second time, single-handedly clears the way for them, and his old student and new friends pause to salute his courage before stepping through the gate.

BACKGROUND
THE PRIM'TA

Jaffa are bred to be the incubators of the larval Goa'uld. In the rite of the prim'ta this genetic destiny is fulfilled. As a Jaffa child approaches the age of twelve, preparations begin for the implantation of the child's first symbiote. Priests test the child on the duties and privileges of becoming a "True Jaffa" – lessons with which all Jaffa have been indoctrinated since birth. If the child is found wanting, the priests assign remedial lessons to the parents as well as the child, and the prim'ta is delayed for a year.

Passing these tests does not always guarantee success. Also required is a series of physical examinations. Using a modified version of the Goa'uld healing device, the priests ascertain that the child has no diseases or genetic problems that could harm a larva or prevent proper implantation. Minor illnesses, even many life-threatening infections, are not a concern – the symbiote can easily deal with them once it is in control of the child's immune system. The goal is to insure against rejection of the symbiote.

The ceremony is performed in a sacred tent, at or near the child's home. The child arrives dressed in the ceremonial garments that leave the pouch accessible. He recites the Jaffa's Oath, a pledge of loyalty to the gods, as inscribed on a tablet of black basalt. Finally the priests perform one last physical examination, using the modified healing device to sterilize the pouch as an added precaution. The rite reaches its climax as the priest gently lifts the Goa'uld larva from a basin and inserts it into the child's abdominal pouch. At this point the larva can reject the child, sensing some problem the priest missed. This halts the prim'ta, and the child must try again at another time.

The last test then begins, as the child's immune system reacts to the Goa'uld as an invading parasite and attempts to drive it out. The resulting fever marks the internal battle in which the larva destroys the child's immune system. In the unlikely event that the immune system wins, the larva dies and the child's fever breaks, but he is thereafter not allowed to attempt another prim'ta without special permission from the Goa'uld. Normally, though, the symbiote asserts itself, and the child recovers through its healing powers. The child is then no longer a child, but a True Jaffa.

Until a Jaffa successfully completes the prim'ta, he or she is a second-class citizen. It is instilled in the Jaffa consciousness that their highest duty is to carry the young gods within them. Those who cannot – or worse, will not – are seen as odd. A Jaffa who has passed the prim'ta knows he is superior to others, even if they play important roles in the community.

It is not surprising, then, that the majority of Jaffa wish their children to undergo the ceremony. As Jaffa populations increase and the number of Goa'uld queens declines, fewer symbiotes are available for implantation, so not every proud parent gets his or her wish. With few exceptions the priesthood controls the selection of the children who are tested (though the Goa'uld, of course, can order it for anyone). It is also the right of every True Jaffa warrior to insist that his sons undergo the ritual at the proper age. The sons of some high-ranking warriors may even undergo the prim'ta at age ten, increasing the odds that they will surpass their peers in size and strength.

For girls, and for all Jaffa of lesser family, the options are fewer. A handful may become warriors, but for most their only real option is the priesthood. All those interested are evaluated, though preference is given to the priests' own families. Those selected undergo a yearlong trial of their devotion, not just to the god they worship, but to all Goa'uld.

KRESH'TAA

The kresh'taa are Jaffa who have failed their gods but been permitted to live, or who have broken a taboo within Jaffa society. In addition to the transgressor himself, it is not unusual for the entire immediate family to be shunned by other Jaffa. Kresh'taa are stripped of their positions and rank, and forced to live outside the cities in makeshift dwellings. On larger Jaffa worlds, there can be several such encampments ringing major communities. Each consists of no more than three dozen Jaffa, often related to one another, pooling their efforts to find food and drinkable water.

Since they live on the debris of ordinary Jaffa society, there are frequent outbreaks of disease and rampant malnutrition. This leads to high mortality rates among the young and elderly. Those condemned to kresh'taa status while incubating larval Goa'uld are allowed to keep them, and are thus protected from the worst of these medical concerns – until the symbiote matures. If still kresh'taa, they will not receive new symbiotes, and will die. Their families are not so protected, and in rare cases a Jaffa has been known to sacrifice his life by implanting his own symbiote within a sick son or daughter. This is called *nom'ka*, a father's right to sacrifice all for his son, and will not be prevented even if the child is sick enough to endanger the symbiote. If he survives, his father's sacrifice is honored by lifting the banishment and allowing the boy to rejoin Jaffa society.

Though shunned, the kresh'taa are in some ways a necessary part of Jaffa society, taking on the jobs that other Jaffa view as beneath them. This includes simple things like garbage disposal, which provides many of the kresh'taa's meager resources. It also includes more illicit activities, such as prostitution and mercenary service. No upstanding Jaffa citizen would think to give his loyalty in exchange for monetary reward – to become a *tolv'al*. The outcasts, however, cannot afford to be bound by these rules. And though they disdain such tactics in public, many Jaffa take advantage of the kresh'taa, secretly contracting them for actions they cannot be seen to perform themselves. Any Jaffa can openly challenge his rival, take the chance of failure, and hope to advance. With a kresh'taa mercenary, the same rival can be targeted secretly with little fear of retribution.

It may be an open secret that some Jaffa use outcasts as spies or assassins, but it is still a secret. Such an arrangement, if revealed openly, would condemn the offending Jaffa to become kresh'taa himself. This guarantees that he will follow through on any arrangements made, if only to take care of the mercenary's family if he is caught and killed. The kresh'taa can also hope that someday, with the patronage of influential Jaffa, he may seek redemption.

The redemption of a kresh'taa, called the *kresht'ma*, is on the mind of every Jaffa from the moment status is lost. It is what keeps them in their place, accepting the scorn cast their way. If a kresh'taa admits to being a tolv'al, which would be necessary to publicly accuse his Jaffa master, all chances of redemption are gone forever. The kresht'ma is achieved by long, hard and distasteful work without complaint, and by the fortune to be recruited by an honorable – and sufficiently powerful – patron. Only the upper ranks of the priesthood or warrior class are able to validate such an offer, so a patron of lesser status may expect years of loyal service from his kresh'taa, as his power and position grow.

For young people raised under kresh'taa banishment, the prospect of a better life sometime in the future is a hazy enticement at best. Their concerns are more immediate. While this makes them a poor gamble for a patron seeking loyalty, one can always find an adolescent scavenger willing take on a one-time task like eavesdropping if it will put a fresh loaf of bread on his family's table or a warmer blanket on a younger sibling's bed.

SHOL'VA: "EVEN BY THE OUTCASTS WE ARE SHUNNED"

Any Jaffa labeled *shol'va*, traitor, is usually killed on the spot – perhaps a kinder fate than what lies in store for his family. If they are otherwise blameless, they are spared as examples to other Jaffa. They are *kresh'taa* by default, but their possessions are destroyed and their house burned. Any trace of their existence is marked with the sign of the shol'va, the serpent trident. For the family of the shol'va, redemption is still possible, but their former lives are gone forever.

While kresh'taa are the outcasts of Jaffa society, they have their own status games. Those marked as shol'va are themselves cast out from the kresh'taa camps. In any kresh'taa population there can be found at least one small camp, set aside and apart from the others, where the shol'va struggle to survive. Within days of such a camp forming, it will be marked with a staff bearing the serpent trident, to warn other Jaffa and kresh'taa away.

THE KADRA'MAL

Chulak has a rare commodity, which makes it a center for Jaffa everywhere: It is one of the few worlds to house an abundance of the larval Goa'uld necessary for implantation. These larvae are birthed by the Goa'uld queens, but it is not uncommon for years to go by without being graced by the presence of a queen, especially as their numbers dwindle. This necessitates the *kadra'mal*, a sacred procession of the immature gods from the place of their birth to the holy sepulchres on Chulak or one of its sister planets.

In ages past, the Goa'uld queens maintained their own young in whatever manner they or their lords chose. This ended after the rebellion of the queen Egeria, who quietly set about building an army of like-minded Goa'uld by modifying her offspring. After Egeria's defeat, the System Lords supported Ra's move to take control of their offspring away from the queens. *(See the Tok'ra sections in the Stargate SG-1 core rulebook for more about Egeria.)*

Though they are still allowed a few larvae to insure they will always have servants of their own line, the queens must relinquish the vast majority of their broods to the care of the Jaffa priesthood. The Jaffa transport the newborn gods in a sanctified cradle (a small tank made of metal and glass filled with the waters in which the larvae were birthed). Thus begins the kadra'mal, the first great journey of a Goa'uld's life. Flanked by eight or more priests, the cradle is escorted to the *chaapa'ai* and sent to one of the crèche planets.

Besides the four Jaffa needed to carry the cradle on poles, two others serve as ceremonial guards – ceremonial, as it is incomprehensible that anyone would dare attack even a newborn god. The remaining two priests are female. The first is always the High Priestess of one of the cults serving on that world. The second priestess is one implanted with a larva from the same queen that spawned the brood being transported. While the High Priestess merely escorts the cradle to the chaapa'ai (passing her duty on to the selected High Priestess at their destination), the "sibling" priestess stays with the cradle during the entire kadra'mal.

Once the procession sets foot on the crèche world, bells are sounded by the local priesthood to announce the birth of a new god. As the bells toll, the kadra'mal proceeds to a sepulchre located apart from the main temple. Though each is maintained by a different Goa'uld cult, the large incubation tanks are used by all. This is by design, and was Ra's insurance against new breeds of traitorous Goa'uld like the Tok'ra.

At the sepulchre, the High Priestess uses a large chalice to transfer the larvae from the cradle to join the multitude already swimming in the larger tank. At this point any tampering with the larvae becomes apparent. Normally Goa'uld larvae spawned by different queens can coexist without incident. But if one has been altered far enough from the common genetic template, the others sense this shift and attack the rogue larva. In this way an entire sepulchre might be sacrificed, but the Goa'uld see this as infinitely preferable to raising a new secret army opposed to them.

If the kadra'mal ends with such an attack, the life of the "sibling" priestess is forfeit. She and her symbiote are killed by the extremely painful method of mingling their blood within the Jaffa's pouch. The bodies of both are then sent back as a warning to the offending queen, along with a cadre of Jaffa warriors to guard the chaapa'ai and prevent her escape. The System Lords are informed, and further action takes place at their discretion.

If during the kadra'mal the Goa'uld being transported comes to harm by any other means, the responsibility falls on the High Priestess. The punishment varies, as it is meted out by the queen who has been harmed by the transgression. Most are condemned to death, but it is within the queen's right to grant mercy. Generally such mercy comes with strings attached. Once the queen's demands in exchange for leniency are known, more than one High Priestess has committed suicide rather than comply.

In recent years the decline in the number of Goa'uld young has meant that the kadra'mal, one of the more sacred rites of the priesthood, has been performed less and less frequently. Fearing this will be seen as evidence of their dwindling power, the priesthood has started to insist that the kadra'mal be performed whenever a Goa'uld larva needs to be transported from world to world. Besides immediately after birthing, larvae are sometimes transported en masse after a battle in which Jaffa were killed, but their symbiotes recovered. Traditionally this has been done by the surviving warriors, and the symbiotes are used to replace losses and swell the ranks of the victorious side. The priesthood now claims this duty, and assert that any re-implantations must occur under their guidance. Some cults have gone so far as to perform the kadra'mal when a single Jaffa has died, in or out of battle, to reinforce their image as the sole authority in these matters.

World Visited: P3X-866 (Oannes).

Thermosphere: Hot (CR 0; close orbit to gas giant; 3d20+50°F).

Atmosphere: Very thin (CR 1; 0.4 atmospheres; Exp. Inc: 10 minutes; SV Fort (DC20); Dmg 1d6 subdual; Recup 2 rounds). *See The Atmosphere of the Ohnes World, page 154.*

Hydrosphere: Desert (CR 2; daily weather 1-92: none, 93: rain/snow, 94-95: dust storm, 96-100: wind 1d10 MPH).

Geosphere: Very Unstable tectonic activity (daily earthquakes 1-90: none, 91-95: minor, 96-99: moderate, 100: major; 10 small volcanoes within 1d10 miles of Stargate).

Seasons: No seasons (1-25: spring unchanged; 26-50: summer unchanged; 51-75: autumn unchanged; 76-100: winter unchanged).

Anthrosphere: 100,000 natives; Star-faring (7 picks, 5 RP); Oligarchy; Suspicious (-1 with disposition checks); Cautious (5,000 soldiers, squad size 1d2 soldiers); Very Progressive civil rights.

Origin: N/A.

Stargate Location (desert region): rocky and sandy terrain in desert, dry desert area pocked with small geysers and gas pockets, bordering a salt-water ocean.

EPISODE SUMMARY

Claxons sound throughout Stargate Command once again as the Stargate comes to life, signaling an off world activation. Confirming SG-1's Iris Deactivation Code, the Stargate controller opens the iris and three members of SG-1, O'Neill, Carter, and Teal'c step through returning from P3X-866, soaking wet and in a state of shock, and inform General Hammond that Daniel Jackson is dead.

After recovering in the infirmary, the surviving members SG-1 debrief with General Hammond, relating the events leading to Daniel's death as best they can recall. Their memories are sketchy, but they all remember diving into a body of water while Daniel was consumed by a column of flame. After the debriefing, General Hammond and Dr. Fraiser discuss SG-1 return to active duty. Hammond wants them to return to duty as soon as possible, while Dr. Fraiser believes they need more time. Hammond agrees to wait seven days. In the meantime, the SGC holds a funeral for Daniel with full military honors.

At the same time, Daniel, still very much alive but dazed and confused, wakes up in an underwater structure of some sort.

At an informal reception after the funeral, the "surviving" members of SG-1 begin to experience flashbacks of both Daniel being consumed in flames and of air bubbles rising through water. O'Neill contemplates retiring in the face of Daniel's death, but General Hammond orders them to clean out and pack Daniel's apartment.

Meanwhile, Daniel attempts to figure out where he is and where the rest of SG-1 has gone. His efforts are interrupted by the arrival of a strange alien that resembles a humanoid fish, with pale eyes, gills on his neck, and fin-like protuberances on his upper body. Apparently, it has abducted Daniel and placed him in an underwater prison of some sort. The alien shows him a panel containing ancient Akkadian cuneiform writing that reads "Reveal Fate Omoroca." When Daniel is unable to provide an answer to that cryptic assertion, the alien attacks Daniel, stunning him.

Later, still in his underwater "prison," Daniel deciphers more cuneiform writing, including the legal code of an ancient Earth kingdom. As he translates more and more of the text, the alien speaks to Daniel, asking "What Fate Omoroca?" threatening to kill Daniel if he doesn't answer.

Back on Earth, O'Neill, Carter, and Teal'c set to work packing up Daniel's apartment, but once again experience flashbacks of Daniel's death and images of rising bubbles; O'Neill voices a growing sense of disbelief that Daniel is truly dead.

The alien returns to Daniel's "prison" again, and informs Daniel that his teammates won't be returning: he gave them the memory of Daniel's death. The alien believes that Daniel serves the Goa'uld, despite Daniel's heated assertions to the contrary. Through further conversation with the alien, named Nem, Daniel discerns that Omoroca was in fact Nem's mate, and that she journeyed to Earth during the era of Babylon. Nem wants to learn her final fate, and insists that Daniel knows what happened to her.

Back on Earth, the other members of SG-1 continue to doubt the truth of their "memory" of Daniel's death, as MRI scans reveal that they have all been subjected to some sort of procedure that altered their brain chemistry. Also, whenever any of them considers the idea of returning to P3X-866, they all suffer acute headaches and refuse to consider the matter further.

Back on the planet, Daniel attempts to escape, but Nem returns, telling Daniel that he will not allow him to leave until he has revealed all he knows of Babylon. In hopes of prompting Daniel's memories, Nem tell him that Omoroca spoke of someone named Belus, whom Omoroca feared. Hearing the name Belus helps Daniel recall excerpts of the history of Belus as recorded by Berossus, a contemporary of Alexander the Great. Since Nem possesses the technology to implant false memories, Daniel asks if he also has the ability to retrieve them. Nem confirms Daniel's suspicions, but is reluctant to perform the procedure on him: it is extremely painful, and could damage or possibly kill Daniel. Despite the risk, Daniel persuades Nem to use the technology on him.

During a meeting with SG-1, SGC psychologist Dr. MacKenzie deduces that their memories of Daniel's death were implanted using a sort of hypnosis, and suggests they try using hypnotherapy to unblock their memories. Carter volunteers, and with Dr. MacKenzie's help, recalls the events of their ill-fated mission to P3X-866.

Upon arriving on the planet, SG-1 found a large body of salt water within a short walking distance from the Stargate. As Carter began to take soil and water samples, an alien emerged from the water. Eyeing the team suspiciously, the alien approached Teal'c, sensing the Goa'uld larva he carried. The alien then drew a number of cuneiform pictographs in the sand, attempting to communicate. Daniel deciphered the pictographs, recognizing the symbols for ancient Babylon, and responded to the alien's writings.

The alien suddenly attacked the team, stunning them all, and then took them to an underwater lab and altered their memories. The alien then released O'Neill, Carter, and Teal'c, who, believing Daniel to be dead, escaped to the Stargate.

As Carter awakens from her hypnotic state, she realizes that they left Daniel behind, and O'Neill tells her that they are going back for him.

Back in Nem's underwater lab, the alien straps Daniel into a device that can extract his memories. Despite the agony of the procedure, Daniel is able to recall more details of the history of Belus:

"And in that place there was Omoroca, a woman who came forth from the heavenly egg, who walked among men by day, but at night, she would retreat to the Great Sea to sleep, one of the beings called Ohnes. The God Belus came down unto Babylon, unto the place of Omoroca, and he cut the woman asunder."

Removing Daniel from the device, Nem at last knows the fate of Omoroca. After millennia of uncertainty and doubt, he finally faces with the truth of Omoroca's fate and can only howl in rage.

O'Neill, Carter, and Teal'c return to P3X-866 and to the ocean where they first encountered the alien. Nem leaves to meet them, and Daniel follows, emerging from the water as SG-1 confronts the alien; he convinces them to lower their weapons. Since Nem now knows the destiny of his mate, Daniel asks to be freed. Nem consents, and allows him and the rest of SG-1 to return through the Stargate.

BACKGROUND
THE OHNES

The Ohnes are an ancient race who have battled the System Lords for thousands of years across hundreds of planets. Fierce warriors and wise scholars, they seek knowledge and understanding, and to rid the galaxy of the System Lords. Their acts are spoken of in angered whispers and raging scowls by Goa'uld nobles. Where you find the Goa'uld enslaving a world, you will find them, fighting to drive the false gods from this life. Where you find ancient mysteries and hidden knowledge, you will find them, seeking to unlock the secrets of the past. They are the Ohnes, and a more loyal ally or terrifying enemy you will never find.

THE OHNES AND THE GOA'ULD

The Ohnes' animosity for the Goa'uld has its origins millennia ago, when the Goa'uld Belus discovered and invaded their home world of Oannes. Driving the Ohnes from their ocean-born cities by bombarding the seas from orbit, the System Lord's slavers waited on the surface to capture the fleeing inhabitants, and transported the new slaves to Belus' ship in orbit. Confident in his victory, Belus left only a token force behind, intent on returning to Goa'uld space with his prize captives. His ship was barely one day away when the Ohnes overwhelmed their captors and moved to seize control. Rather than be defeated by mere slaves, Belus fled his command ship with his First Prime, but not before engaging the ship's self-destruct system, slaughtering the thousands of Ohnes aboard.

At the same time, back on their homeworld, the Ohnes launched a counterattack against the Goa'uld and Jaffa who remained behind. Without their god, the invaders were quickly routed and the Ohnes retook their planet. Interrogation of their prisoners failed to obtain the location of Belus' home world, so the Ohnes used their memory retrieval technology to extract the information from their former masters, killing them in the process.

Within days a group of Ohne warriors journeyed through the Stargate to Belus' world, hoping to find and rescue their captured brethren. Upon arriving, they were themselves captured by Belus' Jaffa and brought before the Goa'uld. Belus ordered all but one of the warriors slain; the survivor was sent back through the Stargate with the bodies to tell his people of the power of Belus and of the System Lords.

What Belus thought would intimidate the Ohnes served only to instill in them a burning passion to confront and defeat the Goa'uld, and free the galaxy from their taint. Belus never had a chance to strike back at the Ohnes again. Within days of receiving his "message", the Ohnes staged a series of strikes against the System Lord, crippling his ships and slaughtering thousands of Jaffa, until Belus had no choice but to flee his former stronghold.

Since that time the Ohnes have waged constant war with the Goa'uld (and in particular Belus), whom they view as a plague infesting the galaxy. Lacking a conventional military and starships, the Ohnes use the Stargate and guerrilla tactics to maximum advantage, making isolated strikes at key facilities that weaken the Goa'uld's ability to maintain control of their domains. The Ohnes utilize no military structure or chain of command amongst themselves. Most warriors never even return to their home; they either die at the hands of their enemy, or more often than not, simply continue to fight the Goa'uld on world after world, going where they are needed rather than awaiting orders.

Today the Ohnes are most often encountered on Goa'uld-occupied worlds, where they help the natives battle against their oppressors. These freedom fighters often work alone or in small groups, sometimes aiding already-existing resistance groups, other times inciting the resistance in the first place. The best-known example of Ohne activity occurred on Earth during the time of Babylon, when a freedom fighter named Omoroca, aided an uprising against Belus. *See page 97 for more information about Belus.*

THE OHNES AND THEIR WORLD

Physically, Ohnes are humanoid in shape, averaging just over six feet tall and weighing approximately 250 pounds. Sharing many traits with fish and other marine life, they sport aqua-blue skin and webbed fingers, spines on their ears, and fish-like features on their faces. The Ohnes are amphibious; they use pairs of nasal slits to breathe air and gills to breathe water, and have pale-blue eyes that grant them excellent vision even underwater. Though they can breathe both water and air, Ohnes must spend at least three hours each day submerged in water or suffer from dehydration. The Ohnes use their strong muscles and hydrodynamic bodies to walk and swim underwater as easily as humans walk on land, adjusting their buoyancy as needed.

The Ohnes are very long-lived; most live up to 5,000 years, showing little signs of aging after reaching adulthood at 200 years. During this period, Ohnes develop the use of a variety of telepathic or psychic abilities, including the ability to communicate with one another telepathically and to focus the power of their minds. The Ohnes can also detect the presence of Goa'uld symbiotes, either within a host or a Jaffa, and are able to emit blasts of psychic energy powerful enough to stun their targets.

Ohnes display a very direct, almost confrontational attitude when meeting members of other species. Not overly concerned with social niceties, they tend to get to the matter at hand quickly. When first contacting other species, they normally evaluate the strangers' status as threats rather than attempting peaceful contact. As centuries-old enemies of the Goa'uld, the Ohnes take no chances when encountering beings from other worlds.

The Ohnes are a deeply passionate species, which carries over to the way they form relationships with each other and with other species, and the way they live their lives. Ohnes mate for life, forming unions similar to human marriages, and remain fiercely loyal to their companions, risking life for one another if need be. Likewise, once they mark someone an enemy, they are an implacable and determined foe.

Two primary passions drive the Ohnes: the search for knowledge and understanding of the universe, and their quest to rid the galaxy and all its peoples of the Goa'uld *(see The Ohnes and the Goa'uld, left)*. In regards to the former, the Ohnes see everything in the universe as pieces in a great puzzle that when solved will reveal the truth of the origins of life. Curious by nature, the Ohnes adopt an analytical and objective stance towards most everything around them.

These twin passions also parallel the separation within the Ohnes' society between those of the warrior caste and the scholar caste. Ohnes of the warrior caste are sworn to battle the Goa'uld wherever they may be. They train in a variety of military and martial skills under the expert tutelage of the Ohnes Warlords, an order of elder Ohnes warriors renowned for the fierce and brutal soldiers they produce. Ohnes of the scholar caste embrace all forms of scientific and academic pursuit, traveling and exploring the galaxy through the Stargate in search of knowledge. This is not to say that only warriors fight the Goa'uld and only scholars seek to learn. While all Ohnes share these two driving passions, those of a particular caste tend to emphasize one focus over the other.

The Ohnes' home world (designated P3X-866 by the SGC) is one of three moons orbiting a gas giant. Volcanoes of varying sizes and stability cover 70% of the surface, with small geysers and gas pockets scattered between. The thin atmosphere, high concentrations of gases, and volcanic activity make the surface of the world uninhabitable. Somewhere between twelve and fifteen salt-water oceans of varying sizes cover the remaining 30% of the moon's surface. Here the Ohnes make their home; Ohnes settlements include both large cities in each of the five largest oceans, and dozens if not hundreds of smaller outposts or towns in and around the cities. These cities are home to approximately 4,000-5,000 Ohnes each, with most towns and outposts housing only several hundred. In addition to the outposts, many Ohnes scholars maintain small one- or two-room laboratories, such as the lab in which Daniel Jackson found himself after SG-1's encounter with Nem. Ohnes architecture tends to utilize materials suitable to an underwater environment such as glass, stone, and translucent polymers, and features dark, aquatic colors, curves, low lighting, and elaborate water-based decorations.

Technologically, the Ohnes far surpass Earth's advances, even rivaling the Asgard in some regards. Their primary energy source is a form of cold fusion that draws its power from seawater, and they also possess technology that allows the forming and shaping of water (which they use as both decorations and barriers between enclosed air environments and the water beyond). These barriers also compensate for differences in water and air pressure when Ohnes (and occasional visitors) move between enclosed water and enclosed air environments.

As advanced as the Ohnes in some areas, they have yet to master space travel (or indeed flight of any kind). They use the Stargate as their primary means of traversing the galaxy, though they've been known to use stolen Goa'uld craft when needed. Though not truly a "star-faring" species, the Ohnes operate sophisticated sensors that monitor the region of space surrounding their solar system, ever watchful for the return of the Goa'uld to their home world.

The Ohnes also have and use memory alteration and retrieval technology, allowing them to implant false memories and extract long-buried ones from subjects. These tools use a laser device that directly accesses the brain. The Ohnes' memory implantation technology leaves traces that are visible on an MRI, and also produce a series of external side effects as well, including headaches and flashbacks. The technology is not without flaws, and hypnosis and other concentration techniques, if applied properly, can circumvent the implanted memories. The technology is extremely painful as well and can cause permanent brain damage and even death if care is not taken in its application. The Ohnes use it only reluctantly, given the dangers associated with it.

Ohnes explorers also use energy weapons fueled by miniature cold fusion reactors, and a device known as a hydrator that allows them to remain out of the water for periods of up to five days.

The Stargate on the Ohnes' home world is located in a desert region of the moon, roughly one mile from one of the larger salt-water oceans. The Ohnes set up a perimeter alarm on the Stargate to alert them of any unexpected

Akkad

Established by Belus and populated by transplanted humans from Earth, the planet and city of Akkad is one of hundreds of worlds once under the domain of Ra. When Ra died and the System Lords struggled to divide his worlds, Akkad remained isolated from the struggle, since it offered relatively little in terms of natural resources and lacks any sort of strategic value.

The Goa'uld Sargon currently rules Akkad, just as his human namesake once ruled the city of Akkad on Earth. Sargon continued to serve Ishtar after Ra's death, and is in turned served by the Warriors of Akkad, the name he uses for his elite Jaffa. These Jaffa are specially trained Horus Guards: formidable soldiers, steadfast in their loyalty to their god.

The city of Akkad and the surrounding villages are home to nearly a quarter of a million inhabitants. Located next a large river, the lands nearby the city offer fertile farmland, and agriculture is one of the planet's few valuable resources.

Most recently, an Ohnes freedom fighter arrived on Akkad and began to instill the ideas of resistance and rebellion in the people. Though the seeds are just starting to take root, it is only a matter of time before the people stand up to Sargon and try to free themselves from his rule.

World: Akkad.
Thermosphere: Warm (CR 0; standard orbit; 2d20+25° F).
Atmosphere: Normal (CR 0; 1.10 atmospheres; Auto None; Exp. Inc: None; SV None; Dmg None; Recup None).
Hydrosphere: Arid (CR 1; daily weather 1-89: none, 90: flood 1d10 MPH or snow 1d4-2 in.), 91-93: rain (1 in,), 94-95: dust storm, 96: hurricane, 97-100: 1d10 MPH).
Geosphere: Stable tectonic activity (daily earthquakes 1-99: none, 100: minor; 1 volcano within 1d10 miles of Stargate).
Seasons: Normal (1-25: spring unchanged; 26-50: summer +2d20° F; 51-75: autumn, unchanged; 76-100: winter -2d20° F).
Anthrosphere: 250,000 natives; Bronze Age (3 picks, 1 RP); Autocracy; Suspicious (-1 with disposition checks); Cautious (500 soldiers (Jaffa), squad size 1d2 soldiers); Poor civil rights.
Origin: Akkadian.
Stargate Location (arid region): Rocky terrain in desert, in a natural rock outcropping near the edge of a large city.

visitors. When an alarm goes off, one or more inhabitants travel to the surface to meet the newly-arrived visitor. The Ohne known as Nem met with SG-1 during the SGC's first contact, and other Ohnes have met with other SG teams on subsequent visits.

The ruling body of the Oannes comprises thirteen members from the eldest families, six from the warrior caste, six from the scholar caste, and one who is neither warrior nor scholar, but is instead of one of the other three lower castes. Members hold their positions for one term of 200 years. New members are selected by existing members from a pool of candidates submitted by the eldest families in each of the castes.

The Ohnes use the Stargate extensively in traveling and exploring the galaxy, and have visited and influenced a number of ancient cultures, including Earth's. (The Akkadian civilization of ancient Earth owes its written language, Akkadian cuneiform, to the Ohnes, who continue to use a variation of the language to this day.)

At any given time there are hundreds of Ohnes warriors and scholars scattered throughout the galaxy, engaged in exploration and discovery as well as battling the Goa'uld. Ohnes warriors most often operate on Goa'uld occupied or controlled worlds, planting the seeds of rebellion and aiding and assisting the locals in fighting their System Lord oppressors. Ohnes scholars can be found on most any sort of world, usually exploring archaeological ruins or searching for lost knowledge. Of the locations explored by the Ohnes, perhaps the most fascinating is the ruins of Heliopolis (see The Torment of Tantalus, page 38), a world recently visited by the SGC, and the one time meeting place of an alliance of four ancient races, the Ancients, the Asgard, the Nox, and the Furlings. Ohnes scholars visited this world long ago (centuries before Ernest Littlefield journeyed there via Stargate), and after decades of study, left in search of other relics of this millennia-old alliance.

SGC teams have encountered Ohnes explorers and warriors on several occasions since SG-1's first encounter with the race, but none of these have lead to any sort of formal relationship. Despite that, the Ohnes remain fairly well-disposed towards the SGC, and may prove to be stalwart allies in the future.

1-12: THE NOX

World Visited: P3X-774 (Gaia).

Thermosphere: Warm (CR 0; standard orbit; 2d20+25° F).

Atmosphere: Normal (CR 0; 1.10 atmospheres; Auto None; Exp. Inc: None; SV None; Dmg None; Recup None).

Hydrosphere: Moist Sub-humid (CR 1; daily weather 1-85: none, 86-87: flood 1d10 MPH, 88-93: rain 1d4 inches or snow 1d6 inches, 94-96: thunderstorm or snowstorm, 97-98: hurricane or blizzard, 99: wind 1d10 MPH, 100: wind 1d10+10 MPH).

Geosphere: Stable tectonic activity (daily earthquakes 1-99: none, 100 minor; 1 volcano within 1d10 miles of Stargate).

Seasons: Normal (1-25: spring unchanged; 26-50: summer +2d20° F; 51-75: autumn unchanged; 76-100 winter -2d20° F).

Anthrosphere: 250,000,000 natives; Asgard (9 picks, 7 RP); Meritocracy; Open (+2 with disposition checks); Absolute Pacifistic; Very Progressive civil rights.

Origin: N/A.

Stargate Location (forest region): Rolling terrain in forest, on a grassy plateau overlooking a forest valley.

EPISODE SUMMARY

The President of the United States and the Secretary of Defense are not satisfied with the progress of the Stargate program to procure technologies that will help Earth defend itself from the Goa'uld. Teal'c points out that there many technologies exist beyond the Goa'uld's capacity, and cites an example of a flying creature on an unpopulated world with powers of invisibility. SG-1 travels to this world in search of the creature, and while busy scouting the area, they turn to discover the Stargate, the DHD, and the drone carrying their gear have disappeared.

> "THE VERY YOUNG DO NOT ALWAYS DO AS THEY ARE TOLD."
> – ANTEAUS

The team splits up to search for their gear (which includes a device that can locate the Stargate). They soon come across what appears to be the invisible creature flying nearby. They move to try to tranquilize it when a staff blast shoots through the sky, narrowly missing the creature. The shot comes from a handful of Jaffa who are on the planet with Apophis hunting the same creature that SG-1 seeks. SG-1 decides that Apophis' presence on the planet with such a small contingent of Jaffa is too good an opportunity to pass up, and plan an ambush. Unfortunately, the trap does not proceed as planned. The Goa'uld and his Jaffa quickly turn the tables, and within moments O'Neill, Carter, and Daniel Jackson are all dead or dying from staff blasts. Teal'c finds himself unarmed as Apophis aims a staff weapon directly at him. Before the System Lord can fire the weapon, however, Teal'c and the rest of SG-1 disappear before his eyes.

Daniel, Carter, and O'Neill awaken sometime later in a primitive thatch hut, only to find their wounds completely healed and their weapons missing. A pair of primitively dressed humanoids, a older male and a female, enter the hut and lead SG-1 out into a small village where they meet two more similarly dressed humanoids, a young boy and an adult male. Within a few moments Teal'c arrives with no memory of what has transpired. One of the locals, the young boy, introduces himself as Nafrayu. His people are known as the Nox.

Meanwhile, a furious Apophis demands to know how Teal'c and SG-1 escaped his clutches, and orders his Jaffa to search the surrounding area.

Back in the village, the Nox offer SG-1 food as Anteaus, the middle-aged male, tells them in near perfect English that he intends to take SG-1 to their "doorway," which he confirms is the Stargate. Astonished at the rate at which these "primitives" learned to speak English, O'Neill asks about their weapons, and is told that they "are gone." SG-1 grows concerned that Apophis will harm both them and the locals. The Nox refuse to explain how they healed SG-1 wounds and will not take SG-1 to their leaders, but they do reveal that one of Teal'c "brothers" is also in the village and will soon be healed. It is Shak'l, a Jaffa who once served under Teal'c when he was First Prime of Apophis. The Nox insist that SG-1 leave despite O'Neill's protests that SG-1 stay to help protect them.

Elsewhere in the forest, Apophis' Jaffa have searched the forest for SG-1 and can find neither.

While O'Neill and Carter fashion primitive weapons, Lya, the female Nox, brings Teal'c to the wounded Jaffa. Teal'c offers Shak'l asylum with SG-1 but the Jaffa refuses. Meanwhile, the youngest Nox, Nafrayu, seems fascinated with the humans and follows O'Neill to a clear where he intends to test his newly crafted bow and arrows. As O'Neill shoots some nearby trees with his arrows, a Fenri, the creature SG-1 came to hunt, swoops down into range. O'Neill tries to shoot it with his bow, but misses. Anteaus appears suddenly to chastise O'Neill for attacking the Fenri and for teaching Nafrayu about weapons and violence.

At the same time, Daniel talks with Ohper, the eldest of the four Nox, who explains the close relationship they share with the forest. Daniel also learns that the Nox are very long lived and extremely intelligent, far beyond what their primitive appearance suggests.

In the village, Anteaus explains to O'Neill that the Fenri possesses no unique powers. It is the Nox who protect it. SG-1 wants to take custody of Shak'l, but the Nox refuse. While Teal'c and Lya sit in the hut with Shak'l, he rises and attacks and injures them both, and escapes into the forest. The other three Nox perform a ritual by which they heal Lya. As they perform the ritual, the Nox fade in and out of sight. When asked about this later, Anteaus explains that they are not able to remain hidden while performing the Ritual of Life.

Realizing that Shak'l has likely witnessed the ritual and will report what he's seen to Apophis, O'Neill and Teal'c head out in pursuit and Nafrayu tries to follow. Shak'l locates one of Apophis' Jaffa and describes all he has seen, as Nafrayu comes across Apophis and the rest of his Jaffa.

A short time later, the Nox and SG-1 find the boy in the forest, unconscious. Anteaus carries Nafrayu back to the village where he and the others can use the Ritual of Life to save him. Suspecting that Apophis intends to follow the Nox back to their village and attack, SG-1 tries to persuade the Nox to come with them back through the Stargate to safety.

The Nox refuse and make preparations to begin the ritual as SG-1 pretends to leave, intending to attack and ambush Apophis when he arrives at the village. Just as planned, Apophis and his Jaffa approach the village and SG-1 attack, Before combat can escalate, however, the Nox intercede, causing Apophis and his Jaffa to disappear before SG-1's eyes.

Anteaus tells the team that the Nox sent Apophis and his Jaffa back through the Stargate. O'Neill expresses concern about the aliens' ability to defend themselves against the Goa'uld in the future. To reassure him, Anteaus reveals a massive floating city, hovering over a nearby valley and hidden by their cloaking abilities. The Nox possess a level of technology far beyond that of the Goa'uld, and are more than capable of protecting themselves from any attack. The gate appears and instantly activates. As SG-1 stares at the floating city before them, Anteaus says "Fear not," and he and Nafrayu disappear, leaving SG-1 to return home.

BACKGROUND
THE NOX

The Nox are one of the oldest and wisest of species that inhabit the galaxy, yet few know of them. Physically, they resemble primitive humans, with faint gray skin color, and grass-like hair from which branches and leaves appear to grow. The Nox wear primitive clothing in colors that combine gray and colors ranging form gray-blue to violet and scarlet. Slightly shorter than average humans and generally slight of build, they present an unassuming facade that belies their capabilities. The Nox are strict vegetarians, getting all their nourishment from fruits, vegetables, roots, and other natural foods found in the forests of their native world.

The eldest among them reach ages close to 500 years. Nox children reach adulthood at the age of 18 years, at which point their aging slows to an all but imperceptible rate; they remain young adults for nearly 300 years before beginning to show signs of aging. Only during the last two centuries of their lives do the Nox begin to appear old, and even then their outward appearance fails to reveal their true age.

The Nox have a symbiotic relationship with all of nature, but in particular with the forests on their world and all the living things (both plant and animal) that make their home in it. In the Nox view of the universe, all living things are parts of a greater whole that they simultaneously contribute to and receive from. This belief prevented the Nox from allowing their technological advances to compromise the natural beauty of their world. Nox scholars long ago discovered that "life" (the energy or force that keeps physiological beings alive) is in essence a dynamic energy field that interacts with, feeds off of, and contributes to a myriad of other energy fields that exist outside the physical body. The Nox believe that these "external" fields comprise the "life force" of their planet and the universe beyond. The "individual" field (sometimes referred to as "consciousness" by Earth psychologists) shares an interdependent existence with "external" fields such that it cannot exist without them. Likewise, "external" fields are at their strongest when they interact with and feed off of the dynamic energy fields of individual beings. Of course, the Nox don't refer to these fields (both individual and external) in such terms. Preferring a simpler approach, they explain this complex relationship with the oft-heard phrase "We get Life from the Forest. We get everything from the Forest."

The Nox are extremely intelligent and perceptive, able to perform complex arithmetic in fractions of a second. They also have an astounding ability to comprehend and retain information, and possess near perfect memories. They use the same five senses as humans, sight, hearing, touch, taste, and smell, but their senses are far more acute than most humans, picking up details and subtleties around them that most others miss completely. Their keen perceptive nature and heightened senses give the Nox abilities that border on extra-sensory perception (ESP). In addition, the Nox seem to possess an innate ability to tune into the bio-electrical energy fields within other beings, in a sense "reading" them at a level far beyond normal senses. The Nox channel their natural heightened perception into a number of extraordinary abilities, including the ability to learn languages after hearing them spoken for only a short time, a mild form of mind-reading that allows them to detect nearby surface thoughts, and the ability to heal others. They can use this latter ability, which they refer to as the Ritual of Life, to completely heal even the most severe wounds, and even resurrect beings that have recently died. So long as even the tiniest hint of molecular activity and bio-electrical energy remains in the body, the Ritual of Life can repair it. The Ritual requires at least three Nox to perform, and intense and focused concentration that interrupts their ability to employ their technology *(see Nox Technology, page 150).*

THE JOURNEY OF LIFE

Most Nox follow a path through life that leads them from early stages of learning about the world and the universe, to traveling and exploring world beyond their own, to eventually returning to their home world so that they might teach the young, feeding a never-ending circle of learning, experience, and teaching. The Nox sometimes refer to this as the Journey of Life.

During the first stage, young Nox seek to understand and know all they can of their world. They possess a near insatiable curiosity and a certain level of naiveté, often making choices they know aren't wise simply for the sake of understanding the folly of them.

During the second stage of the journey, adult Nox leave their home world to travel the galaxy, most often using the Stargate, though some have journeyed along with other star-faring races, using the stealth technologies to remain hidden. It was Nox travelers such as these who first encountered other races, including the Asgard and the Ancients, with whom they would one day join in an alliance *(see The Torment of Tantalus, page 38).* This exposure to other species also prompted the Nox to develop the stealth technology they now regularly employ. They learn to master most of their technological feats while travelling, so as better to hide their presence among other races.

During the third and final stage of the journey, the Nox return to their world so that they might share what they have learned with other travelers just starting their own journey. Elder Nox are also leaders of both families and communities, and spend much of their time communing with nature and the forests of the Nox homeworld, ever deepening their connection to life around them.

NOX SOCIETY

The Nox practice a philosophy of absolute pacifism and non-violence so strict that they refuse even to defend themselves when threatened. When placed in such situations, the Nox typically hide using their stealth technologies, or to use their abilities to remove the aggressors and their weapons. The Nox enforce this devote pacifism and nonviolence on others when necessary as well, such as when SG-1 confronted Apophis and his Jaffa during their mission on the Nox's world. In these situations, the Nox refuse to allow visitors to employ violence against one another, and usually take the visitors' weapons from them as well.

The Nox value freedom, both for themselves and for others, and refuse to impinge on another's right to free choice, save when others choose violent or war-like ways. The Nox respect no authority on their world beyond themselves, and refuse to allow one party to impose their wishes onto another. For example, the Nox refused to hand Shak'l over to SG-1, as doing so would have meant denying Shak'l' his freedom of choice.

The Nox live in two distinct types of communities: massive floating cities above the six major continents of the planet, and in small forest villages scattered across the surface. Permanent residents of the floating cities are referred to as City Dwellers, and include Nox leaders as well as most scientists and scholars. In contrast to the primeval forests, Nox cities feature advanced architecture and metal and plastic construction. Copious trees, vines, and other plants adorn nearly all their buildings, forming a sort of "forest apron" which helps the Nox residents remain within close proximity nature at all times. While on the surface, the Nox live in tiny settlements of thatched huts, most comprising only a single family. Thousands of these settlements cover the forests, most within a day's walk from each other. All property is communal among the Nox, and it's not uncommon for the same family to live in a different settlement every time they return to the forests. Nox refer to those fortunate few who permanently reside on the surface as Forest Dwellers. They are mostly older Nox who prefer to remain within the forest for the final years of their lives.

The Nox government is a meritocracy; comprising a council of five elders selected their peers. Each member carries out a term of 25 years, with a new member selected every 5 years. For a race as long-lived as the Nox, this means an almost constantly changing ruling council, leaving very little time for political maneuvering (which while mostly absent, still occurs from time to time).

Gaia, the Nox Home World

The Nox world is a large planet with six large continents separated by three oceans. Small polar ice caps comprise roughly 20% of the planet, with the rest of the surface covered equally by land and water. The terrain of the planet is mostly forests and mountains, with patches of grasslands and rolling hills between the larger forests. The Nox refer to their world as Gaia, and like the Earth hypothesis of the same name, refers to their belief that their world, like all planets in the galaxy, is in reality a living organism.

Though obviously populated, the Goa'uld and many other star-faring races believe the Nox world to be unpopulated. The Nox find this misunderstanding beneficial, remaining for the most part isolated from the rest of the galaxy for the last several thousand years. Still, travelers from other worlds do occasionally arrive through the Stargate, whom the Nox maintain a careful watch over for the duration of their stay. The forest settlement nearest to the Stargate (within an hour's walk) serves as a guard post of sorts, and the family residing there acts as guardians, monitoring the Stargate for unwelcome guests. The Stargate is outfitted with sensors that automatically alert the guardians when visitors arrive. The guardians then cloak and/or shift the nearby floating city and any nearby creatures to maintain the illusion that their world is uninhabited. The guardians also observe the visitors closely, ensuring they don't threaten or harm the Nox or any of the living beings on their world.

In addition to the Stargate guardians, the Nox also use powerful sensors to monitor space around their world to alert them of any incoming spacecraft.

The Nox and Other Species

Though largely unknown to other races, the Nox do interact with certain species from time to time, both on their home world and on other planets as well. The Nox view themselves as "teachers" and believe it is their roles to instruct the "Young," whether they be young Nox or young species such as humans. Though they limit their contact with other species, the Nox try to take advantage of any and all opportunities to teach others their ways.

The Fenri Hunters

The most common visitors to Gaia are parties coming to their world to hunt the Fenri, a large flying creature native to the Nox world. The Nox use their stealth technologies to protect and defend the Fenri. Over the centuries, tales of the invisible creature resulted in false legends of "a flying beast with powers of invisibility on an uninhabited world." Over the past several hundred years countless hunters have arrived in search of the mythic creature, all of whom met with failure. This legend also led both SG-1 and Apophis to the Gaia, and in turn exposed the Nox's existence to the Goa'uld.

The Nox and Goa'uld

Until recently the Nox remained unknown to the Goa'uld, despite their participation in the Heliopolis alliance with the Asgard. Apophis' recent visit to Gaia ended their isolation, and made the System Lords aware of their extraordinary powers. At SG-1's suggestion, the Nox buried their Stargate in hopes of preventing the Apophis from returning. Apophis responded by charging his son Klorel with the task of returning to the Nox world to locate, capture, or (if all else failed) destroy the primitive people who so easily bested him. Arriving in a ha'tak warship, Klorel and his Jaffa spent days searching the planet for any signs of the Nox, only to leave disappointed. Apophis hasn't given up on finding and dominating the Nox, but other more pressing matters keep him from returning. Since his initial visits, word as spread among the other System Lords of a people with fantastic abilities, and several Goa'uld have since visited Gaia, only to leave empty handed.

The Nox and the Tollan

A few months after SG-1's visit to their world, the Nox unburied their Stargate to aid a race of technologically advanced beings known as the Tollan (a small group of whom were saved by SG-1 before their former world destroyed itself). Stranded on Earth and unable to travel to their new home via Stargate, this small group was set to be imprisoned by the NID when Daniel Jackson convinced Omoc, the leader of the Tollan to use their advanced technology to contact the Nox. The Nox responded quickly, traveling to Earth and offering the Tollan refuge on their world. Once on Gaia, the Tollan contacted their fellows and were picked up by a Tollan starship shortly thereafter (see Enigma, page 62 for more information).

Nox Explorers and the SGC

If you were to ask Daniel Jackson or anyone in the SGC if they keep in contact with the Nox, their answer would likely be "No." What the SGC doesn't realize is that Nox have encountered SG teams on several occasions since SG-1's visit to their world, but avoid making direct contact, preferring to observe the humans and their actions. Some of these travelers have considered making contact with the humans so that they might interact with them in a less covert manner, but none have yet done so. That may change in the future, however, especially if the SG team in question displays the sort of compassion and value for life which the Nox themselves so purely embody.

1-13: Hathor

World Visited: Earth.

Episode Summary

While exploring an ancient Mayan pyramid, two archaeologists, Dr. Cole and Dr. Kleinhouse, discover an Egyptian sarcophagus. Incredulous, they cannot imagine how such an artifact came to be so far away from Egypt. However, Kleinhouse remembers reading an article by Daniel Jackson that postulated a connection between ancient civilizations and wonders if perhaps he was correct. Before the archaeologists can speculate further, the sarcophagus opens, revealing a woman who asks them the location of Ra. When she realizes they are not Goa'uld, she uses her ribbon device to kill them.

Word of the deaths of the researchers reaches Jackson at SGC, as does word of their find. He believes that the sarcophagus might be a Goa'uld device like the one Ra possessed on Abydos, which can, among other things, revive the dead. If so, whoever was in the sarcophagus must be a Goa'uld. While discussing this with Hammond and SG-1, an airman interrupts and says that a woman has been captured attempting to enter Cheyenne Mountain. She knows that the Stargate is there and asks to be allowed in.

The woman in question is named Hathor, whom they meet in a holding cell. Hathor is the ancient Egyptian goddess of fertility, inebriety, and music. She is said to have been both the daughter and wife of Ra. When asked, Hathor says she was drawn to the Stargate. Jackson asks that she be released from her handcuffs. Hammond complies and while Jackson removes them, Hathor breathes a pink mist on him, which briefly startles him. He recovers and quickly advocates that Hammond and the others "humor" her by playing along with her belief in her divinity and being "the mother of all pharaohs." Before he leaves her and Jackson alone, Hathor breathes pink mist on the General's hand. He too is briefly startled before seemingly regaining his senses.

Alone, Hathor interrogates Jackson about Ra. Reluctantly at first, he tells her that Ra is dead, killed by humans, including himself. Instead of being upset, Hathor is delighted. She tells Jackson that she owes him her gratitude. She suggests that she might choose him as her new beloved and kisses him. Jackson then goes to the briefing room and explains to Hammond and SG-1 that Hathor must be a Goa'uld who was imprisoned on Earth two thousand years ago and has been in stasis ever since. He suggests that she in fact a good Goa'uld, who was attempting to free humanity from Ra. Jackson cites tales of Hathor as a friend of humanity, but neither O'Neill nor Teal'c believes him. Jackson then asks that Hathor be allowed to debrief them to prove his point. Inexplicably, Hammond agrees, although he consents to closing the blast door so that she cannot see the Stargate from the briefing room.

When Hathor enters the debriefing room, she asks for a drink of water, which Hammond asks O'Neill to get. She thanks O'Neill for killing Ra and touches his hand, breathing pink mist on him. He is momentarily startled and then returns to his seat at the briefing table. Hammond then offers Hathor every courtesy, which deeply offends and worries Captain Carter, who protests. Hammond rebuffs her, as does O'Neill, leading Carter to worry about the mental state of her companions.

Hathor is taken to a guest room. She convinces Hammond and O'Neill not to post guards at her door, despite protocol. When they leave, she asks Jackson to remain and tells him that he will be her Chosen One. At her suggestion, Jackson takes Hathor to the gate room, where her sarcophagus is being held. She reveals that she is a Goa'uld queen, the source of all Goa'uld larvae. To do this,

though, she needs a source of human DNA to ensure compatibility between her brood of young and the eventual host species. She intends to take this DNA from Jackson. Meanwhile, Carter expresses her concerns to O'Neill, who once more rebuffs her. He claims Hathor is their friend and that there is no reason to worry.

Still worried, Carter goes to speak with Dr. Janet Fraiser, who also expresses concern at the way the men on the base are acting. Together, they surmise that Hathor may be using airborne pheromones to control the men of Cheyenne Mountain. They gather several female airmen and give them weapons, hoping to defeat Hathor before she can take over the base and turn it into her nest. Teal'c joins them, saying that the Goa'uld larva within him protects him from Hathor's pheromones. The women and Teal'c find Hathor reclining alone in a hot tub, but before they can act against her, a large band of soldiers appear and take them prisoner.

O'Neill is slowly coming to his senses. He approaches Hathor and begins to ask her questions. Before he can get very far, she overpowers him with her pheromones and yanks a device from the mid-section of her dress. It is a Jaffa creation device, which she uses on O'Neill so as to form a pouch in his abdomen – the first to hold her new brood of larvae.

Carter, Fraiser, and the captured female airmen trick their guards into entering the holding cell by taking advantage of the men's heightened libidos. Once inside the cell, they overpower the guards, take their weapons, and flee. Hammond appears and attempts to stop them, but Carter hits him on the head and knocks him unconscious. They free Teal'c and make their way to the locker room where they last saw Hathor.

In the locker room, they find O'Neill in a hot tub, which is now full of Goa'uld larvae. The strongest will enter his pouch and turn him into a Jaffa. Carter and Fraiser pull him out before this occurs. However, his condition is not good, since he no longer possesses a human immune system. Teal'c suggests they take him to Hathor's sarcophagus to be cured. They place O'Neill inside, but Hathor objects. Airmen under her control attack them. Shortly after O'Neill is removed, Hathor uses her ribbon device to destroy the sarcophagus. Now cured, O'Neill is determined to defeat the Goa'uld queen.

They find her in the locker room, where Jackson attends her. She attacks Carter with her ribbon device, seemingly knocking her unconscious. In reality, the Captain is only wounded. She fires her pistol into Hathor, who collapses into the hot tub, which bursts into flames, sending Goa'uld larvae everywhere. As the whole room bursts into flames, Hathor escapes to the gate room, where she activates the Stargate and steps through to Chulak.

General Hammond is pleased with Carter and Fraiser. He recommends them both for commendations for their quick thinking. Without their efforts, SGC would have fallen entirely under Hathor's control. Though she escaped, at least she did not turn Cheyenne Mountain into her new nest and take over Earth as she had planned.

BACKGROUND
THE NETJERIANS

The planet Ta-Netjer had, in the distant past, been Hathor's personal seat of power. This was the world from which she ruled before she entered into the alliance with Ra that made her his queen. Though Hathor gained immense power as a result of this alliance, she also lost much of her independence and freedom of movement, two things that she valued dearly. It is little wonder then that she rejoiced upon learning of Ra's demise at the hands of the Tauri. She had hoped one day to eliminate the great System Lord herself, although the opportunity to do so never arose.

Ta-Netjer survived the departure of Hathor but not without some terrible repercussions. Its inhabitants were anthropomorphic aliens who had worshiped the Goa'uld queen as a goddess. Indeed, she formed the basis of their entire culture, with the Netjerians building great monuments in her name and creating entire arts and sciences simply to sing her praises. Once she was gone – and gone she was for Ra did not wish his queen to possess an independent base of power – the aliens found themselves bereft of the one thing in their lives that had always seemed a constant.

Not surprisingly, the early days after Hathor's departure were not pleasant ones. Many Netjerians committed suicide en masse rather than accept a life without their goddess. Others attempted to bring her back by religious devotion bordering on insanity. They fasted, burnt offerings in her name, and undertook other rituals intended to call her back through the Stargate. None worked. Within months of Hathor's departure, the entire world was thrown into chaos and, by any outside standard, it should have eventually fallen into barbarism forever. That it did not is a testament both to the unique qualities of the Netjerians and to the role Hathor had played in their lives.

Over the course of several decades, the Netjerians created a new society, one that did not take Hathor as its inspiration but rather the Netjerian people themselves. While there was no doubt that they had achieved much of what they had due to the influence of the Goa'uld queen and her Jaffa, the Netjerians had nevertheless done much on their own. The new society that arose lauded the average Netjerian's capacity for greatness, which laid the groundwork for many later changes that would one day make Ta-Netjer a beacon in the galaxy – a rare example of world that survived Goa'uld domination and thrived in its aftermath.

Of course, it also created a schism in Netjerian society. Most Netjerian came around to the idea that Hathor had not in fact been a goddess but merely a very powerful life form possessed of great technological advancement. In fact, many Netjerians came to revile her as the personification of evil. In many ways, this was a natural reaction to their abandonment. How could a truly benign deity simply leave them behind without instructions for what to do afterward? How could a loving goddess abandon her people at all?

It did not take long for the whole of Netjerian society to look upon Hathor with revulsion. Unfortunately, a few aliens refused to accept the new outlook on their former Goa'uld mistress. They remained true to her, despite their seeming abandonment. They argued that if Hathor were as evil as her detractors claimed, why then did she not simply destroy them all when she no longer had need for them? Why had she simply left the Netjerians to their own devices rather than eliminate them as she could have? To these true believers, Hathor's departure was a test of her people's faith and determination. What could they achieve in her absence? How much better could they make Ta-Netjer while she was gone?

So it was that they joined in the efforts to rebuild the planet even though they did not share the rationale for doing so. Unlike most of their fellow Netjerians, the true believers longed for the return of Hathor so that they might be rewarded by being made Jaffa. These Netjerians formed a secret culture within the planet's overarching culture,

TA-NETJER

World: Ta-Netjer.

Thermosphere: Hot (CR 0; close orbit to gas giant; 3d20+50°F).

Atmosphere: Very thin (CR 1; 0.4 atmospheres; Exp. Inc: 10 minutes; SV Fort (DC20); Dmg 1d6 subdual; Recup 2 rounds).

Hydrosphere: Desert (CR 2; daily weather 1-92: none, 93: rain/snow, 94-95: dust storm, 96-100: wind 1d10 MPH).

Geosphere: Very Unstable tectonic activity (daily earthquakes 1-90: none, 91-95: minor, 96-99: moderate, 100: major; 10 small volcanoes within 1d10 miles of Stargate).

Seasons: No seasons (1-25: spring unchanged; 26-50: summer unchanged; 51-75: autumn, unchanged; 76-100: winter unchanged).

Anthrosphere: 10,000,000 natives; Star-faring (7 picks, 5 RP); Republic; Neutral (+0 with disposition checks); Cautious (5,000 soldiers, squad size 1d2 soldiers); Very Progressive civil rights.

Origin: N/A.

Stargate Location (desert region): Rocky and sandy terrain in desert, dry desert area pocked with small geysers and gas pockets, bordering a salt-water ocean.

which revealed itself only occasionally. As the centuries and millennia wore on, the true believers came to see Hathor as a savior who would free them from their bondage among the heathens of the planet and lead them to a promised world where they could again worship Hathor and serve her as she deserved. The more radical of the true believers, though, engaged in acts of violence against mainstream society. From time to time, they would arise in large enough numbers to spark wars and military incidents, but they were never sufficiently powerful to cause any permanent damage.

In time, the Netjerians learned to reproduce much of the Goa'uld technology that had been left behind on their home world. They used it to improve their society rather than to enslave as their former mistress had done. Eventually, they even gained the ability to travel first between planets and then the stars themselves. When they did so, the Netjerians were saddened to learn of the existence of other Goa'uld who had conquered other worlds and thrown their inhabitants into bondage. The galaxy was indeed an unpleasant and brutal place and the Netjerians did not know how best to react to it. Should they withdraw to their homeworld and avoid contact so as to preserve themselves? Or should they do what they felt was right and battle against the Goa'uld?

The decision to oppose the System Lords did not come easily. True believers still existed in their ranks and argued that the Goa'uld were not evil but beneficent; it was only the Netjerians' limited understanding of these matters that obscured this truth. While this line of reasoning – if it could be called that – held little appeal for the vast majority of the population, there was still much trepidation when the planetary republic finally decided to fight the Goa'uld whenever and wherever they could. Though far more advanced than many races in the galaxy, the Netjerians were still far behind the Goa'uld technologically. Their weapons were no match for the System Lords and their ruthlessness was insufficient in light of the brutal tactics needed to give the Goa'uld a serious fight.

Thus far, no System Lord has taken an interest in the Netjerians. They are considered a nuisance rather than a serious threat. Unlike the Tauri, they have never dealt a serious blow to the Goa'uld, although that may change in the years to come. Emboldened by the tales of the Tauri's success, the Netjerians are themselves becoming braver in their own fight. Indeed, they are seeking out the Tauri in the hopes of forming an alliance. They believe that they have much to offer the people of Earth, particularly starships and pilots capable of flying these vessels. In addition, they themselves have made allies on other worlds that suffer under the dominion of the Goa'uld. The Netjerians wish to share their knowledge in exchange for assistance from humanity.

It is worth noting that, as of Season One, the tales of Hathor's return are widely circulated on Ta-Netjer. Although she was defeated by the Tauri, she was not destroyed. Rumors are abroad that the former queen of the planet has plans to re-establish her rule once she is strong enough to do so. As one might expect, this has led to a resurgence in true believer terrorism and acts of violence,

as well as a sense of unease among the Netjerians. The race's numbers are small and its increasingly bold initiatives against the Goa'uld might well prove to be their undoing. Consequently, their desire for an alliance with Earth is almost desperate – if only they could make contact with the fabled warriors of the Tauri.

1-14: COR-AI

World Visited: P3X-1279 (Cartago).
Thermosphere: Warm (CR 0; standard orbit; 2d20+25˚ F).
Atmosphere: Normal (CR 0; 1.1 atmospheres; Auto None; Exp. Inc: None; SV None; Dmg None; Recup None).
Hydrosphere: Moist sub-humid (CR 0; daily weather 1-85: none, 86-87: flood, 88-93: rain/snow, 94-96: thunderstorm or snowstorm, 97-98: hurricane or blizzard, 99: light wind, 100: moderate wind).
Geosphere: Stable tectonic activity (daily earthquakes 1-99: none, 100: minor; 0 volcanoes within 10 miles of Stargate).
Seasons: Very mild (1-42: spring unchanged; 43-50: summer +2d6˚ F; 51-92: autumn unchanged; 93-100: winter -2d6˚ F).
Anthrosphere: 1,000 natives; Iron Age (3 picks, 1 RP); Gerontocracy; Neutral (+0 with disposition checks); Extremely Cautious (5 soldiers, squad size 1d4 soldiers); Very Progressive civil rights.
Origin: Carthaginian.
Stargate Location (upper region): Flat terrain in forest, village in a large clearing.

EPISODE SUMMARY

Arriving on the planet Cartago – home of the Byrsa and a favorite among the Goa'uld as a source of hosts – SG-1 finds a village, apparently deserted mere minutes before their appearance. The meeting hall seems equally deserted until a small group of men armed with crossbows confronts them. O'Neill demonstrates SG-1's goodwill by lowering his weapon first and the villagers relax – until their leader sees Teal'c. Despite SG-1's assurances that their teammate's intentions are peaceful, the leader, Hanno, will not back down. This Jaffa, he says, killed his father. Teal'c asserts that he has never seen the young man before. One of Hanno's compatriots does not recognize the Jaffa, and cautions him against taking hasty revenge against the Mandates of their people. If Teal'c is guilty, his fate will be determined by *Cor-ai*. Hanno agrees, and leads SG-1 to meet the Elders.

Outside, villagers emerge from hiding as it becomes clear that the strangers are not Goa'uld despite having arrived through the *circ kakona* (a term Jackson translates from a curious mixture of Latin and Greek roots to "circle of woes"). To O'Neill's surprise, the chief Elder tells him they may go, but the catch is quickly clarified: Teal'c must remain. Hanno challenges Teal'c's claim not to know him by holding up a carved wooden crutch. Teal'c recognizes it, and by extension Hanno – the now-grown son of its owner, a man he killed at Apophis' order years ago.

During a recess, Jackson explores the village, puzzled to see no residences. The woman who was to have been Teal'c's voice explains that they sleep in the Hiding: caves and tunnels extending in all directions. When the Stargate begins to activate, they retreat to these caves before the marauders come through. Jackson comments that the Goa'uld must therefore only catch the slowest among them, but the woman assures him that they would never leave anyone behind. They all go, or none of them do.

Armed with this insight, Jackson returns to the Cor-ai and pins Teal'c down on the reason he chose Hanno's father. Hearing Apophis order Teal'c to kill one of the villagers to intimidate the rest, the crippled man reached out to him. Both knew that without him among them, next time they might escape. Apophis chose seven women and released the rest; the sacrifice of Hanno's father had saved his son and his clan. Hanno hears Jackson out, commending him on the wisdom of his argument, but he has reached a decision. At noon the next day, the Jaffa will die by his own weapon.

Meanwhile O'Neill has returned with Carter to the SGC for reinforcements to extract Teal'c under threat of force. Hammond refuses, and an appeal to the President elicits the same answer: Whatever their personal feelings, they cannot commit forces to such a morally ambiguous action.

O'Neill and Carter return to find the village in flames and under the control of several Serpent Guards, including Shak'l. *(See The Nox, page 49.)* Cut off from their escape routes, the villagers are surprised to see SG-1, including Teal'c, fight in their defense. When the Jaffa have been defeated, Teal'c gives his staff weapon to Hanno, prepared to meet his fate. The young man, though, declares that the Jaffa who killed his father is already dead, that Teal'c has killed him. SG-1 leaves Cartago in friendship, promising to help the Byrsa defend themselves in the future.

Hanno, after seeing Teal'c safely incarcerated, tells SG-1 that they are welcome to stay. As soon as the villagers have left, O'Neill begins to outline a plan, but Teal'c refuses to disrespect the Byrsa by escaping. Jackson agrees with him, but O'Neill remains unconvinced that the Cor-ai will be a fair trial. He is not reassured when a woman arrives and explains that she has been chosen to serve as the Jaffa's "voice," and must witness his *pecca-ve* – his confession. She is baffled by O'Neill's anger at the assumption of Teal'c's guilt, but acquiesces when O'Neill says he will be Teal'c's voice in her stead. When Carter and Jackson express doubts about his diplomatic skills, he compromises by saying they will all defend their teammate.

To Teal'c's surprise, Hanno opens the Cor-ai by asking his forgiveness for threatening his life in anger, counter to Byrsa Mandates. Teal'c grants it, setting off a murmur of discussion through the meeting hall. When it becomes clear that Hanno is to conduct the proceedings, O'Neill's vehement objection is met with confusion by the Byrsa. The idea of an impartial judge is foreign and incomprehensible to them; only the one who has suffered, the chief Elder says, can fairly choose the punishment. Ignoring O'Neill's order to the contrary, Teal'c answers his accuser's simple question. He is the one who killed Hanno's father. With that, a bell tolls and the Byrsa file out of the hall.

Though forced to admit that the confession was not a surprise, O'Neill is frustrated by Teal'c's unwillingness to defend himself. Apophis gave the order, and must take at least part of the blame. To Teal'c, though, he alone is responsible, for the death of Hanno's father as well as countless others. He will not deny Hanno his retribution.

His friends refuse to accept this, and when the Cor-ai resumes they set out to prove he does not deserve to die. Teal'c is not the same Jaffa, they argue, that he was when he killed Hanno's father – or even when his selection of Jackson's wife condemned her to possession. He has demonstrated this by sacrificing his former privileged position – and everything else he knew – to fight the Goa'uld beside them.

BACKGROUND
THE BYRSA

The Byrsa are a simple people living lives of quiet harmony... punctuated by terrifying raids from the Goa'uld. While their home world of Cartago is not occupied by any one System Lord, their healthy stock and technological inferiority makes them the prized target of raids. Despite such horrors, the Byrsa remain a peaceful people, interested only in caring for themselves and their loved ones.

While many Byrsa words stem from Greek or Latin, other words and most names point to the Phoenician roots of ancient Carthage, the ancestral home which they refer to as Lu'Cartago, "before Cartago." Cartago itself means "new home," an echo of the Phoenician *Kart Hadasht,* "new city," from which the name Carthage derives. Byrsa is also the name of the hill on which the ancient city was founded, a detail lost to their history before the coming of SG-1. To them the name means "simple way," and indeed their culture reflects a rejection of the wealth-based Carthaginian power structure (which the Byrsa equate with the arrogant excesses of the Goa'uld). The simplicity and harmony of Byrsa life prompted Daniel Jackson to characterize it as "a very lovely existence." Their clothing is clean-lined and functional, employing subtle color coordination and modest trims, with head coverings customarily worn by both men and women.

The village near the Stargate consists primarily of open-sided round wooden structures roofed with palm branches. The Byrsa's outdoor lifestyle is well suited to Cartago's mild climate and the need to quickly evacuate in the event of a Goa'uld raid. Only the meeting hall, the *kaleo*, is a conventional enclosed building; it is also the only stone structure in the village, decorated in a more elegant version of the Byrsa's restrained style. The kaleo's main level consists of a single large room, with high seats used by the Elders at one end. The smaller dungeon level houses a single prison cell, and serves as an emergency shelter during severe weather. Accessible via two stairwells, it has also been used as a stopgap hiding place for villagers unable to reach the Hiding during a Goa'uld raid. Byrsa tradition holds that their ancestors found the kaleo empty and in disrepair upon their arrival; it took two generations to renew it, in remembrance of that which was good in Lu'Cartago. This is probably essentially accurate: the Byrsa have neither the knowledge required to build such a structure from scratch nor any interest in doing so.

Due in part to the depredations of the Goa'uld, but also by their own choosing, the Byrsa population is small, expanding no more than a day's walk from the village. The *kaleo* is the physical and symbolic center of their community. They have considered the possibility that moving farther away from it (and the Stargate) could discourage the Goa'uld from their frequent raids, but believe that the secret cave system called the Hiding affords more reliable protection. Farmers in outlying areas still consider themselves part of the community, though they may visit the village itself only once or twice in a month. These families build houses more substantial than the workshop structures of the village — sometimes incorporating the same native stone found in the kaleo — using a similar circular framework. The craftspeople and Elders, together with their families, spend their days in the village, retreating at night to the Hiding to sleep. While daily labor tends to be divided along traditional gender lines, female blacksmiths or male weavers are neither unknown nor censured.

The manageable size of the Byrsa community allows for an egalitarian and consensus-driven social structure. Reason and wisdom are highly valued, and respected in all members of the community regardless of their age, trade or gender. Parents usually have no more than two children, to ensure a steady population and keep resources from becoming taxed. The Byrsa frown upon emotional decision-making, and their Mandates expressly forbid it in serious matters affecting others. Leadership is accorded to a council of three Elders, one from each of the clans. Once selected, they serve for life or until they choose to retire, and the seniormost — in service, not necessarily age — is designated chief Elder, sometimes called "Holder of the *Pauma*." This epithet refers to a staff of office topped by a branched bronze ornament, which signifies that its holder has final say in conflicts.

Though they commonly refer to the Goa'uld as "gods," the Byrsa do not worship them. Indeed, they claim that no such worship has ever existed on Cartago . The kaleo's relative grandeur and its position adjacent to the Stargate — which the Byrsa call the *circ kakona,* "circle of woes" — suggest that it might once have been a temple, but it is reasonable to believe that the Byrsa have always used it for its present secular purpose. None of those taken through the circ kakona have returned in living memory, but the Byrsa have drawn fairly accurate conclusions about the Goa'uld's true nature from old tales of evil gods wearing the stolen faces of loved ones. They remember the names of the gods of Lu'Cartago — Ba'al, Tanit, Melkart — with open loathing.

THE HIDING

While the activities of daily life are carried out in the village, the Byrsa protect themselves at night by sleeping in the Hiding. Each clan claims a cave section some distance removed from the village, affording an additional measure of security. Sleeping areas, while comfortable, are kept scrupulously neat, with clear paths between them, in case evacuation proves necessary. This is especially important since the Goa'uld became aware of the caves' existence.

The Byrsa have also had to devise new escape routes for daytime evacuations. Since they must vanish with very little warning, cave entrances nearer the village are designated for this purpose. These arrangements are also organized by clan, and no one leaves the village until all clan members are accounted for. Typically this means everyone must be present, although a person may accompany another clan whose gathering point is closer to his location. In such a case, it is imperative to communicate his intention to his own clan — usually a simple hand signal understood to mean "I am going with them," acknowledged by an answering signal from one of his clan. The answering party is then responsible for informing the clan leader that the other is accounted for, and with which clan he is traveling.

During an evacuation, five to seven armed men remain behind to observe the invaders and make certain they do not discover the hidden villagers. The structure of the village affords several concealed vantage points which, while by no means as secure as the Hiding, generally serve their purpose well enough. Immediately following each raid, the Byrsa choose which group will serve as guardians for the next evacuation, usually by a combination of volunteering and drawing lots. A few young men who are particularly adept at this dangerous duty, or who simply feel the need to do more for their people than run, tend to volunteer frequently. This has led to the rule that every individual must go to the Hiding with their clan at least once in every five evacuations.

Following SG-1's visit, the SGC sent an Engineering Corps team to Cartago to assess the Hiding. They were impressed with the Byrsa's own improvements on nature, which include smoothly-graded floors and solid wooden supports shoring up high-traffic passages. To further enhance safety, the engineers recommended a number of changes, including sealing off compromised entrances and creating new ones, as well as opening up new cave sections that were not previously habitable. Respecting the Byrsa's pride in their self-determination, they have worked closely with native craftsmen to implement the changes, using local materials whenever possible, and employing methods that can be replicated – or at least maintained – without access to Earth technology.

THE HIDING

Following the Engineers Corps' visit, several innovations were made to the Hiding, Compromised entrances to the network of caves have been filled with tons of rock, to a minimum depth of 20 ft. (Hardness 8, Wound Points 3,600). Additional entrances were created within a quarter-mile of the buried routes, with concealed doors made of 6 in. reinforced steel (Spot DC 20, Hardness 12, Wound Points 200, Break DC 32 (force open door)). Since the Byrsa do not wish to bury their Stargate *(see "New Friends," right)*, the SGC hopes that these measures will help keep them safe during any future raids by the Goa'uld.

THE MANDATES

The highest moral authority on Cartago lies in the Mandates, laws defining the individual's responsibility to the community. As Dr. Jackson observed during Teal'c's Cor-ai, many of the principles underpinning the Mandates resemble those found in the Jewish Talmud. (SGC researchers are investigating the apparent link between this similarity and the kinship between the Hebrews and the Phoenicians.) In addition to typical prohibitions such as theft and murder, the Mandates outline requirements such as the care of the elderly or infirm, the imparting of knowledge to the young, and the maintenance of communal property such as the kaleo.

The Mandates are set down in writing – a bonanza for SGC linguists – but all Byrsa learn them from earliest childhood, and only rarely need to consult these documents to settle a dispute. The motivation of conscience is augmented by a system of honor and shame in which a violation of the Mandates reflects on the transgressor's clan. The wronged party may choose to forgive him at any time, at which point the shame is erased. If he does not forgive, or in the case of serious crimes such as murder, more involved proceedings are called for.

COR-AI

The centerpiece of Byrsa justice is the Cor-ai. While the roots of many Byrsa names and words are readily apparent, this one remains a puzzle, though Dr. Jackson has speculated that it might be related to the Hebrew *kor* (Latin *corus*), an ancient Hebrew and Phoenician unit of measure. It is important to note that the Cor-ai serves not to establish the guilt or innocence of the accused, but to determine the appropriate penalty for one already known to be guilty.

Preliminary to the Cor-ai, the Elders name an individual to serve as the transgressor's "voice." Any adult can be chosen; members of his own clan are exempted, but may volunteer. This duty consists primarily of witnessing the *pecca-ve,* (roughly translatable as "confession") Only the voice and two secondary witnesses are typically permitted

to hear the pecca-ve, though the transgressor may choose to have others present. The purpose of this formality is twofold: The pecca-ve cannot be taken back, ensuring that the transgressor cannot unexpectedly deny his crime in the Cor-ai; and if he is ashamed to state it in public, the voice may repeat the pecca-ve for him. Theoretically the transgressor could stall the Cor-ai indefinitely by refusing to give his pecca-ve, but there is no record of such a gesture lasting very long. The Byrsa acknowledge that in rare cases an innocent person has been put through Cor-ai. Since the pecca-ve is by definition truthful, an innocent person would be unable to give one, but they insist that the truth invariably comes to light within a few days.

The Cor-ai itself is conducted in public. In the initial phase, the *posco,* the transgressor sits or stands on the small railed platform in the center of the kaleo, facing the high seats of the Elders. Like the rest of the Byrsa, however, they are present only as witnesses; the wronged party leads the Cor-ai, in accordance with the Mandate that only the one who has suffered understands the pain which has been inflicted. If the wronged has mocked, threatened or otherwise retaliated against the transgressor, he must ask the transgressor's forgiveness before he can begin. If it is not granted, the shame of his own actions will remain with him and his clan even after the Cor-ai is finished and the transgressor pardoned or punished.

While Cor-ai is in session the chief Elder relinquishes the pauma to the wronged, acknowledging his right to final say in this matter. The wronged begins the posco by asking the transgressor if he is the one who committed the crime. Despite the phrasing of the question, "yes" alone is not a sufficient answer. The transgressor must state that he is the one who committed the crime, or if he prefers (or refuses to speak), his voice will repeat his pecca-ve. While emotional displays on the part of the wronged or the transgressor can prolong it, the posco is normally very short. When it is complete bells sound and the Byrsa withdraw briefly from the hall. Family and close friends are permitted to remain, and a violent offender may be guarded, but typically the transgressor reflects on his actions alone.

The main and final phase of the process is the *decerno.* The transgressor has the opportunity to enumerate any mitigating factors that might sway the wronged to forgive or to exact a lesser punishment than that mandated for the offense. At the discretion of the wronged, others may also be permitted to speak on his behalf. Even in the most straightforward case, the transgressor may have compelling arguments for leniency, which the wronged is obligated to hear and thoroughly consider, so it is not unusual for the decerno to stretch out over several days before he reaches a decision.

Throughout the proceedings, the transgressor, even a violent offender requiring imprisonment, is treated with the same courtesy as any other member of the community. The Byrsa's remarkable commitment to this Mandate was evident in their conduct toward Teal'c – not only a stranger, but a Jaffa – during SG-1's visit to the planet.

New Friends

As promised by SG-1, follow-up missions have assisted the Byrsa in putting new defense measures in place. Teal'c initially accompanied them to contribute his expertise in Jaffa strategy and tactics, and received a hero's welcome that – despite the Byrsa's deeply-ingrained caution – was soon extended to the newcomers beside him. Upon evaluation of the Byrsa's resources, the SGC has helped them make several improvements to both active and passive defenses. The goals are relatively modest: in the short run to better enable the people to evade capture, and in the long run to make Cartago less attractive as an easy and convenient source of hosts. One means of achieving this goal has been to modify the Hiding, as noted above. Maslih, the chief Elder and an accomplished stoneworker herself, participated in the modifications with the SGC engineers. This insured not only that the Byrsa's input was incorporated into the changes, but also that the techniques used would be available for them to make their own modifications later on. Though they appreciate the help, Maslih and the other Elders wish to keep from becoming too dependent on anyone.

SG-1's defeat of Shak'l and his raiding party provided the Byrsa with several staff weapons, and Teal'c trained a select group of young men, led by Hanno, in their use. He continues to visit on occasion to coach the more advanced students, and to satisfy himself that his adapted Jaffa instruction drills have enabled them to teach others effectively. The *kest* will remain important, however, even if additional staff weapons are acquired in the future. Smaller and easier to maneuver in and out of tight hiding places, the slower speed of its bolts also allows them to penetrate a Goa'uld personal shield.

Faced with the Byrsa's unwillingness to relocate, the Engineering Corps team briefly considered the possibility of moving the Stargate instead. They abandoned this idea early on, however, due to the extent of the Hiding and the fact that escape routes and utilized cave sections extend in all directions from the village, with farms beyond. Transporting the gate far enough to avoid endangering these traditionally safe locations would be no simple operation even with the SGC's resources, and – being an impossible task for the Byrsa alone – would be likely to draw unwanted Goa'uld scrutiny. Burying the gate is a last-resort possibility that the Byrsa have agreed to consider should the raids grow more frequent or severe, but they hope to avoid having to shut out friend as well as foe.

1-15: SINGULARITY

World Visited: P8X-987 (Hanka).

Thermosphere: Cool (CR 0; Terran Orbit; 2d20° F).

Atmosphere: Normal (CR 0; 1.0 atmospheres).

Hydrosphere: Sub-Humid (annual rainfall 25-47 in.; daily weather 1-85: none, 86-87: flood 1d10 mph, 88-93: rain, 1d4-1 in. or snow 1d6-1], 94-95: thunderstorm or snowstorm, 96: hurricane or blizzard, 97-98: wind 1d10 mph, 99: wind 1d10+10 mph, 100: wind 1d10+20 mph.

Geosphere: Flat; Very Stable tectonic activity (daily earthquakes – N/A).

Seasons: Normal (1-25: spring unchanged; 26-50: summer +2d20° F; 51-75: autumn unchanged; 76-100: winter -2d20° F).

Anthrosphere: Originally 2,000 natives; Renaissance (5 Picks, 3 RP); Oligarchy; Friendly (+1 Disposition Modifier); Absolutely Pacifistic (no soldiers); Progressive civil rights. Now none.

Origin: Lithuanian.

Stargate Location (plains region): In a field surrounded by crops.

Episode Summary

SG-1 enters the Stargate embarkation room talking about the impending mission to a world where they will observe a black hole during an eclipse. Once through the gate they arrive on planet PX8-987, also known as Hanka, with a primitive pre-industrial culture. Teal'c wonders where the member of SG-7 are; they had arrived in anticipation of the eclipse and were expected to greet them. The team soon finds a body apparently killed by some disease and takes appropriate precautions. Col. O'Neill assigns Teal'c and Dr. Jackson to check out the local village while he and Capt. Carter go to the observatory. Once there they discover all the members of SG-7 dead in their bunks, also from the disease. Teal'c and Dr. Jackson return shortly to report that the entire village has been wiped out be the mysterious plague.

Upon returning to the pre-fabricated scientific outpost, the team is decontaminated and examined by Dr. Fraiser. After being cleared from infection, the SG-1 travels back to Hanka for further investigation. Dr. Jackson reveals that the locals had told him that the impending darkness was an sign of the apocalypse, but that he had – apparently falsely – reassured them that it was simply a natural phenomenon.

Capt. Carter quickly discovers they are being watched from the wheat fields. Teal'c goes to find the cause only to discover a small girl, who trusts his uncharacteristic smile and allows him to lead her out of the bushes. She is inspected by Dr. Fraiser, who hazards a guess that the disease is caused by a virus. Capt. Carter tries, unsuccessfully, to try and talk to the girl to comfort her, but the girl demonstrates she fiercely believes she will become like the others very soon by latching on to a body identification tag.

Dr. Fraiser finds traces of naquadah in the girl's blood; impossible, yet it is there. She then goes on to reveal that the entire area has been contaminated by the disease, both in the ground and the water. While Teal'c and Col. O'Neill decide to remain on the planet to observe the eclipse, Dr.

Fraiser and the other members of SG-1 return to Earth with the girl. After being decontaminated in the gate room, the girl is taken by Capt. Carter to quarters on the base where she attempts to again comfort her.

Dr. Jackson and Dr. Fraiser debrief with Gen. Hammond, explaining that the disease has wiped out 1,432 people; the entire population of the planet. The girl is believed to have an immunity. The SGC is mystified as to why SG-7 did not report the disease.

Informing the girl she must return to Hanka, Capt. Carter tries to explain Dr. Jackson will see to her. Afraid, the girl meekly asks her, "Please don't go." The girl goes on to reveal that her name is Cassandra and that she has a in pain in her chest. Dr. Fraiser and Capt. Carter check her out in the med-lab only to discover that her bloodwork shows a marked potassium deficiency. When she leaves the med-lab, Cassandra goes into cardiac arrest. The emergency team is called in to save her life... and discovers an odd mechanical pump-like sound in her heart. An x-ray reveals a device there which a previous exam, ten hours earlier, failed to reveal. The SCG begins exploratory surgery on her to determine the object's exact nature. But when contact is made with the bio-mechanical device, Cassandra goes into cardiac arrest; the object has the ability to shut down the girl's heart in an instant, and cannot be removed without killing Cassandra. The girl eventually stabilizes, but her dilemma remains.

Seeking answers, Capt. Carter performs an experiment by contacting a microscopic particle of iron and potassium with naquadah. The result is an immense nuclear explosion. A similar biochemical reaction is at work in Cassandra: the fatty layer between the two sides of the device is decaying slowly, which will cause an explosion a million times more powerful than the one Carter instigated.

The entire affair seems to have been a set-up. The Goa'uld killed the entire population of the planet, except for Cassandra, because they knew the humans would not leave her behind. The device was designed to assemble itself using the microscopic particles in the girl's body after it had been activated by passing through the Stargate.

Dr. Fraiser goes further to suggest that they may have even turned the device on with a jolt of electricity to resuscitate Cassandra after her initial cardiac arrest. The girl is nothing more than an unwitting Trojan Horse, and they have less than two hours before the fatty tissue finishes decaying. Gen. Hammond tells Carter and Jackson that the girl must be returned to the planet, as the device cannot be removed.

Meanwhile, during the eclipse on Hanka, Col. O'Neill spots what appears to be a Goa'uld attack vessel in orbit above the planet. Teal'c explains that the starship belongs to the Goa'uld Nirrti, an enemy of Apophis. She had previously sent an emissary of peace to negotiate with Apophis over a Stargate he had seized. The negotiation was a ploy; as soon as the emissary entered the Stargate there was a massive explosion.

As attack gliders descend from the ship, Col. O'Neill and Teal'c race back to the Stargate and dial in, beating the SGC who were attempting to dial out to Hanka. While doing so Cassandra slips into a coma in the embarkation room. Col. O'Neill quickly orders the girl to be removed from the presence of the gate.

Teal'c then debriefs Gen. Hammond, explaining that if Cassandra is taken through the gate, the device will explode, destroying the Stargate and the SGC. Looking for a safe place to put the girl until the bomb explodes or the danger is passed, Col. O'Neill recommends an abandoned nuclear facility close-by. SG-1 takes Cassandra there by truck, and Carter volunteers to take her down the thirty stories to the bottom of the complex. Col. O'Neill warns her the elevator takes three minutes to get to the bottom, giving her four minutes to start back up.

In the elevator, Cassandra wakes up in Capt. Carter's arms. Once at the bottom, Samantha then walks Cassandra out into a dark foreboding room, where she tries to explain the situation. Earlier, she had promised never to leave the girl alone, but now it seems as if she must break her word. Sealing Cassandra in the room, Carter returns to the elevator to where she begins her ascent. Partway up, she changes her mind and returns to Cassandra. Col. O'Neill tries to dissuade her via intercom, but Samantha disobeys his direct order and remains with the girl.

The time elapses, but the bomb does not go off, to everyone's relief. Carter then explains to Col. O'Neill that, from her understanding, if Cassandra stays far enough away from the Stargate the bomb will not go off.

Some time later, the bomb dissipates, apparently reabsorbed into the girl's system. Cassandra is allowed to remain on Earth, and is instructed to keep the Stargate a secret, and to tell others that she was born in a place called Toronto. Dr. Fraiser contemplates adopting Cassandra as her own.

VILNA

The people of Hanka began life on Vilna, a small planet whose technological progress had been stalled by Nirrti at the pre-industrial level. Its populace became a pool of human resources which Nirrti would extract and transfer to other planets for her experiments.

Vilna's populace lives relatively peaceful lives, dominated by working their fields and paying homage to their goddess. Nirrti rules with a relatively relaxed hand – she doesn't want to waste her stock putting down petty rebellions – and leaves a series of administrators to govern day-to-day affairs. Technology beyond a certain level is forbidden, and all unions must be approved by the goddess (so as to better guide the genetic pool), but other than that, the people are generally left to their own devices.

With Nirrti's imprisonment in Season Three, Vilna fell into the hands of Cronus, who himself was slain before he had a chance to properly claim it. Left to their own devices, the people continued more or less as they always had, confident that their goddess would one day return.

World: Vilna.

Thermosphere: Cool (CR 0; terran orbit; -[1d%]° F).

Atmosphere: Normal (CR 0; 1.1 Atmospheres).

Hydrosphere: Sub-Humid (Annual Rainfall 25-47 in.; Daily Weather 1-85: none, 86-87: flood 1d10 mph, 88-93: rain, 1d4-1 in. or snow 1d6-1, 94-95: thunderstorm or snowstorm, 96: hurricane or blizzard, 97-98: wind 1d10 mph, 99: wind 1d10+10 mph, 100: wind 1d10+20 mph.

Geosphere: Rolling; Very Stable tectonic activity (Daily Earthquakes N/A).

Seasons: Normal (1-25: spring unchanged; 26-50: summer +2d20° F; 51-75: autumn unchanged; 76-100: winter -2d20° F).

Anthrosphere: 250,000 natives; Renaissance (5 Picks, 3 RP); Oligarchy; Friendly (+1 Disposition Modifier); Absolutely Pacifistic (No soldiers); Progressive civil rights.

Origin: Lithuanian.

Stargate Location: In a forest a short distance from a path leading to a village surrounded by clear fields among hills.

BACKGROUND
THE MACHINATIONS OF NIRRTI

The Goa'uld Nirrti is one of the most cunning and duplicitous of all System Lords. Considering how manipulative the species is, that is quite a statement. The planet Hanka (derived from the original word "ankh" meaning "life") is a breeding ground which she uses for subjects in her experiments – one of many in her domain. Nirrti took a sampling of people from another planet, in this case Vilna, and seeded them here in the attempt to bring certain genetic traits to the fore. Usually this type of eugenics involves inbreeding to bring out recessive traits, but on Hanka Nirrti wished to develop extrasensory perception among the populace. Once she identified the appropriate genes, she would then experiment with the subjects to see how they could be manipulated to create more powerful individuals.

Nirrti's experiment on Hanka never reached its final stages. Around 100 years after the colony was founded, SG-7 arrived through the gate. In Nirrti's eyes, this contaminated the experiment beyond repair... and delivered unto her a grave insult. After some thought she decided to turn the botched experiment against the intruders. She abducted a young girl from the colony, then gave her the vaccine to a virulent disease . She also implanted a specialized miniature naquadah bomb in the girl's heart. Nirrti had created a version of the bomb that could absorb from the body of the victim the materials needed to reach a critical mass and explode. Two of the minerals, potassium and iron, were already in Cassandra's body, but the third, naquadah, had to be injected in a solution into her body.

With her "Trojan Horse" now prepared, Nirrti unleashed the disease of Hanka, killing the entire population – including SG-7 – within hours. She then waited for the SGC to bring Cassandra back through the Stargate, knowing that the bomb would explode the minute it reached the other side. Luckily for Earth, the weapon was flawed, and did not immediately explode when it passed through the Stargate for the first time. Instead it began a slow build-up, assembling itself over a course of time. The SGC discovered her plan in time and were able to save the girl – and the Earth – by keeping her away from the Stargate.

More on Nirrti – including her other experiments – will appear in the upcoming *System Lords* sourcebook.

1-16: ENIGMA

World Visited: P3X-7763 (Tollan).

Thermosphere: Warm (CR 0; standard orbit; 46° F).

Atmosphere: Normal (CR 0; .9 atmospheres; no additional effects).

Hydrosphere: Semi-arid (daily weather 1-88: none, 89: flood, 90-92: rain/snow, 93: thunderstorm, 94: dust storm, 95: hurricane, 96-97: wind 1d10 MPH, 98: wind 1d10+10 MPH, 99: wind 1d10+20 MPH, 100: wind 1d20+30 MPH).

Geosphere: Unstable tectonic activity (daily earthquakes 1-98: none, 99: minor, 100: moderate; no volcanoes near Stargate).

Seasons: Severe (1-25: spring unchanged; 26-50: summer +4d12° F; 51-75: autumn unchanged; 76-100 winter -4d12° F).

Anthrosphere: 10,000,000 natives; Goa'uld (7 picks, 6 RP); Meritocracy; Cautious (-1 with disposition checks); Defensively Pacifistic (100 soldiers, squad size 1d2 soldiers); Very Progressive civil rights.

Origin: Indeterminate.

Stargate Location (upper region): Rolling hills in scrub terrain, near the outskirts of the capital city.

World Visited: P3X-7763 (Cataclysmic Tollan).

Thermosphere: Furnace (CR 3; close orbit; 285° F).

Atmosphere: Ultra-thick (CR 4; 35 atmospheres; -12 Int/Wis penalty, -10 speed; Exp. Inc: None/1 round; SV Fort (DC 30); Dmg 1d10 normal; Recup 16 rounds).

Hydrosphere: Exotic (dry) (daily weather 1-85: none, 86-90: dust storm, 91-94: wind 1d10 MPH, 95-96: wind 1d10+10 MPH, 97-98: wind 1d10+20 MPH, 99: wind 1d20+30 MPH, 100: wind 1d20+50 MPH).

Geosphere: Cataclysmic tectonic activity (daily earthquakes 1-50: none, 51-75: minor, 76-95: moderate, 96-100: major; 2 small and 1 medium volcano within 10 miles of Stargate).

Seasons: No seasons (unchanged).

Anthrosphere: None; see alternate P3X-7763 entry for prior inhabitants.

Origin: Indeterminate.

Stargate Location (upper region): Surrounded by lava flows and city ruins.

EPISODE SUMMARY

Traversing through the Stargate to P3X-7763, the members of SG-1 are surprised to find themselves in the midst of a torrential downpour of ash and sulfur. In the distance, a volcano belches forth rivers of lava and the suffocating temperature makes it clear that the world is in a dramatic state of change since the last MALP uplink a week ago. Taking no chances, Colonel O'Neill immediately orders a return through the Stargate to Earth. Before doing so, Daniel pleas for an opportunity to study the destroyed remnants of the city that lies around them. There, he makes a startling discovery: a humanoid body, recently fallen, indicating that some kind of civilization must still reside on P3X-7763.

Fanning out, SG-1 finds several more unconscious or dead humanoid forms, all attired in the same kind of clothing and carrying unusually advanced equipment. Who they are, or how they came to be on P3X-7763, remains a mystery. As SG-1 takes stock of those that are still alive and able to be assisted, a dying figure reaches out and implores Daniel: "don't help us."

Of the bodies near the gate, over half are already dead or dying; a scant ten survivors are brought back to Earth. Little is discerned from their appearance, other than they are human and carry highly advanced equipment. As General Hammond points out, the SGC have discovered humans before on any number of worlds – perhaps these humans and their technology may be willing to share their knowledge with Earth. One of the survivors, Omoc, requests to speak to those that would have saved them, making it clear that he and his people – the Tollan – did not wish to be rescued. Omoc's gruff manner and inhospitable nature leaves General Hammond no choice but to acquiesce to their wishes and return the aliens to P3X-7763, where a transport vessel will collect them.

Prior to doing so, Captain Carter prepares an Unmanned Airborne Vehicle (UAV) to be launched through the Stargate. From the SGC they will be able to monitor events as they unfold on Tollan. However, the project is placed on hold when one of the Tollan survivors seeks to speak with Carter. Narim, thankful for his rescue, appears more approachable and open than Omoc. Through Carter, the SGC is able to learn more about the Tollan and what befell their world: a horrible disaster of planetary scale, as the neighboring world of the Sartians plunged into war, destroying their own world and laying waste to Tollan by shifting its orbit. The source of the Sartian's newfound weapon was technology provided by the Tollans. Narim explains how the Sartians – at a level of technology similar to that of Earth – were unprepared to deal with the consequences of such power, instead using it to wage war amongst themselves. Omoc has good reason to be wary of the Tauris' intentions.

The UAV is sent through to Tollan, returning data on the climatic conditions around the Stargate. The air is saturated with sulfur, ash, and pyroclastics. Temperatures range from 200 degrees to 1,500 degrees in some areas and near the capital city, just beyond the Stargate, a volcano sends lava down towards the gate. It is clear that Omoc's people are unable to return to Tollan and meet with the transport ship that would take them to their new home. Omoc acerbically laments how nature succeeded where they failed; their singular mission was to stay behind and seal the gate on Tollan forever. General Hammond arranges for quarters for the refugees and pledges the assistance of the SGC in finding a new world suitable for them.

Restricted to the multipurpose room on level 5, an alarm is raised when the Tollans are discovered missing. After a brief chase, Omoc and his people are found on the surface, gazing longingly at the stars. With armed escorts, Omoc notes how the Tollans seem to be prisoners rather than guests; the Tauri resort to force as their first instinct, just like the Sartians.

Unable to fully determine how the Tollans escaped, Colonel O'Neill suggests that the SGC call in some off-world favors in the hope of finding a world suitable for Omoc and his people. Among those interested are Tuplo from the Land of Light (P3X-797), who meets with Omoc and generously offers all that his world has to offer, willingly, to the Tollan. Omoc tosses the offer aside – the people of the Land of Light are far too primitive for the Tollan's taste.

The arrival of Colonel Harry Maybourne of the NID complicates matters further. Colonel Maybourne, under the authority of the Pentagon and the President, has orders to relocate the Tollan for questioning. The Colonel sets an ominous tone for the NID's priorities when asked about the Tollan's rights, making it clear that in his eyes – and the Pentagon's – that the aliens have no freedoms at all. With

the gauntlet thrown down, General Hammond arranges for the transfer of the Tollan after they have been medically cleared... again. That gives the SGC a little more than a day to hold Maybourne at bay.

Disturbed by the turn of events, SG-1 confers for a possible solution to the Tollan plight. While the members of the SGC can not directly disobey a direct order, Daniel – a civilian – can. Meeting with Narim and Omoc, he attempts to convince the Tollan that SG-1 wishes to help them escape. Colonel Maybourne and the NID are not representative of all the Tauri, he explains. Omoc grudgingly accepts Dr. Jackson's plan and using a Tollan phase device, moves freely through the facility to the surface. There, Daniel and Omoc send a message to the Nox who can help the Tollan escape.

Narim meanwhile makes his good-byes to Captain Carter, to whom he has grown affectionate. Through the use of a Tollan recall device, Narim is able to impart to Captain Carter the emotions she has instilled within him. The Tollans, Narim explains, must leave tonight, one way or the other.

At the appointed time the Tollans use their phase devices to make for the gate room, much to the displeasure of Colonel Maybourne. The SGC marines are unable to pro-

vide any resistance as the Tollans – literally – walk right through them. An inbound wormhole from the Stargate carries a singular traveler – Lya of the Nox – notes that the people of Earth still have learned nothing, resorting to violence to solve matters and agrees to offer refuge to the Tollan.

Colonel Maybourne, confronted with losing perhaps the greatest advanced technology recovered through the Stargate yet, authorizes the use of deadly force against the Tollans; they are not to leave at any cost! Lya, drawing upon the resources of the Nox, summons a wormhole and disarms the assembled marines, taking the Tollans with her. As the Tollan disappear through the Stargate, Omoc confides his thanks to Daniel for all that they have done. his faith in less advanced cultures has been partially restored by SG-1's actions. With the Tollan safely away and beyond the reach of Colonel Maybourne and the NID, Daniel reflects on the wisdom of the Nox once again: "The young do not always do what they are told."

THE LOST COLONY

(**Note**: Basic information on Tollan and its inhabitants can be found in the *Stargate SG-1* core rulebook. The events detailed here represent the situation as of the finale to Season One.)

The technology level of the Tollans is approximately 800 years ahead of Earth's. In that time the Tollans have harnessed limitless energy and developed faster-than-light travel. Primarily a defensively pacifistic and non-expansionist species, the Tollan have investigated a large number of worlds, particularly after their own shortsightedness wrecked havoc with their native ecosystem. A number of colony worlds exist with small settlements of Tollan. In many cases these settlements are little more than research outposts; no long-term colonization plan has been put forward to the Curia by the Expeditionary Forces. It was only after the disaster on Sartian that the Tollans were forced to move ahead and relocate as many of their people as possible – not all were able to make it.

When Sartian was destroyed, the orbital rotation of Tollan was irreparably altered. Dramatic changes in the axial tilt of the planet shifted weather patterns and wrecked havoc with the tectonic plates of the world. Severe alterations in the planet's magnetic field caused great upheavals of earth and entire oceans ran rampant over the surface. These changes came swiftly and with little warning – the Tollans had just over a week to try to rescue their civilization. The Expeditionary Forces mobilized all available ships, but these would only transport a fraction of the Tollan populace. Those that could used the Stargate to evacuate to other worlds, but even then any hope of recovering these lost pockets of Tollan survivors was deemed slim.

SARTIAN SURVIVORS

The Sartian world was inconceivably destroyed through a series of massive explosions that ripped the world asunder. The Sartian took the Tollan technology provided to them – designed simply to provide clean and limitless power – and instead twisted it into a deadly weapon so powerful that the Sartian had no understanding its limits. Their world, fractured by centuries of petty bickering and strife, had always been on the verge of devastating war. Now they sought to wage that war. The results were as predictable as they were final.

After the destruction of Sartian, many straggling ships returned to their dead husk of a world. The Sartian had developed rudimentary space travel and had numerous ships beyond the reach of the solar system at the time of the planet's destruction. What little they were able to piece together, they learned that the Tollans had been involved. Why the Tollan would seek to destroy Sartian – and their own world in the process – was unknown, but vengeance flowed through the veins of every remaining Sartian from that point on. Makeshift fleets were formed and a great crusade began – a crusade to wipe the every Tollan from the stars.

At first the Sartians surprised and destroyed a large number of Tollan transports. Not expecting an attack, the Tollans were quickly overwhelmed by the tenacity of their foes. Those Sartian vessels not armed with neutrino cannons or fusion-tipped torpedoes would instead ram the Tollan craft, which destroyed a great number of Tollan survivors seeking only passage to Tollana. Some of these vessels were captured and then used to further wage war against their creators.

Now the Sartians wage a single-sided war against the Tollans. United for the first time against a common enemy, they pursue any signs of a Tollan vessel with dogged deter-

mination. Using captured information and star charts, they attack the last remaining colony worlds and even now (i.e., as of Season One) seek the final lone convoy that heads for their enemies' new home of Tollana...

THE FINAL JOURNEY

With news of the Sartian attacks against Tollan ships, the Tollans have assembled what few vessels remain into a lone convoy, hoping that safety in numbers will dissuade Sartian attacks. The convoy slowly makes its way towards Tollana, ever vigilant for Sartian pursuit. Occasionally it will stop at suitable worlds to take on supplies – or even search for a Stargate – but it can never linger for too long. The Sartians may be just behind them.

The Sartians continue to ruthlessly hunt the Tollans, always one step behind in their stolen or makeshift vessels, their singular purpose in life to extract vengeance from the aggressors that destroyed their homeworld. Thus far they have rebuffed any attempts to communicate with the Tollans, focusing solely on revenge. Until such time that a dialog can be established, the Sartians may never learn that the destruction of their world was solely their responsibility.

ASHES TO ASHES

Ever since the creations of the Stargate Program and the SGC, the NID has been hard at work to place personnel within the organization sympathetic to their cause. After the discovery of the second Stargate in Antarctica (see *Solitudes*, page 69), the NID has even begun to take part in their own off-world missions. Among their efforts is a private "emergency recovery" operation – one that yielded some promising results.

Operating with the utmost secrecy, Colonel Maybourne authorized sending of an NID team through the Antarctic Stargate to P3X-7763, shortly after the Tollan survivors were recovered by SG-1. With climate conditions becoming increasingly worse by the moment, the NID team was only able to scout within a very small perimeter of the Stargate. While they were not able to salvage any sizeable equipment or weapons they were able to recover a Tollan body, found underneath collapsed rubble near the gate. They also uncovered a number of Tollan devices. Unfortunately their extended exposure to the heat and elements of P3X-7763 rendered the devices inoperable... for now.

Scientists at Area 51 continue tinker with the devices, many of which emit low-levels of some unknown radiation. Using captured footage from the SGC security monitors, they believe that at least one of the devices appears to be a phased energy generator, which allows the Tollan to pass through matter unharmed. Unfortunately, Colonel Maybourne's inability to secure any Tollan prisoners – or functional devices – has dampened what was otherwise a successful undercover operation; as of the end of Season One, the SGC has no knowledge of the NID's involvement or their possession of the Tollan technology.

DAMAGED GOODS

In the NID's possession, locked safely away at Area 51, are a Tollan phase device, inverted phase communicator, and recall device. All three are currently inoperable due to their prolonged exposure to extreme heat and pressure. (Internally , the phase discrimination crystals have been fused – the crystals must be entirely replaced or some adequate solution MacGyver-ed to repair them.)

The devices have suffered threshold damage level 3 (*see page 208, Stargate SG-1 core rulebook*) and since adequate replacement parts are unavailable, the repair DC is increased by +15. Thus, the NID is taking great care in researching the devices, hopeful that at some point they may be able to get their hands on more Tollan technology. More likely is that the NID will at some point attempt to acquire personnel familiar with Tollan technology and "persuade" them to assist in the items' repair. The ability to walk through walls – as a small example – provides a significant advantage to a spy or military force working to protect the interests of the nation from aggressors (whatever the NID's definition of that term may be...)

1-17: TIN MAN

World Visited: P3X-989 (Altair).

Thermosphere: Hot (CR 0; normal orbit; 5d20+20° F).

Atmosphere: Thin (CR 0; 0.6 atmospheres, Int/Wis penalty -1, exposure increment 1 hour, Fort save DC 15, 1d3 subdual damage, recuperation time 1 round).

Hydrosphere: Exotic (wet) (daily weather 1-72: none, 73-75: flood 1d10 MPH, 76-77: flood 1d10+10 MPH, 78: flood 1d10+20 MPH, 79-88: 1d6 inches of rain, 89-95: acid rain storm, 96-98: acid rain hurricane, 99: wind 1d10 MPH, 100: wind 1d10+10 MPH).

Geosphere: Stable tectonic activity (daily earthquakes 1-99: none, 100: minor).

Seasons: Normal (1-25: spring unchanged; 26-50: summer +1d10° F; 51-75: autumn unchanged; 76-100: winter -2d10° F).

Anthrosphere: Less than 20 natives; Cybernetic (6 picks, 5 RP); Pantisocracy; Friendly (+1 with disposition checks); Defensively Pacifistic (0 soldiers).

Origin: Unknown.

Stargate Location (interior): Underground facility inhabited by an artificial life form and filled with massive machinery.

EPISODE SUMMARY

The members of SG-1 arrive through the Stargate to find themselves inside a massive facility of relatively high technology. Dr. Carter theorizes that the original inhabitants of the world must have developed a technology level equal to or even surpassing that of Earth, and her suspicions are quickly confirmed as they come an advanced computer system. Otherwise, the facility seems completely abandoned and void of life. As the voices of SG-1 echo throughout the facility, Captain Carter begins investigating the computer system they found and sets off an alarm. Colonel O'Neill orders SG-1 to fall back to the Stargate, but before they can do so each member of the team is engulfed in a bright flash of white light and falls to the ground, unconscious.

Slowly, SG-1 awakens only to find that much has changed while they were asleep. Their uniforms and equipment are completely gone and each of them is lying on a small platform extending outward from some sort of mechanical construct in the middle of the room. When O'Neill asks if anyone is injured, the surprising answer comes that not only is each member of the team unharmed but also in better health than any of them can remember. Dr. Jackson no longer needs his glasses, and Colonel O'Neill's hair has darkened to its original shade of brown. Each member of the team feels better than they ever have, yet they know that something was done to them while they were unconscious.

Moments later, a balding man wearing strange clothing waddles into the room with a joyous shout of "Komtraya!" He introduces himself as Harlan and the world they are on as Altair. According to Harlan, he has been alone on Altair for some time, which explains his eccentric behavior and strange mannerisms. According to Harlan, the facility they are in is deep underground. The surface of Altair is highly radioactive and acid rain storms constantly plague the planet's surface. As O'Neill becomes more and more irritated at Harlan's roundabout way of answering questions, the members of SG-1 come to realize that each of them possesses a significantly greater intellect in addition to their newfound health and physical strength. Finally, O'Neill becomes so frustrated that Harlan will not explain what has happened to them that he orders all of SG-1 back through the gate, ignoring Harlan's pleas not to leave.

Back at the SGC, Dr. Fraiser notices something wrong with the members of SG-1. When Colonel O'Neill appears to have no heartbeat, the doctor insists on taking a blood sample. Instead of drawing blood the syringe fills up with some kind of milky white fluid. In a panic, Colonel O'Neill snatches up a scalpel and slices into his own arm, peeling back his skin to reveal mechanical devices where his internal organs should be. Simultaneously, Teal'c opens his shirt to reveal that his symbiote and pouch are gone, despite being able to feel its presence. Dr. Fraiser slaps the alarm button and calls General Hammond to the infirmary. The androids that look, think, talk, and act like the members of SG-1 are taken into custody and escorted to holding cells.

Aggravated by their detainment, SG-1 begins to reason out what happened. They come to the conclusion that Harlan, who claimed to have been alone for 11,000 years, must have also been an android. When Hammond comes to question them he gets no more than a few questions out before all four android members of SG-1 collapse in pain. Realizing that Harlan's pleas for them to stay were more than just a desire for companionship, the androids must return to Altair in order to survive. General Hammond offers to send another SG team through to help, but the android O'Neill recognizes the threat and instructs him to send no one through. As SG-1 stumbles through the gate and emerges on the other side, the pain subsides and they once again find themselves energized.

Harlan once again greets the group on the other side and explains that they cannot stray far from the power source within the Altairan facility. He then goes on to relate how he came to be in his current position. Eons ago, Altair's surface became inhospitable and the population was forced to move underground. Realizing that their frail bodies could not survive the intense conditions, Altairan engineers managed to transfer their minds into android bodies in order to survive. Unfortunately, many lives were lost when developing this technology and only a thousand of the original Altairans survived in their new bodies. Among those thousand were several who could not tolerate their new existence and left with portable power generators. The last ones departed and died over 11,000 years ago, leaving Harlan alone ever since.

Demanding they be put back in their original bodies, the android members of SG-1 learn that Harlan has disposed of their original human forms. As they contemplate their new existence, O'Neill discovers that Harlan needed to create them in order to maintain the facility. The android Teal'c, on the other hand, seems deeply disturbed and goes off alone. After a few minutes, alarms begin to sound all over the facility, and Harlan desperately pleads for the three remaining members of the group to help with repairs. They reluctantly agree, but the android Teal'c suddenly ambushes the android O'Neill and the two of them fight, inadvertently releasing the pressure buildup that caused the malfunction. Harlan arrives and disintegrates the android Teal'c, saving O'Neill from destruction.

Soon, the androids discover the truth that Harlan has hidden from them. Their minds were not transferred to android bodies, but duplicated. The original members of SG-1 are alive and well, but the androids, who have all the same knowledge and feelings as their human counterparts, are stunned to learn that they are little more than artificial copies. The human members of SG-1 return through the Stargate, while their android counterparts stay behind, bury the Stargate, and help Harlan maintain the facility.

BACKGROUND
THE ALTAIRANS

The original inhabitants of Altair all died or left the world over 11,000 years ago. Their civilization reached its peak while the people of Earth were drawing on cave walls and living in nomadic societies. Yet Harlan is remarkably human, and the androids that he creates are able to mimic human senses, feelings, and consciousness with uncanny perfection. The logical conclusion is that the Altairans were themselves humans, else they would have been unable to create technology that so closely resembles humanity. Regardless of their origins, SGC has learned a few facts thanks to Harlan's limited ramblings and eccentric tales.

Altair was once a lush and fertile planet similar to Earth in many respects, capable of supporting a vast array of wildlife and providing the Altairans with a comfortable life. As Altairan society developed and their knowledge of the sciences grew, so to did their capacity for creating weaponry. It was their own scientific advances that led to their planet's destruction. Over time, the Altairans produced weapons capable of destroying entire civilizations and making the entire planet inhospitable. Unfortunately,

these weapons were used on their own world and plunged it into ecological disaster. All wildlife on the surface was killed, vast swathes of land were leveled by explosions, and the ecosystem became harsh and unforgiving. Destructive acid rain eroded the last vestiges of their civilization, and Altair became a dead planet.

Fortunately, many of the Altairans survived by moving to facilities underground. Here, they transferred their consciousness into android bodies to better survive. Unlike Harlan and his fellow engineers, most of the Altairans living in the subterranean city were actually politicians and military leaders. Believing that the destruction of their world was actually an attack by some unknown enemy, they stockpiled weapons and secured their new home as a military base. The Altairans never realized that their world was destroyed by their own weaponry, and remained cautious to the point of being paranoid. When the secondary strikes never came, these politicians and soldiers began to grow impatient. Since several of them had begun investigating the Stargate that was uncovered during the construction of the underground facility, the leaders decided to send explorers and colonists to find a new world where they could regain their old lives. Many left Altair, except Harlan and a group of scientists that felt it too unsafe to rely on portable generators for power. Over time, the rest of the inhabitants of Altair were destroyed or departed, some even terminating their own lives rather than live such a melancholy existence.

THE NEW HOME

Those Altairans who chose to leave their home eventually found and settled another planet within the Stargate network. Designated P3X-637, the colony world of the Altairans is not the idyllic paradise that Altair itself once was. The world is dry, with very little water, and covered in hard stone. The Altairans chose this world because it offered the least environmental hazards to cause problems with their electronics. It features several mountain ranges and seems to have been shaped by extensive tectonic activity in the past. The androids from Altair selected P3X-637 for abundant natural resources and a lack of water, dust, sand, and other fine particles that can lock servos and interfere with electronics.

The Altairans dubbed the world Naltoros, a derivative of their own word for colony. As soon as the world was designated safe for colonization, the androids began constructing buildings and preparing a new home almost immediately. Since they could no longer reproduce, their small city remained relatively unchanged over the millennia; with no population growth and little need for a large urban sprawl, the Altairans were content to simply live a relatively stationary existence. The first priority, of course, was recreating the power generators that keep the androids alive. Fortunately, this was not difficult. Of all the structures built on Naltoros, the power plant is the largest and most extravagant, a massive spire stretching hundreds of feet into the air capable of broadcasting the power signal across their entire world. In this way, the Altairans ensured that they may travel all over their planet and the Power Spire remain a dazzling sight to behold.

Since many of the Altairans that colonized Naltoros were former military personnel, their society evolved into a highly disciplined and militaristic (if not aggressive) form. A rigid system of rank and order dominates almost every aspect of their lives, and any citizen that violates this organization is severely punished (and usually demoted in rank). Additionally, the defense of their colony ranks among the group's top priorities, and each Altairan is required to contribute in some way to the world's security.

Encounters between the Altairan androids and the Goa'uld have occurred, though little has come of them. Since the Altairans can no longer be taken as hosts for the Goa'uld, the System Lords have little use for them. Their advanced technology and weaponry, on the other hand, is of great interest to the Goa'uld. Thus far, the Altairans were able to repel their first few attempts at conquest, and quickly erected an energy shield over their civilization. The Stargate is kept under constant vigil so that no Goa'uld forces can slip onto the world, and the advanced physical abilities and superior intellect of the Altairans makes them more than a match for even several legions of Jaffa. Having been rebuffed several times, and seeing that the Altairans are no threat to them due to their inability to expand further out into the galaxy, the System Lords have deigned to leave the android colonists alone. Some Altairans are proponents of taking the fight to the Goa'uld, but given their small numbers and limited mobility few have joined this crusade.

Naltoros

World: Naltoros.

Thermosphere: Warm (CR 0; normal orbit; 2d20+25° F).

Atmosphere: Normal (CR 0; 1.1 atmospheres).

Hydrosphere: Arid (daily weather: 1-89 none, 90 flood 1d10 MPH, 91-93 1 inch rain, 94-95 dust storm, 96-100 wind 1d10 MPH).

Geosphere: Very Stable tectonic activity.

Seasons: Normal (spring 1-25, +0° F; summer 26-50 +1d10° F; 51-75 autumn, +0° F; 76-100 winter -2d10° F).

Anthrosphere: Less than 500 natives; Cybernetic (6 picks, 5 RP); Stratocracy; Suspicious (-1 with disposition checks); Defensively Pacifistic (100 soldiers, squad size 1d4); Very Progressive civil rights.

Origin: Altairan.

Stargate Location (interior): Interior facility, in the middle of the primary city of Naltoros.

ALTAIRAN TECHNOLOGY

With a head start on Earth of over 11,000 years, it comes as no surprise that the Altairans' technology level is vastly superior to that of most human cultures. Unfortunately, since few Altairan survivors were scientists or engineers, and since their resources have been limited by the destruction of their home world, the technology level on Naltoros has remained the same as it was when they first colonized the world. Since so much knowledge was lost during the retreat underground (and later during the exodus to the new planet) the Altairans have only made small technological advances despite the great time span. What technology they do have is put to practical use, and the androids spend little time on research or experimentation.

The android city on Naltoros was built slowly but evolved into an efficient and productive urban area. Refineries and manufacturing facilities were built in order to process raw ore (including some rich deposits of naquadah) gathered from across the world. Since the androids have no need to eat or drink, no technology has been wasted on agriculture, and only mining and industry have advanced in any appreciable manner. Despite the fact that the Altairans are capable of mass producing their own technology, their static population size gives them little reason to do so and, once each member of the society received the weapons and technology they needed, the manufacturing plants were shut down. They occasionally start up again to replaced lost or worn-out equipment (or when new fortifications are needed), but usually remain inert.

In response to their early encounters with the Goa'uld, the Altairans made their first effort at scientific innovation and created a massive energy shield to protect them from orbital attack. The shield is capable of deflecting any fire from orbiting Goa'uld craft as well as disrupting the energy beam used to teleport matter in a ring device. Unfortunately, the energy shield requires massive amounts of power, and while it is in use, the range of the Power Spire's energy broadcast is reduced to within the city itself. In the event of an attack from space all the Altairans congregate within the city and defend it fiercely.

As Captain Carter discovered when first entering the underground facility where Harlan lived, the Altairans had developed computer technology in a similar fashion to that found on Earth. More than that, the Altairans had mastered the art of creating a controllable artificial intelligence. In fact, almost all of the major control systems in the facility on Altair were operated by artificial intelligence routines that allowed Harlan to survive alone for a long time. The Altairans that went to Naltoros took this technology with them, and for a time used it to create drones that could do the mining and heavy labor while the sentient androids spent their time doing more important things. Unfortunately, large chunks of the android creation technology were lost when the creator of the system died, and as a result the new androids were imperfectly constructed. Little more than a metal endoskeleton with exposed wires and circuitry, the drones were not durable enough to last in the long run and eventually faded from use. Additionally, their inability to create perfect replicas of their current bodies led the Altairans to realize that they must be careful, since even death in an android body would now be permanent.

ALTAIRAN DISINTEGRATOR

A piece of technology sought by both the Goa'uld and the SGC, the Altairan disintegrator is the peak of the androids' weapons technology. Roughly the size of a zat'nik'tel, the disintegrator can turn any large object into thousands of atoms in a matter of seconds. It works on a principle that everything is held together on the atomic level and that by breaking those bonds any item can be separated into its individual atoms. The development of such a weapon was far more complicated than the theory, and many accidents almost spelled the end of Altairan civilization. The disintegrators were developed long before the eco-logical disaster that made Altair inhabitable, and in many cases entire research facilities were lost during the testing phase. Fortunately, the disintegrators were perfected before too much damage could be done.

The hand-held disintegrator is most effective on nonliving matter, but can still function against a living being. Additionally, the Altairans perfected the disintegrator tech-nology to the point where the weapons themselves deter-mine how much is to be disintegrated. Thus, firing a disin-tegrator at a person will not simply disintegrate the cloth-ing they are wearing, but also that person and any belong-ings or weapons he or she carries. Yet the disintegrator will not damage anything the character is touching (but not holding) such as floors, walls, and other stationary objects. One quirk that the Altairans were never able to eliminate, however, was that any time a conscious being is targeted with the disintegrator the beam from the weapon would not function; the target needed to be unconscious or asleep for the weapon to function. As Harlan discovered when he dis-integrated the android replica of Teal'c, however, androids and artificial constructs could be disintegrated just as eas-ily as nonliving matter, despite the living tissue covering the android's body.

STUN FIELD GENERATOR

In order to capture SG-1 and make android replicas of each of them, Harlan activated a security measure that had been installed long before the other Altairans left to colo-nize the new world. Altairan scientists had long ago creat-ed an anti-intrusion device, but thus far neither Harlan nor his former companions had ever had cause to use it. The stun field generator was a surprisingly effective means of immobilizing intruders, in this case SG-1, and could affect several targets simultaneously. Unlike conventional weapons, which had to be fired at a single target, the stun field generator affected all within its range.

Each stun field generator appears to be a large, conical device that attaches to a wall or to the ceiling, with the wide base of the cone extending outward. This projects a sensor field that identifies targets within the generator's reach. When the generator fires, all targets within that sensor field receive a stunning blast of energy capable of taking down even the toughest soldier. The stun field generator can only be fired a certain number of times before needing to be recharged, a process that requires one hour of being hooked up to a proper power generator.

BETTER... HOW?

The entire time SG-1 was questioning Harlan, he contin-ued to insist that he had made each of them better. What he actually meant was that the conversion process into an android had made them smarter, faster, and stronger than they were before. Thanks to the nature of the computer processors that served as their brains, each android copy of SG-1 could perform complex mathematical calculations instantaneously. The android bodies are able to perfectly process and duplicate human senses and are sophisticated enough that even the consciousness transferred to the new bodies could not tell the difference until taken back to the infirmary. In truth, the android bodies are perfect replicas of the human body as far as the senses of the mind are concerned.

Creating an android replica is painstak-ing and requires lots of time and extreme attention to detail. Though an automated process within the underground facility's machines handles much of the creation of the physical body, the creator of the androids must monitor the transfer of the human consciousness in order to ensure that the android's mind is intact. Harlan, having never encountered a Jaffa before, was unaware that the dual-minds of Teal'c and his larval Goa'uld would come into conflict when placed in a single android body. As such, any attempts to transform a Jaffa, Tok'ra, or Goa'uld into an android will result in murderous insanity if both minds are transferred into the android body. As a result, only one mind (that of the host or Jaffa or that of the symbiote) can have con-trol over the android body.

THE DATABANKS

Though it appeared that Harlan could not create an android without a subject to copy, in truth he was simply unaware of a databank that contained hundreds of stored personalities in case anything ever happened to one of the android bodies. The creator of the androids, who died long ago, prepared backups of each consciousness to be trans-ferred so that an error in the process would not result in the permanent death of a human mind. Unfortunately, he took the secrets of this process to his grave and the scientists and engineers that remained had no knowledge of his databank. Additionally, every time a consciousness is transferred into an android body, a copy of that consciousness is made and stored in the databanks. Each time such a copy is made, a complete genetic blueprint is stored along with it in order to replicate the proper body. In essence, there is a permanent blueprint for creating a perfect android replica of thousands of people just waiting to be discovered on Altair.

Unfortunately, one of those minds stored in the database belongs to a very ingenious criminal. A man called Koryn, a leading military mind of the Altairans, set off the weapon that destroyed Altair's surface. Though many considered him a tactical genius, he was also criminally insane, and caused the disaster in an attempt to convince the Altairan government that he needed more power and resources to fend off attackers (which successfully distracted others from investigating the true cause of the disaster). Should anyone ever discover a means of accessing this databank, there is always the possibility of creating an android replica of Koryn and unleashing him on the unsuspecting galaxy.

HACKING AN ANDROID

Since much of an android is made up of machinery and computers, it is actually possible to alter its knowledge and thoughts. In fact, Harlan did so when he created the android copied of SG-1 by planting knowledge of the maintenance and workings of the facility in their minds to more quickly enlist their help. Unfortunately, this alteration can also be abused and an android can have its thoughts altered to reflect whatever the programmer desires. The programmer can designate certain people as friendly and some as hostile, or erase all knowledge of a particular subject. Though most androids operate on a system drastically different from that which most computers use, creative programmers can find a way to bypass the system barrier and make changes. Rules for doing so can be found on page 135.

THE WASTELAND

The surface of Altair was made uninhabitable long ago, but since then the planet has slowly begun to recuperate from the horrible ecological damage it suffered at the hands of the Altairans. The surface of the world is still plagued by radiation storms and acid rain, but life survives, though not in exactly the way most picture it. On the surface, vast ruins of the abandoned cities remain, heavily eroded by acid rain and left to decay under the ravages of time. Towering skyscrapers are now little more than half a dozen stories tall and vast swathes of the land reveal nothing but stones underfoot.

Explorers who are careful and wear environment suits can move around on the surface with relative ease. Though Harlan was never adventurous enough to go to the surface himself, others may do so and investigate what is left of the lost world of Altair. Other underground bunkers from before the planet's destruction remain untouched, holding stockpiles of weapons, shields, and other pieces of technology.

1-18: SOLITUDES

World Visited: P4A-771 (no designation).

Thermosphere: Hot (CR 0; normal orbit; 3d20°+50° F).

Atmosphere: Normal (CR 0; 1.1 atmospheres).

Hydrosphere: Arid (daily weather 1-89: none; 90: flood 1d10 MPH wind; 91-93: 1 inch of rain; 94-95: ash storm; 96-100: 1d10 MPH wind).

Geosphere: Very Unstable tectonic activity (daily earthquakes 1-90: none; 91-95: minor; 96-99: moderate; 100: major; volcanoes 1-98: none; 99: small (20%); 100: medium (20%)).

Seasons: Normal (1-25: spring unchanged; 26-50: summer +1d10° F; 51-75: autumn unchanged; 76-100: winter -2d10° F).

Anthrosphere: 60,000 natives; Iron Age (3 picks, 1 RP); Theocracy; Extremely Hostile (-3 with disposition checks); Expansionistic (10,000 soldiers, squad size 2d4 soldiers); Poor civil rights.

Origin: Egyptian.

Stargate Location (desert): clay desert surrounded by towering columns, 8 miles from nearest settlement).

EPISODE SUMMARY

When the SGC gets a surprise gate activation followed by SG-1's GDO code transmission, Hammond and other technicians rush to the gate room to investigate. As the wormhole forms and the SGC monitors traffic over the wormhole, the Stargate begins drawing more and more power and blows stabilizers and surge arrestors into shards of metal and wire. Teal'c and Dr. Jackson, propelled by some force at high velocity, are hurled from the wormhole and crash to the ground just seconds before the Stargate deactivates in a shower of sparks. Bewildered at the absence of half of SG-1, General Hammond orders the two of them to the infirmary and sets about repairing the gate.

Meanwhile, Captain Carter and Colonel O'Neill have emerged from a different Stargate altogether, this one placed inside a mysterious ice cave. The Stargate barely has room to operate and is crusted with frost, while only the formation of the wormhole (and the accompanying matter disintegration) has kept the area in front of the Stargate clear of ice and debris. Colonel O'Neill has sustained several injuries, including cracked ribs and a broken leg, while Captain Carter seems to be little more than shaken. They too wonder what happened to their companions and how they ended up in this strange place, noting that Daniel might have dialed the wrong coordinates or, more likely, that there was some kind of malfunction.

Back at the SGC, Jackson and Teal'c reveal that SG-1 came under attack by the forces of an unknown Goa'uld. Energy weapons, including bolts of what appeared to be staff weapon fire, were used to chase them back into the wormhole. The weapons came from too far away to identify the assailants, though Teal'c and Daniel are sure that they were Goa'uld forces. Teal'c is convinced that Carter and O'Neill were no more than a few steps behind them when they came through the Stargate and is unable to accept the idea that his companions were captured or killed. Repairs to the Stargate are slow going, despite General Hammond's best efforts to motivate the repair crews; for the time being all the two men can do can do is rest and hope that the Stargate is fixed quickly.

Meanwhile Captain Carter and Colonel O'Neill discover a dial home device embedded within their bleak surroundings. With it, they speculate that they should be able to return to Earth in a timely fashion if only it can be uncovered. O'Neill has begun to show the first signs of fatigue and is becoming lethargic in the cold, but continues to assist Carter in digging the device out of the frozen cave floor. The digging is tiresome and their enthusiasm begins to flag quickly, and even the Colonel's dry humor can't break the melancholy mood each of them feels. Finally, the dial home device is uncovered and Samantha attempts to dial Earth. The seven symbols lock into place, but when Carter attempts to initiate the wormhole the Stargate simply rattles the cave, neither engaging nor deactivating.

With repairs finally finished at the SGC, General Hammond does not hesitate to send through a MALP to investigate the situation on P4A-771. Teal'c is eager to mount a rescue for his companions, but the MALP sends back images of heavy energy weapon fire (resulting in the destruction of the probe itself), and Hammond rules out the possibility of a rescue. Dr. Jackson, however, proposes a different theory about what might have happened to them. Theorizing that the wormhole may have jumped to another gate thanks to the energy surge, he reasons that rather than searching across thousands of worlds where their friends might have been taken if captured by the Goa'uld, instead they should search worlds nearby on the path of the wormhole to see if they exited somewhere else. Hammond agrees, and the first search and rescue missions begin.

O'Neill is beginning to succumb to both hypothermia and internal bleeding, leaving Dr. Carter on her own to continue working towards unlocking the Stargate and getting the two of them home. After a preliminary investigation outside the cave reveals a barren arctic wasteland for miles and miles, Carter begins digging down to the base of dial home device in order to reset the power. When she finally reaches the base, the gate resets to its idle status. O'Neill is no longer capable of helping, or even coherent speech, and as Carter dials Earth once more – only get the same result – all hope seems lost.

After many failed rescue missions return, one with severe injuries to members of SG-3, General Hammond is forced to call off the search. Unable to accept the loss of his friends, Daniel continues to diligently work on a solution. Standing in the briefing room, he notices serious vibrations in the gate room and surrounding area. In a fit of inspiration, he realizes that the vibrations are similar to those that the Stargate made when dialing out before dampeners were put in place. He theorizes that the vibrations he witnessed were those of *another* gate right here on Earth, and using earthquake-sensing technology pinpoints the source of the vibrations: in Antarctica. The SGC mounts a search to the location of the vibrations and Carter and O'Neill are rescued in the nick of time. SGC and Area 51 personnel helped move the Antarctic Stargate to a secure location in order to prevent this situation from ever occurring again.

BACKGROUND
THE ANTARCTIC GATE

The gate that was found by the SGC in Antarctica was a mystery to those that discovered it. The Stargate was actually the original gate placed on Earth by the creators of the Stargate system; the gate found at Giza was actually brought to Earth years later by Ra in order to make transport between Earth and Abydos faster and more efficient. The second gate was already lost by the time Ra and the other System Lords began transferring the human race across the galaxy.

Long before Ra came to Earth, another System Lord – Apophis – discovered the world and had begun quietly staging attacks against Ra from this location. Since the planet was completely unknown to Ra, staging attacks from Earth was a simple matter. To be safe and ensure that none of Ra's forces would come to Earth via the gate network, Apophis moved the Stargate to the Antarctic, setting up a temporary base of operations there. With the gate safely in his control, Apophis began using humankind as slaves and launching attacks on Ra's forces.

Eventually, Ra traced the attacks to the primitive world and traveled there in his spaceship. Catching word of Ra's impending arrival, Apophis and his forces hastily gathered up their possessions and traveled through the Stargate to a safe world. Ra, suffering as his host body degraded uncontrollably, arrived at Earth intending to wipe out the rebels that were attacking him in his weakness. To his own surprise his enemies had unwittingly delivered to him the means of his own salvation: humanity. On Earth, Ra discovered the human race and became the first to take them as hosts and transport them to the worlds under his control. Unable to locate the other Stargate (which had sunk into the ice in the time since its abandonment by Apophis) Ra placed a new gate on Earth at Giza and began his domination of the humans there. Apophis was incensed at inadvertently providing his enemy the means of staying alive despite having him on the brink of defeat and vowed to return with vengeance.

IN THE ICE

When Captain Carter and Colonel O'Neill first arrived in the ice cave where the Stargate was located, they discovered evidence that the Goa'uld were aware of its existence. Inside the ice was a Serpent Guard like those used by Apophis, frozen and preserved. In addition, since the System Lord had used the Antarctic gate to stage raids and strikes against Ra, a large cache of weapons and armor was left behind in their haste to flee. At the time of the rediscovery of the gate by the SGC, dozens of staff weapons, zat'nik'tel, and sets of Jaffa armor (complete with Serpent Guard helmets) remained deep beneath the icy floor of the cave. Thanks to the ever-shifting nature of the Antarctic, these caches sank deep into the ice and were not discovered by the teams moving the Stargate.

Moreover, numerous bits and pieces of Goa'uld technology thought to have been lost before Ra came into power are buried in the ice as well. Among them is a Goa'uld tablet that describes the location of P4A-771 – the very planet SG-1 was exploring when they encountered the Antarctic gate – which once serves as a secret base of operations for the forces of Apophis. Though Ra would later discover the planet and have its Stargate coordinates inscribed with the others on Abydos, for centuries P4A-771 remained a stronghold guarded by the Goa'uld underlord Mehen. The tablet contains means for getting onto P4A-771 without being blasted by the Jaffa that constantly monitor the gate. A certain set of protocols are used when traveling to the world in order to indicate that the incoming travelers are welcome visitors; these include opening and closing the gate twice before sending travelers through, tossing all weapons through the gate before entering the wormhole, and passing a tablet through with a complete list of those who would be arriving on the planet.

Unfortunately, one final remnant of the forces of Apophis was left behind: an incredibly destructive weapon intended for use against Ra while in his weakened state. Apophis' original plan was to have the weapon carried as a gift to Ra by a turncoat Jaffa. The device was based on the staff weapon technology but could be activated even if the Jaffa carrying it failed to get a clear shot at Ra. The weapon was an orb roughly one foot in diameter that sported several nozzles spreading out from the center of the device. When activated, the weapon would fire a spray of staff weapon blasts in all directions, acting as a longer-range (and potentially devastating) grenade weapon. The device was left behind in the rush to leave P4A-771 and was never used, though its power cells (capable of activating the weapon once) remained charged and ready for use.

LYING IN WAIT

When SG-1 was attacked on P4A-771, they were unaware that they had violated the security of a secret base of the System Lord Apophis. For millennia, since the first attacks against Ra, the planet had been a safe refuge and highly defended fortress where Apophis could recuperate after evading pursuit. Following Ra's death, Apophis continued to use the planet as a safe refuge and a staging point for attacks against other System Lords.

An underlord of Apophis named Mehen, who was often associated with serpents and snakes in Egyptian theology, rules the planet and ensures that no one violates the safety of the world. Though Egyptian tales describe Mehen as a protector of Ra, in truth the tales had been twisted such that the protector of Apophis, Mehen, became the protector of Ra. Mehen makes extensive use of Serpent Guards to carry out his master's will and is one of his most devoted subjects, explaining why he was entrusted with the task of safeguarding P4A-771.

Lines of columns surround the immediate gate area, each one depicting hieroglyphs that tell a tale of the greatness of Apophis. These columns serve two purposes: the first is to ensure that all Jaffa and human servants on the world are constantly aware of their god's power, but they also provide cover behind which the Jaffa launch attacks on incoming travelers. Only those who employ the right procedures, as detailed on the tablet left behind on Earth, may arrive on the world without coming under immediate fire.

P4A-771 is covered in dirt and clay that is so red it borders on crimson. The world isn't as harsh as the desert climate of Abydos, but still demands a certain strength and

SEARCH & RESCUE

The dangers of Stargate use often result in lost team members, or even entire teams. Since the beginning, the SGC has had search-and-rescue protocols in place to determine how they go about retrieving lost team members. Due to the unique nature of Stargate Command and its missions, the search and rescue protocol which they use has been altered from that of standard military procedure. Stargate Command uses the following protocols in the eventuality of a search and rescue situation.

Debriefing: When an SG unit returns from a trip through the gate without a member of the team, the search and rescue protocols are enacted. The SG team is given an extensive debriefing to determine the exact cause and situation of a team member's loss. If any characters returning from the mission are injured, they are treated in the infirmary first and then debriefed.

MALP Deployment: After the debriefing, a MALP is sent through the Stargate to the planet where the mission took place. Its primary goal is to look for any indication of hostiles on the other side of the gate. If no indication of hostility is given, a search and rescue mission may be authorized. If hostility is detected, or if the SG unit indicated during debriefing that they came under attack from enemy forces, a search and rescue mission is postponed until more information can be gathered.

Establish Communications: Since all SG team members are equipped with radios for communications, the first attempt at information gathering will be made. Typically, this involves the deployment of a UAV to the planet, except in the cases where the likelihood of a UAV being shot down by enemy fire is high. The UAV is used to establish radio contact and to send back telemetry based on any signals received while on the other side. Based on the findings of the UAV and any communications established with missing team members, tactical planning for search and rescue missions begins.

Contact Allies: If any allies exist that may have information on the missing team member's whereabouts, they are contacted and informed of the situation. Any information provided by such allies is used in mission planning.

Search and Rescue Mission: A search and rescue (SAR) mission is planned to recover the missing team member. This mission is prepared and executed as per a standard SG team mission, and follows all mission planning protocol.

Declaration of Missing in Action: If a search and rescue mission fails, the missing team members are formally declared Missing in Action (MIA). This declaration does not preclude further SAR missions, however it does give the soldier the same status as one lost during combat on Earth. Additionally, the GDO codes used by missing team members are locked out and the remaining members of that team are given new codes.

These guidelines are in place not only to help find a missing team member, but also to protect the SGC and associated personnel from danger should classified information known by a captured team member fall into enemy hands.

toughness to survive. Water is not in abundant supply, and red clay does little to diffuse the heat. Additionally, several active volcanoes still litter the landscape and have caused numerous natural disasters. Though not dangerous enough to cause Apophis to relocate his forces, hundreds of his servants have died from the clouds of ash that occasionally sweep across the scrublands. Most of the world remains undeveloped except for the village where the Jaffa and human slaves live, as well as a great temple and palace where Apophis resides during his visits.

WEAPONS ON P4A-771
LIGHTNING CANNON

Energy weapons striking the gate on P4A-771 caused the power surge that caused the wormhole to jump from the primary Stargate in the SGC to the gate in the Antarctic. However, a mere staff weapon blast is not enough to cause such a jump, as evidenced by the number of times an SG unit has come under fire from Jaffa forces while trying to return to Earth. The cause of the power surge was actually a powerful energy blast from a lightning cannon, called a *nek'sed,* which is used by Mehen to defend the area around the Stargate.

A lightning cannon appears to be a two-pronged energy weapon roughly the size of a death glider's weapons. The nek'sed is attached to a portable naquadah generator. When powered up, the lightning cannon hums and electricity crackles between the two prongs. If the cannon is fired, a solid arc of blue electricity leaps from the end of the cannon, striking an opponent with immense amounts of energy capable of killing even the toughest Jaffa. The lightning cannon is a formidable defense due to the fact that it can smite a group of targets instead of just one. This is particularly deadly to groups of Jaffa, who tightly cluster together when traveling through the Stargate, and wear metal armor that conducts electricity very easily.

The lightning cannon was originally designed for the System Lords by Goa'uld engineers but is rarely used due to its size and need for a portable power source. Additionally, Jaffa often engage in close combat, casualties to both sides are commonplace when the lightning cannon is used on a melee. Still, when placed a great distance away (as was the case on P4A-771) it can be absolutely devastating when targeting invaders coming through the Stargate.

FORCING THE JUMP

Though it was simply an accidental strike of an energy weapon against the Stargate that caused the wormhole to jump to the Antarctic gate, there are methods of forcing such an event. The process is a delicate one, however, and failure could permanently damage a DHD or, worse, disable the Stargate altogether. Still, in the case where a foothold situation might occur or some other reason prevents an SG unit from returning to Stargate Command, being able to force a jump to another Stargate is a valuable ability.

The process involves hooking up a power generator of some kind to the Stargate, one capable of producing large amounts of energy. Rather than simply attaching the generator to the Stargate and powering it up, care must be given to produce the power surge at the right time. Most often, the power generator is brought online but allowed to idle without sending current to the Stargate. Once the gate is dialed and a wormhole has been established to the target world, the generator sends a sharp spike of energy to the Stargate in an effort to overload it and cause the jump. If successful, the wormhole will flicker for a moment as it makes the transition to the secondary Stargate, and then establish a solid connection. Failure, however, causes the wormhole to dissipate and the Stargate to go inactive.

There are many dangers associated with this process. If there is not a second gate on the world they are targeting, the Stargate will make the wormhole jump to another world. Massive power surges can knock out the DHD, or even disable the Stargate itself. Additionally, some characters passing through the Stargate may be transferred to the default gate on the world that was dialed, while others might be sent to an alternate gate location. This process is very risky and is only used in the most dire situations. Rules for forcing a jump can be found on page 154.

1-19: THERE BUT FOR THE GRACE OF GOD

World Visited: P3R-233 (Former Camil home world).

Thermosphere: Exotic (radioactive) (CR 5; standard orbit; 189° F).

Atmosphere: Very thin (CR 1; .35 atmospheres; -2 Int/Wis penalty; Exp. Inc: 10 minutes; SV Fort (DC 20); Dmg 1d6 subdual; Recup 2 rounds).

Hydrosphere: Semi-arid (daily weather 1-88: none, 89: flood 1d10 MPH, 90-92: acid rain 1d3-1 in., 93: thunderstorm, 94: dust storm, 95: hurricane, 96-97: wind 1d10 MPH, 98: wind 1d10+10 MPH, 99: wind 1d10+20 MPH, 100: wind 1d20+30 MPH.

Geosphere: Stable tectonic activity (daily earthquakes 1-99: none, 100: minor).

Seasons: No seasons (radioactive wasteland).

Anthrosphere: None; destroyed civilization.

Origin: Indeterminate.

Stargate Location (underground): Science directorate access chamber, near research laboratories; deserted.

EPISODE SUMMARY

Traveling to P3R-233, SG-1 investigates what appears to be a vacant world and the remains of what look to be technology left behind. However the area around the Stargate — located deep underground — is devoid of any signs of life. As SG-1 looks around, there appear to be no indications as to why P3R-233 is uninhabited. That is, until Teal'c makes an alarming discovery: several weapon strikes near the Stargate appear to have originated from a Goa'uld staff weapon. A warning symbol found by O'Neill is also recognized by Teal'c: it means *korush-nai,* or "turn back." The Jaffa explains that the world they are on is surely lifeless, the surface above bombarded and destroyed by the Goa'uld; a radioactive wasteland. No one on the world is left alive.

Concerned that the Goa'uld may still have an interest in P3R-233, O'Neill orders the team to reassemble and dial the Stargate back to Earth. In a nearby room Dr. Jackson and Captain Carter have found what appears to be a collection of ancient artifacts from across the galaxy, some of Earth origin and tagged. With the team's imminent departure, Daniel hurriedly attempts to collect as many as he can to return to the SGC. Among the items is a small, alien hand-held device. Upon touching it, Daniel notices a black stone obelisk with a mirror-like surface – a surface that returns no reflection. Intrigued, he touches the mirror, receiving a small shock of energy for his troubles. Returning to the Stargate to request help in returning the item to the SGC, Daniel is surprised to find the area empty – SG-1 is gone.

Dialing back to Earth, Dr. Jackson is surprised to find himself confronted with several heavily-armed marines. General Hammond, who apparently does not recognize him, instructs him to identify himself or be shot. Furthermore, Hammond isn't a General, but instead a Colonel, a development which makes no sense at all. A confused Dr. Jackson is taken away and locked up.

After a medical checkup, he awakens in secured quarters, a prisoner. Calling for help, he is surprised to be met by Dr. Katherine Langford, his old mentor responsible for introducing him to the Stargate during Project Giza. Dr. Langford, however, maintains that Daniel is not a member of the Stargate program. Furthermore, Captain Carter is not a member of the military but a civilian astrophysicist. Daniel protests that this must be some kind of cruel joke, although he can't explain what is happening.

Things don't improve much when he is brought before General O'Neill, head of the Stargate program, who confesses that he doesn't know who Daniel is and doesn't have time to listen to the ravings of a madman. In desperation, Daniel reveals his knowledge of O'Neill's background, the circumstances that surrounded the Abydos mission, and the death of Jack's son, Henry. Upon mentioning Chulak, the Jaffa home world, O'Neill takes interest in Daniel's story, particularly the gate address.

Daniel is relieved when Samantha Carter arrives but, as Katherine said, she is not a member of the military. Sam brings news that two more cities, Philadelphia and Washington, have been lost. "Lost?" Daniel asks. Taken down to the gate control room, Daniel is shown a map of the world where the Goa'uld have attacked, systematically taking out city after city from orbit. The Earth is under assault and billions have died from the onslaught.

With the realization that something terrible happened returning from P3R-233, Daniel searches for answers. With the help of Drs. Langford and Carter, they theorize that Daniel somehow was transported into an alternate dimension or reality, similar yet different than his own. Since the Stargate is unable to perform such an act, Katherine theorizes that it could have been the unusual device on P3R-233 – the mirror – that Daniel discovered.

General O'Neill, however, has his own problems to contend with. Armed with the gate address to the Jaffa home world, O'Neill sends a nuclear bomb through. Although millions of innocents may die, it is nothing compared to the destruction the Goa'uld have already inflicted. Daniel's pleas for mercy fall on deaf ears. As the President's plane is destroyed by the Goa'uld, a mothership heads for Cheyenne Mountain. Evacuation plans are cut short as an incoming wormhole keeps the Stargate busy, preventing escape to the Beta Site. The Goa'uld intend to capture the Earth's Stargate.

Preparing to mount a last stand, General O'Neill looks for recommendations. Until the wormhole is broken off, no one can dial out to escape, so a defensive perimeter is set up, blowing the secondary elevator shafts.

Forced to wait, Daniel translates a deep space telemetry message, originating from the direction of P3R-233, "and your mirror," explains Katherine. The message, spoken in ancient Egyptian, is similar to the dialect of Abydos. Daniel is able to translate it: "Beware the destroyers, they come from $3 - 32 - 16 - 8 - 10 - 12$." Using video footage that Daniel took while on P3R-233, they are able to determine that world's unique point-of-origin symbol and assemble a Stargate address – the home world of the Goa'uld?

The Stargate disengages and a race begins to dial out. If the Stargate can be dialed in time to the Beta Site then an escape route can be made for the base personnel. However, the dialing computer is too slow, and another incoming wormhole effectively cuts off any means of escape. Confronted with the fact they may, at best, get only one more shot at dialing out, plans are proposed. Armed with the gate address of "the Destroyers," O'Neill favors sending another bomb. Daniel points out that this, ultimately, will do nothing; the destruction on Earth – their Earth – has already happened. "The Earth that I know still has a chance." If they use their last opportunity to dial out to P3R-233 Daniel may be able to return to his reality and prevent a Goa'uld attack from happening there.

The option is considered academic, as the Jaffa are too strong and will easily make it down to the lower levels by then. Daniel offers a plan to buy them some time, by bargaining with Teal'c – First Prime of Apophis – to turn against his master and let the Tauri go. Armed with Daniel's video footage, General O'Neill agrees to give it a shot; perhaps diplomacy can succeed where bullets have failed.

O'Neill meets with the alternate Teal'c, head of Apophis' forces, and shares his fanciful story of alternate realities and a Teal'c that stood up against the False Gods. Teal'c is unmoved by O'Neill's story or proof, instead stating that they have received word from Chulak about the bomb that went through. All that Teal'c cared for is now dead.

With forces overrunning the base, the wormhole is disengaged and the base struggles to dial out to P3R-233. Samantha dies, taking several Jaffa with her and Katherine is trapped in the gate control room as the self-destruct of the base counts down. As the Stargate opens, Teal'c appears in the gate room, confronting Daniel. Making a mad dash for the Stargate, a glancing shot hits Daniel from Teal'c's staff weapon as he is flung through the gate. Teal'c stands victorious before his prize as the entire base is destroyed around him…

Returning to P3R-233, badly injured, Daniel makes his way to the artifact room, touching the mirror. Collapsing to the floor he is discovered by Colonel O'Neill and SG-1. Daniel grips the Stargate address in his hand and emphatically states, "They're coming."

BACKGROUND
THE LAST BATTLEFIELD

The planet of P3R-233 was once home to a near-human species, the Camil. Decedents from a long-lost world formally under Goa'uld control, these humans settled on P3R-233 in an attempt to prosper beyond the grasp of their sadistic masters. With little knowledge of their history or origins, the Camil spent several lifetimes in pursuit of their heritage, attempting to learn more about the world from which all human life originated. To this end, they became galactic scholars, visiting a number of planets – some still under Goa'uld control – in an effort to build an accurate accounting of their history. One such world was Abydos, where the Camil obtained great insight to the origins of the Tauri, although never the exact gate address.

Across these worlds the Camil also assembled a large number of cultural and technological relics, all helping to form a picture of the origins of humanity. On one such world, an arctic wilderness, the Camil discovered signs of prior Goa'uld occupation – Jaffa remains, frozen for all time. There they also found a Goa'uld stronghold, holding several pieces of technology, some clearly of Ancient design. Among them was an odd-shaped obelisk device made of naquadah and a control mechanism – the quantum mirror.

Eventually the Camil earned the wrath of the Goa'uld and off-world agents were captured and tortured for information, revealing the gate address of P3R-233. The System Lords launched a devastating attack, assaulting the planet through the wormhole and from space. The technological might of the Goa'uld was overwhelming, obliterating the cities of the Camil from orbit and leaving the surface a radioactive wasteland.

In this desperate hour a handful of survivors escaped through the quantum mirror into alternate realities, one day hoping to return to their own.

THROUGH THE LOOKING GLASS

The quantum mirror is a powerful artifact in its own right but framed within the context of a Stargate SG-1 campaign, it is an even more powerful plot device. The introduction of the quantum mirror allows the GM to expand the scope of the series to include not only new worlds, but new realities. Each reality is a potential macro-campaign setting, made up of smaller adventure settings. This presents any number of possible story ideas. Some ideas on how to use the quantum mirror and alternate realities in your campaign are included below.

RA LIVES!

The quantum mirror provides an easy tool to bring back fallen foes. While death has always been a shaky proposition at best with the looming presence of a sarcophagus, now even long-thought dead foes (or allies) can rise again within your campaign. Since there are an infinite number of realities, there are an equally infinite number of possibilities – some so subtly different that on the surface they appear identical. Even more so, characters traveling through a quantum mirror have no way of knowing just how different the reality is, perhaps days, months, or even years later.

A reality where Ra successfully disarmed the nuclear bomb sent up by Colonel O'Neill is certainly plausible as is a reality where Major Kawalsky was not infected by a Goa'uld and instead leads the highly-decorated team of SG-2. As the exploits of SG-1 continue on the small screen, Goa'uld foes fall left and right – the quantum mirror allows you to bring them back in perpetuity.

Fallen characters could also make return appearances, or perhaps even shift realities into that of the campaign. A key character that fell in battle at the hands of a System Lord could be easily reintroduced back into the game via the quantum mirror, either as part of a "guest appearance" or as a long-term addition to the team. Such considerations should be carefully considered and have meaningful consequences; too much "script immunity" could lead players to act recklessly with their characters (and your story), asserting that a duplicate copy of their character is only a brief trip through the quantum mirror away.

NEW WRINKLES

As a plot device, the quantum mirror also allows the GM to revisit old storylines and view them from an alternate perspective. For example, the characters could be thrust into a reality where Abydos is actually held by loyal Goa'uld subjects who are not oppressed but instead lead opulent lives. There, slave labor from the world of the Tauri is brought through on a regular basis to mine (and die in) the naquadah mines.

The attraction of such "one off" adventures is that there need be no consequences or downsides to the character's actions. It's perfectly acceptable for the characters to take extreme measures or even fail in the end – perhaps it is not possible to free Abydos from the Goa'uld – instead it helps illustrates the darker points of the traditional Stargate SG-1 campaign setting. The episode There But For the Grace of God is one such episode; in the end, pretty much everyone dies. But, that is also a very powerful narrative tool to help demonstrate the seriousness of the situation, or in this case, the foreshadowing of the eventual Goa'uld attack in Within the Serpent's Grasp.

Getting to Know Yourself

Whenever you travel into an alternate reality there is always the possibility of meeting one's self. Within the game this does have meaningful repercussions, specifically the quantum flux affect. Player's could be tasked with a dual role: playing not only their regular characters but their other selves as well. Alterations between the characters can allow players to experiment or take their characters in new directions safely. Some changes can be even more extreme and require additional work on the part of the GM and player, say for a character that chose to follow the path of a scientist, rather than a pointman. These special "guest appearances" by alternate characters provide a fun way to liven up a GM's adventures.

They also provide an opportunity for players to realize lost chances or see their characters in a new light, helping to expand his or her development. An alternate reality character who tends to fly by the seat of his pants and doesn't hesitate to intervene for his friends provides a stark contrast to the normal player's character that lurks in the background and looks out only for himself. Some of these traits – positive or negative – may be adapted by the core character after the adventure is over. Depending on how it's presented by the GM this could provide a reasonable catalyst to introduce change.

Galactic Reboot

Regardless of the GM's best intentions, a campaign may sometimes go astray – key plot hooks are outright missed, much-beloved NPCs die accidentally, or characters fall prey to several sessions of particularly bad die rolls. The quantum mirror provides an opportunity to "reset" or reframe an entire campaign. Such tactics should not be frequently used, however, and the ramifications must be seriously considered. Altering the events that took place in the past and effectively starting the campaign over can breed a sense of apathy among players. Such changes should be for the better and used sparingly.

Galactic reboots also allow players to take the opportunity to alter or even redo their own characters, based on their experiences with the game. For example, a player that created a scientist character and found himself getting into much more combat than originally imagined, deems that his character would make a better explorer. During a reboot of the campaign, the player discusses with the GM some alterations to his character which essentially redesigns him with the appropriate changes in mind. The key events in the character's life still happen, but they take slightly different turns. A civilian in one reality may be a respected member of the military in the other or a Tok'ra host in the next. Other times it can be as simple as a new hairstyle.

The Same... But Different

Should you employ the quantum mirror and send the characters to an alternate reality, here are some suggestions on how to make subtle differences that, individually, do not alter things significantly but provide some unique flavor.

Rank: Shift ranks and responsibilities around. The quiet, unassuming officer who controlled the dialing computer might now be in charge of base security. General Hammond is now the base's Operations Officer and second-in-command and a deceased character may be alive and well, functioning as the Base Commander.

Uniforms: Alter appearances and clothing. Dressing everyone in black with knee-high boots can help impart a more dictator-like atmosphere and a foreboding sense of seriousness. Likewise, disregarding military trappings and placing the Stargate under civilian control can show a more progressive reality.

Appearances: Characters with expertly maintained hair are now bald. Other characters show off new ponytails or even new hair color altogether. The nerdish medical aide in the infirmary is now a stunning redhead without glasses.

Décor: Change symbols and paint schemes. Offices now have wood paneling and red carpet on the floor. Common patches and identification symbols are replaced with more functional or utilitarian designs. Doors now open upwards instead of sliding aside and halls once formed from stark concrete are instead covered in sheet metal with handrails.

Alliances: Friends are now bitter enemies, or never heard of the characters before; former foils and villains may be fast friends or respected contacts. The group's greatest enemy is now married to one of the characters – and misses her dearly!

Names: Alter abbreviations and introduce new nomenclature to underscore the characters being caught out of their element. The SGC can become the Stargate Alliance (SGA) or the Stargate Directorate (SGD) and SG Teams instead of SG Units or Stargate Squads. Teams don't carry GDOs, but instead use Remote Iris Deactivation Devices (RIDDs).

Attitude: Perhaps the NID got what they always wanted and have unilateral control of the Stargate. Teams now go through and plunder alien worlds for technology, uninterested in maintaining friendships. Or it's a pacifistic reality where SG teams travel offworld without weapons of any kind, acting as emissaries of peace. It might even be a General Hammond more prone to shoot first and ask questions later, unwilling to listen or compromise.

Shaking Things Up

Finally, you shouldn't be afraid to use the quantum mirror and alternate realities to make sweeping changes and introduce something new. The ability to play new or interesting nuances of their own characters shouldn't be underestimated by the players. Taking characters in new directions or revisiting old storylines framed in a new backdrop provide endless "what if" opportunities.

Equipment Descriptions

Quantum Mirror

This unusual device was developed by an unknown culture, but is likely another lost device of the Ancients. Shaped as a large, jagged obelisk made of a rough quartz-like material (naquadah), this unassuming artifact provides no immediate indication as to its function. Similarly, a small hand-held device that controls the quantum mirror provides no feedback that the two items are, in fact, linked as one.

The control device, when activated, generates a quantum field on the surface of the obelisk appearing, as the name implies, as a mirror. However, instead of a reflection, the mirror shows the location of an alternate reality on the other side, at that exact spatial point. Following established popular quantum mechanical theories, there could exist any number of alternate realities that are widely different or nearly identical to our own. The mirror provides a gateway to these alternate realities and transports a person through the mirror, to the other side.

How each reality differs is unknown; it is entirely possible than an alternate reality exists that is identical to our own in every conceivable way, save the most miniscule detail. This detail, however, could potentially alter the development of the reality in some small, subtle way. Other realities may be so different that sentient life on Earth, as an example, may never have existed. Within these two spectrums lie an infinite number of possibilities.

A significant limitation of the quantum mirror is that no two entities from different realities can coexist within the same reality. The result is temporal entropic cascade failure on the cellular level – which eventually will prove fatal. The "native" entity does not suffer these effects, only the alien one. If the traveler leaves the reality back to his or her own (or another reality), the entropy ends; unless the reality they travel to presents the same problem. Another alternative is to eliminate the other's double entity.

Resource Points: 20. Following the events of Season One, the quantum mirror has been deemed off-limits to all personnel. It is far too dangerous to be used. The GM may, however, devise certain plot lines incorporating the device, in which case the resource points above will apply.

Mechanics: Use of the control device is a somewhat haphazard affair; there is little feedback to allow one to determine which reality they have reached. A small touch-sensitive scroll pad allows the user to select a reality; the more one deviates from the center point – their current reality – the greater variance exists in the target reality. Moving the control device to either extreme generates a reality entirely different from our own. Selecting a specific reality requires a secret DC 20 Electronics skill check. For every additional significant alteration that exists in the destination reality (GM's discretion), raise the DC by 2 as the user attempts to find it. Unfortunately the quantum mirror provides no immediate feedback that the user was able to successfully select their desired reality. In this case, the player may request an Inspiration check with a DC equal to the original reality selection DC. If the GM activates a threat, the device locks onto a similar reality that is indistinguishable from our own until such time that the

players can investigate for themselves (by traveling through the mirror). Selecting a reality is a full round action and multiple retries may be attempted in subsequent rounds.

Once a reality has been selected, any number of persons can travel through the mirror by touching it. The use of the mirror utilizes a quantum charge, meaning that all persons planning to travel through should touch the mirror simultaneously. Touching the mirror is a free action and traversing to the opposite side happens instantaneously. While not inherently disorienting, it does take a full round to reorient oneself on the other side. After use, the mirror requires 1d10 minutes to recharge its quantum field. During that time users can still view through the mirror to either side, but may not travel from one reality to the other.

The quantum mirror does allow a traveler to move spatially, but only to the location of the mirror in the other reality. For example, a mirror on Earth that looks to a reality in which that mirror is on P3R-233 will send its travelers to P3R-233. This is uncommon except in realities that have a DC higher than 30; frequently those realities are so different that the mirrors may be in several varying locations.

Travel through the mirror is two-way at all times, and includes energy as well as matter. Using the control device to disengage the quantum field effectively "closes" the door and requires the destination to be reacquired. The quantum mirror cannot operate without its control device.

Should temporal entropic cascade failure occur, the target must make a DC 25 Fortitude save every hour. Failure results in a loss of 1d4 points of Constitution. Removal of the other's duplicate entity or leaving the reality will end the loss and healing will begin as normal. Using the mirror to escape to another reality with another duplicate entity does not halt the temporal entropy.

1-20: Politics

World visited: Earth.

Episode Summary

Dr. Jackson, fresh from his return from P3R-233, is in the infirmary, explaining the imminent attack of Apophis to the other members of SG-1. Unable to find anything wrong with Daniel – aside from the staff weapon wound in his shoulder, provided by the alternate reality Teal'c – the members of SG-1 are dubious of his fantastic tale. Undaunted, Dr. Jackson reiterates the mysterious message from P3R-233: "Beware the destroyers."

General Hammond, accompanied by the now-promoted Lt. Colonel Samuels, wants to look into Jackson's claims, but now is not the most opportune time. Samuels, visiting from the Pentagon and Stargate Mission Analysis, is here for the upcoming inquiry at the SGC to which the members of SG-1 will provide testimony. Senator Kinsey, Chairman of the Appropriations Committee, has traveled to the SGC to review the Stargate program directly and determine if the necessity outweighs the risk. For now it is determined that Dr. Jackson's potential Earth-saving information must wait.

As the proceedings commence, Senator Kinsey confesses his interest in seeing "the drain through which the money flows" – the Stargate. The Senator, General Hammond explains, was informed of the existence of the Stargate Command and its expenditure of $7.4 billion in hopes of swaying Senator Kinsey to realize the importance of the program. At the President's insistence, the Senator is prepared to listen to SG-1 and review the SGC's records prior to making a final determination.

However, it becomes readily apparent that Kinsey has no great love for the Stargate Program and views it as a burden which unduly puts the nation at risk. The Senator likens the Stargate to Pandora's Box; a potential danger that must be "closed" lest the secrets within doom them all. Furthermore, the Senator is alarmed by the secrecy of the SGC – designated as line item Area 52 – and his belief "that which grows in shadow, but withers in the light of day, does not belong on the vine."

After reviewing several mission reports of SG-1, the Senator dismisses the overall threat of Apophis and his kind, citing that the SGC has had no difficulty in defeating the aliens thus far. Furthermore, should the Stargate be buried, the Earth would remain safe from these potential aggressors. Should the Goa'uld attack from space via their ships, the Senator vows that they will be dealt with by the most powerful nation on the planet. Blinded by his patriotism, he refuses to acknowledge the danger of the Goa'uld. Teal'c's assurance that the Goa'uld are a legitimate threat is equally dismissed.

After reviewing the bulk of the missions of SG-1, the Senator's position – regardless of his promise of a fair hearing – seems solidified; the Stargate Program serves no useful function and is, in fact, a dangerous liability. Frustrated by Kinsey's shortsightedness, Dr. Jackson reveals the information brought back from the alternate Earth. Devoid of any tangible proof, the Senator condemns the use of an outrageous 11th hour claim to stay his hand. Citing the destruction of Ra – one of the most powerful System Lords – and his unyielding faith in God and country, the Senator reports that the Stargate Program is to be shut down, effective immediately. All, it seems, is lost.

Teal'c explains that, if the Tauri are unwilling to continue their battle against the Goa'uld, then he would leave this world to continue his fight. Unfortunately, General Hammond explains, beyond returning any SG teams on assignment, the use of the Stargate is now forbidden. Faced with the threat of a possible impending attack by the forces of Apophis, and an even more sinister enemy to the Stargate Program in the guise of Senator Kinsey, SG-1 stands powerless to intervene... for now.

Background
Reluctant Allies

The National Intelligence Division – more sinisterly known as the NID – has had their eye on the workings of the SGC and the interests of Senator Kinsey for some time. Once it became clear that the Senator's interest the Area 52 was more than passing, the NID took steps. Senator Kinsey, sensing that the contents of Area 52 were more than just clandestine operations, began to push further for details.

Applying heightened political pressure – and the threat of blocking funding for Area 52 outright – the President and the Joint Chiefs decided to provide the Senator access to the records of the SGC in the hopes of bringing him around to the necessity of the program. The NID closely watched every step.

Rocks & Shoals

Where the SGC used the Stargate as a means of exploration and discovery, seeking to find new allies and technology to counter the threat of the Goa'uld, the results thus far have been less than extraordinary in the eyes of the NID. Realizing the potential that the Stargate provides, the NID sees the methods of the SGC as lacking. Their inherent black ops nature forces them to work from the shadows and manipulate events, as opposed to directly intervening. Thus, while eventual control of the Stargate fell out of their hands into the military and the auspices of the Air Force, the NID continues to make its influence felt. Those sympathetic to their cause, such as Colonel Maybourne, provide important intelligence and ready access to the results of the Stargate program. The NID can then use these assets to gain access to equipment and intelligence normally denied to them, such as the incredibly powerful technology of the Tollan.

Once Senator Kinsey's intentions to shut down the SGC became known, the NID moved to counter his plans, for in their eyes, an active Stargate Program operated by any agency is better than no operational program at all.

Executive Decision

As a member of the minority party (as of Season One) seeking a nomination for the Republican Presidential candidacy in the next election, Senator Kinsey's aspirations for public office are sky high. Thus, his placement on the Appropriations Committee – and the closure of the SGC – is simply one more step on his path towards the White House.

Once the Senator became aware of the Stargate Program and the funds being channeled into it, he realized an opportunity: while the President favored the SGC, the secret nature of Area 52 makes the Stargate a distinct political liability. The Senator's threat to reveal the program carried little weight, but its closure – and the inability to block it – provided him with a powerful political weapon. Once the NID stepped in, the Senator saw an even greater opportunity.

With the SGC shut down, the NID could begin their own Stargate program using the Antarctica Stargate. Were the Senator to aid them in removing the SGC as an obstacle, the NID would be willing to assist in his political aspirations. Thus, an unholy alliance was born. The Senator, determined to dismantle the SGC and pave the way for the NID, made a token inquiry to appease the President but with the help of Lt. Colonel Samuels, he already had all the information necessary to close the gate. In return for this effort, the Senator will find that the political playing field in the coming years is increasingly clear of opposition.

Securing Funds

The current operating budget of the SGC is $7.4 billion, classified as "Area 52," by the White House Budgetary Proposal for the Fiscal Year 1997. These funds are used in all aspects of the operations of the SGC, including salaries, research, procurement, and security of the site beyond those funds appropriated for NORAD. The operational budget is submitted by the offices of the SGC and forwarded by the Base Commander, General George Hammond. This proposed budget is sent to Washington and then reviewed by the Joint Chiefs and Executive Branch. Approval of the proposed amount is via its inclusion into the Congressional Budget, otherwise the budget is returned to the Command for reclassification and alteration. Within the Congressional Budget are a number of line items classified as Top Secret. In many cases these items are funded based on the stipulation of the Office of the President and the Joint Chiefs as necessary to the function of the nation. In actuality, the amounts are but a small blip on the radar (of some $1.9 trillion) and since they cannot be disclosed to the general public, have no political ammunition to them. On copies presented to the general public, these line items – and others – are simply blacked out. The final budgets are prepared by the Congressional Budget Committees via the levels set by the Budget Resolution.

Final approval of the budget and dispensation of funds from the Treasury requires the approval of the House of Representatives Appropriations Committee and the Senate Committee on Appropriations (more commonly also referred to as the Senate Appropriations Committee). Each of these Committees is actually comprised of a number of smaller Subcommittees that deal with specific areas of spending, such as Defense (under which the Stargate Program can be found). Prior to final approval by the Committee a series of hearings are held to delve deeper into budgetary concerns and to provide due disclosure as to the appropriation of funds. In the case of items of national security, only the head of the Appropriations Committee (or designated representatives) can take part in such hearings.

In the case of the SGC, Senator Kinsey, as head of the Senate Appropriations Committee conducted the hearings himself; the other members of the committee were not involved.

Stargate Mission Analysis

After every mission, SG team members and team commanders file an after mission briefing report – more commonly referred to as a Destination File. These reports are then compiled into a single docket that represents the sum of the information gathered for most missions, and then reviewed by the Base Commander and SGC staff (in some cases, addendums or follow-up reports may be called for to expand or detail additional areas). In addition, other SGC personnel may be required to file supporting documentation, such as post-mission medical analysis if applicable. In the event that these post-mission reports contradict one another, the Base Commander may assign administrative SGC staff to conduct a Mission Analysis Inquiry. These inquiries, while uncommon, do happen on a fairly regular basis. In most cases an inquiry quickly determines and resolves a point of confusion within a report. As a matter of procedure, inquiries are also conducted on a random basis for SG teams.

All reports, after final review of the Base Commander, are then filed via computer and hardcopy and transmitted to Stargate Mission Analysis, located in the Pentagon. This office, comprised of approximately 12 personnel, sifts through all the destination files and briefs the office of the Pentagon and the Joint Chiefs on any strategic or tactical threats discovered by the SGC. Stargate Mission Analysis (SMA) also looks for trends on worldwide Earth events or even historical markers that might signify a potential connection. For the most part, the SMA provides governmental oversight for the SGC and weekly briefings to both the Joint Chiefs and the President.

The Office of Stargate Mission Analysis is currently headed up by Lt. Colonel Bert Samuels who also serves as liaison officer to Stargate Command.

Using the NID

Throughout the first season, the NID have appeared in a number of episodes, either directly or indirectly. Their inclusion, however, can add an additional layer of complexity to any storyline. In many cases the involvement of the NID may not even become readily apparent to the players until long after the adventure is over.

In some cases the Gamemaster might be inclined to take a story with no NID involvement and retroactively add these elements at a later date. This is a perfectly acceptable ploy and is sometimes mandated by particularly clever or unpredictable players. Do not feel compelled to craft elaborate plot upon elaborate plot in an effort to foreshadow NID involvement for a later date; instead, rely upon inspiration and happenstance to turn steadfast allies into shadowy NID supporters.

The NID fields no standing army or waves of assailants; instead they use pawns and misdirection to counter their foes. A highly-placed operative, such as Colonel Maybourne, can simply draw upon those under his command to deal with NID concerns.

What the NID do have in ample supply is access to information and secrets. These are their weapons, which they will bring to bear against the player characters without hesitation. The NID falls within a shade of gray – their methods are despicable but their intentions are sometimes laudable. The moral quandaries they represent are an opportunity to place the characters in situations that require difficult decisions. While the SGC may not have a prime directive to guide them, they do strive to "do the right thing" whenever possible. Are the lives of a handful of primitive natives worth more than the safety of the Earth? In the eyes of the NID, probably not, and forcing the characters to confront that reality can make for excellent gaming.

51 Pickup

With the limited space of the SGC and personnel available to conduct long-term research, items and technology brought back through the Stargate traditionally are kept at the Cheyenne Mountain Complex for a short period of time. Once the threat of any possible contaminants or infiltration has been removed, the items are then processed for delivery to Area 51: the infamous Top Secret military facility located in the Nevada desert, considered a haven for all matter of secret and clandestine projects fielded by the government (including reports of captured alien spaceships).

Also known as The Groom Lake Facility located at Nellis Air Force Base in Nevada, Area 51 has taken on a level of heightened mystique that provides a near bulletproof cover against the operations of the Stargate Program. The irony being, of course, that nearly everything said about Area 51 is true but too fantastic for the general populace to even consider; it becomes the stuff of urban legends, believed only by the truly deluded. Under that cover, Area 51 has thrived.

The capabilities of Area 51 are numerous, providing a comprehensive storage and research facility to house items and technology recovered via the Stargate. Here, sequestered scientists – both military and civilian – work to unlock the secrets brought back in order to facilitate quantum leaps in our own technology. Work currently progresses on the hand-held alien weapons and their function, as well as a way to defeat Goa'uld shield technology. The study of naquadah – the quartz-like material of which the Stargate is comprised – and its fantastic energy-producing ability remains one of the most important discoveries thus far. Numerous laboratories work on using the technology brought through the Stargate for day-to-day use, including cures for Alzheimer's, advanced metallurgy processes, geology, and anthropology. A recent breakthrough in a naquadah-enhanced missile payload is considered the best prospect for protecting the Earth from a Goa'uld-launched attack from orbit.

While a military installation, Area 51 has a number of oversight and controlling bodies, among them the Intelligence Oversight Committee and the National Intelligence Department (NID). Several NID operatives, including Colonel Harry Maybourne, can frequently be found at Area 51 reviewing the latest advances provided by the Stargate.

Playing For Keeps

Perhaps the greatest discovery of the Stargate program was not brought through the gate, but the actual existence of another Stargate on Earth. Originally discovered in Antarctica by Colonel O'Neill and Captain Carter, this second Stargate – dubbed the Antarctica Gate – was recovered and returned to Area 51 for study. *(For additional details, see Solitudes, page 69.)*

With a second Stargate to study, the scientists at Area 51 hoped to learn more about the gate process and refine the existing dialing program. However, the functioning of two Stargates was concurrently determined to be an impossibility, both scientifically and financially, and the Pentagon ordered the Antarctica Stargate secured away.

Or so it was believed.

Shadowgate

Following the mothballing of the second gate, the NID made preparations to "acquire" the Antarctica Stargate for their own purposes. Theorizing that a second gate could be operated – clandestinely and concurrently with the main gate at the SGC – the NID prepared to launch their own rogue Stargate program. With Senator Robert Kinsey threatening to shut down the SGC, the NID viewed such a program as a failsafe measure. They launched a shadow operation and replaced the Stargate from Area 51 with a replica, transferring the gate to a remote facility in the Utah desert just south of the Black Mountains.

For a number of months the NID worked to find a way to operate their gate without the knowledge of the SGC, even though they had access to their own DHD. The use of either gate with the DHD was theorized to set that gate as the "primary" gate, shunting all off-world travel to it. Thus, in order to operate covertly, the NID would need to have their Stargate effectively disabled and their DHD disconnected, until needed. In order to mask their gate activity, the Shadowgate – as dubbed by the NID operatives – would be used only concurrently with the SGC gate. Utilizing resources available to them, the NID launched a covert operation within the SGC to gain monitoring access to the SGC dialing computer. The fact that the SGC operates several teams on pre-determined schedules and windows of operation made this feat easier.

With their plan in place, the NID stands ready to launch their own full-fledged Stargate program whenever it suits their needs.

Breakthroughs

While the Stargate Program has not to date yielded any overwhelming examples of technology that vastly expand the abilities of Earth, there have been a number of important scientific discoveries. In time, it is hoped that even more can be realized – even beyond simple military applications – to benefit mankind as a whole.

Triactive Serum 337B: This experimental serum contains enhanced regenerative properties. Designed to be used as a "super anti-toxin," 337B has thus far failed to meet expectations. However, one side effect has been a strong success rate at curing symptoms of Alzheimer's. Serum 337B appears to concentrate and repair the affected neural pathways degenerated by the condition and restore a sense of normalcy. As of the end of Season One, the drug is not yet ready for human testing, but the outlook is promising.

Theoretical Chemistry: The volume of data recovered from planet P3X-972 by Drs. Littlefield and Jackson have provided insight into a number of new chemical compounds and building blocks outside the scope of traditional science. Dr. Littlefield studied the formulae for several years, theorizing that it served as a "universal language" of sorts. Linguists have also been examining the possibility of further translating the language or using it as a near-unbreakable code for the US military.

Pheromones: The SGC's encounter with the Goa'uld Hathor has provided new details as to how pheromones may be concentrated to affect a person. Typically outside the realm of traditional science, the near-hypnotic quality of Hathor's pheromones and ability to seemingly control men's minds has provided a powerful onus to investigate the matter more directly. Blood samples taken at the time of the event at the SGC as well as trace amounts of the chemical harvested from the base have provided promising results.

Particle Physics: Study into naquadah technology — including the Stargate — continues to yield new data on particle physics and the generation of cleaner energy sources. The stability of naquadah and miniscule amounts required to produce a significant output makes it attractive as an alternate power source — or even a weapons system. Unfortunately, supplies of naquadah are difficult to come by, even for the Goa'uld (whose entire civilization is based on the substance, even incorporating it into their blood). Attempts to synthesize naquadah thus far met with failure.

Quantum Physics: Encounters with the Tollan and reports by Captain Carter have yielded new insight into quantum physics. Security footage of the Tollan and their fantastic technology — the ability to literally walk through walls — are of significant interest to the military and the NID. Unbeknownst to many, Area 51 is actually conducting experiments on non-functioning Tollan technology, recovered from P3X-7763 prior to the destruction of its Stargate (*see Enigma, page 62*). The recent recovery of a quantum mirror, thought to provide access to a variety of "alternate dimensions" is of particular interest to several physicists.

Nanotechnology: The replication of SG-1 team members into computer forms (*see Tin Man, page 65*) has provided the first up-close examination of microscopic technology so perfect that it is able to mimic a human being in complete detail. If this underlying nanotechnology can be fully-developed it could extend life spans by several orders of magnitudes and all but wipe out disease and hunger. In addition, the potential construction or "replication" of persons to form an android army would be the perfect counter to the parasitic Goa'uld.

1-21: WITHIN THE SERPENT'S GRASP

Worlds Visited: Earth; Apophis' ha'tak.

EPISODE SUMMARY

After the ill-fated visit with Senator Kinsey (*see Politics, page 76*), the Stargate program and SGC are to be shut down immediately. Colonel O'Neill makes another attempt to convince General Hammond to try to reverse the Senator's decision but it's too late. Hammond attempts to keep the program operational by seeking a reprieve from the Senator, enlisting the aid of the Joint Chiefs — even speaking with the President himself — have failed. The Stargate program is to be buried — both literally and figuratively.

The members of SG-1 — Colonel O'Neill, Captain Carter, Dr. Jackson, and Teal'c — meet to discuss their options, overlooking the soon-to-be sealed Stargate. Daniel, reiterating the death and destruction he saw on the alternate Earth

(*see There But For the Grace of God, page 72*), tells his friends that they have to go through the Stargate to the coordinates provided by the inhabitants of P3R-233; in two days the gate will be permanently sealed and there will be no opportunity to try to save Earth. O'Neill again questions Daniel's experience in the alternate reality, unconvinced that a same fate awaits Earth here. Even without any evidence, Daniel's assertion is too dire to ignore: should they not take the risk, the consequences are too horrible to imagine. The members of SG-1 decide to launch an attack through the gate to the Goa'uld base of attack.

Alarms sound as SG-1 activates the Stargate without permission. Colonel O'Neill seals the gateroom and a MALP is launched to the alien coordinates. On the other side darkness envelops the MALP but infrared shows what appears to be the interior of an Egyptian structure. With base security attempting to gain control of the gateroom, SG-1 deploys through the Stargate just as General Hammond and a security force arrive. SG-1 has defied direct orders in an effort to save the Earth.

When SG-1 arrives they find themselves in a darkened cargo room, sealed in with numerous Goa'uld crates. Preferring to keep their arrival a secret, O'Neill has Daniel send the MALP back to Earth through the Stargate while the contents of the crates are investigated. Each crate holds a number of weapons, making it plain that some kind of assault is being planned. Suddenly the entire room shifts and the team — sans Teal'c — is sent to the ground by the force of a great movement. Surprised, SG-1 regains their footing, unsure of what exactly has happened. Fearing that their arrival may have been detected, O'Neill authorizes Daniel to dial the Stargate back to Earth again. As Daniel does so, SG-1 is surprised to find that the gate will not generate a wormhole. Something inexplicable has happened.

There is no time to discuss their options as the cargo room doors open, forcing the members to scramble for hiding. From their hiding places a number of Apophis' Serpent Guards solemnly enter the room. They open a crate and remove a large spherical device, setting it up in front of the Stargate. Their task complete, the guards leave, unaware of the presence of SG-1.

The team withdraws and investigates the device which Teal'c is able to identify as a long-range communicator, similar to a television. With the location of the room's exit now known to them, Teal'c sets about to the task of opening the door, using a hidden switch. From there, SG-1 is able to leave the room, moving carefully to avoid Jaffa detection.

Moving down the corridors, SG-1 darts into a nearby chamber where they are surprised to find a sarcophagus in waiting. This revelation pales in comparison to the sight of stars streaming by from a nearby window. The team — and the Stargate — are not on a planet, but on a space ship traveling through hyperspace. Teal'c theorizes that the shift they felt earlier was the ship jumping to hyperspace. In transit, the Stargate will remain inoperable until the vessel stops. SG-1 is trapped!

After dealing with a wandering Jaffa guard, the team continues to reconnoiter the facility, finding a landing bay full of death gliders ready for use. It appears clear now that the vessel is heading towards Earth to launch a massive attack. Even so, at the speeds normal for a Goa'uld vessel,

Captain Carter estimates it would take them nearly a year to reach us. Returning to the cargo bay, they discover that several Jaffa have arrived, along with the sarcophagus. The device is activated and the image of Apophis appears before all assembled. The Jaffa bow in reverence to their god. Apophis speaks, detailing how the scourge that plagues them – the people of the Tauri – will be crushed by his might. Until such time that they arrive, the Jaffa will be commanded by Apophis' son, Klorel. At that the sarcophagus opens and a single form emerges... Skaara!

As the gathering ends, SG-1 is left to consider the events thus far. Indebted to his Abydonian friend, O'Neill and Teal'c will attempt to capture Skaara while Carter and Daniel will plant explosives throughout the ship. O'Neill's hope is that they can somehow get through to Skaara and stop the invasion; otherwise SG-1 will have to destroy the vessel before it reaches Earth. The teams move out.

The assault on Klorel/Skaara is swift, as O'Neill and Teal'c take the Jaffa guards by surprise. Klorel attempts to kill Colonel O'Neill but is subdued by Teal'c. Shooting the door to the control room to prevent entry, O'Neill attempts to contact his old friend. Klorel's will is strong, however, and is unwilling to allow Skaara to communicate with O'Neill. Using the zat guns found earlier, O'Neill shoots Klorel, causing the Goa'uld great pain and loosening its control over the host. For a brief moment O'Neill is able to talk with his friend. Meanwhile, Jaffa guards begin their assault on the room in an effort to rescue their lord.

Klorel regains control as the Jaffa break into the room and a standoff ensues. Ultimately, O'Neill and Teal'c relent, unwilling to sacrifice their lives – or Skaara's – while an alternative still remains. The Goa'uld is pleased by the prize he will be able to offer his father.

Meanwhile Captain Carter and Daniel move to the glider bay and plant a series of explosives, then return to the cargo bay and plant more on the Stargate. When detonated, the Stargate will destroy everything around it utterly. Carter and Daniel are surprised as Serpent Guards enter, accompanied by Klorel, Colonel O'Neill, and Teal'c. Activating the communications device, Klorel contacts his father, Apophis. The Serpent God is clearly pleased by the turn of events. Their moment of triumph at hand, Apophis orders the death of Teal'c and O'Neill for the many crimes they have committed against the System Lords. They are to be taken to the *peltak* and executed.

Carter and Daniel move to rescue their comrades but the safety of Earth must come first. Carter sets a timer on the C-4, setting it to detonate in 24 hours. Should they be captured there is still hope for Earth.

On the peltak Klorel mocks O'Neill who would try to save his friend. He offers to show O'Neill his planet one last time and decelerates the ship. O'Neill is surprised to see the ha'tak passing the rings of Saturn; the vessel moves considerably faster than just 10 times the speed of light!

Meanwhile on Earth, the SGC moves into action as early reports from deep space telemetry show a large vessel approaching. The forces of Apophis have arrived – just as Dr. Jackson predicted.

On the ha'tak, Carter and Daniel assault the control room, taking out several of the Jaffa guards while O'Neill and Teal'c spring into action. The battle is swift but in the confusion, Klorel grabs Daniel and uses his ribbon device on the young archeologist. O'Neill is left with no alternative and opens fire, killing Klorel/Skaara. As he slumps to the ground, O'Neill apologizes to his young friend.

There is no time for mourning as the image of Earth grows in the view screen, showing that the Goa'uld vessel has arrived at its destination, much faster than anyone thought possible. Captain Carter reveals that in a matter of moments the death gliders will be launched and the assault on Earth will begin – SG-1 has failed, perhaps dooming all life on Earth.

To Be Continued...

BACKGROUND
COUNTING COUP

Considering the age and might of the Goa'uld empire – including several Dynasties and thousands of worlds – why the world are the Tauri such a pivotal point of contention to the System Lords? More so, why is the success of the Tauri – small, yet measurable – even of a concern to the likes of Apophis? It is the Goa'uld psychological makeup and famed ego that makes such affronts unbearable. Among the System Lords, such a show of weakness – even in passing – is enough to question one's ability to be a leader, or as a precursor to attack from other Goa'uld.

A FAMILY MATTER

Throughout this chapter, and other books, there may be references to the Goa'uld family structure of brothers, sisters, fathers, and mothers – not to mention queens and kings – used to illustrate the relationship between the various System Lords. In reality, because of the biological makeup of the Goa'uld and their methods of reproduction *(see pages 110-111 of the Stargate SG-1 core rulebook)*, these monikers are used for simplicity's sake. While Apophis and Heru-ur are not "brothers" in the traditional sense, they do share a kinship – even begrudging respect for one another – that denotes a level of intimacy between them. In fact, the extremely long lives of the Goa'uld and their limited numbers make all System Lords, by choice or not, a member of a much larger extended family. Over several lifetimes of bickering, confrontation, and backstabbing, the Goa'uld have come to form this larger "family unit" that helps define their various roles. These roles are even more easily confused when one considers that the Goa'uld can change sexes by changing hosts, as often as their whim dictates. Last centuries' "brother" may now, in fact, be a "sister."

The transient nature of these relationships also defies establishing permanent relationships between the various System Lords. Bitter enemies for thousands of years may put aside their differences after a millennia to become wary allies. For all their power, the Goa'uld are often fickle and hard to predict. Hence, while two System Lords may wage a century-long war and decimate millions of lives in the process, two thousand years later they can just as easily find each other opportune friends... for a time.

GOA'ULD PRESTIGE

Every Goa'uld is constantly seeking prestige; those that have it seek to keep it and those without it require it to survive. The entire culture of the Goa'uld is built upon the premise that the strong will survive and that the week will serve... or worse. To this end, to achieve power a Goa'uld must possess prestige. The Goa'uld admire and covet it and it is the only way to ever achieve the rank of System Lord.

The most common ways of achieving prestige are measured on the field of battle through victory, overcoming one's opponents, or by possessing power over another. The possession of power can also be measured by the Goa'uld material assets; having access to a sizable cache of naquadah, for example, would garner significant prestige even though the owner may never had success on the field of battle.

Internal fighting is the most common way of earning prestige. Victory, in Goa'uld terms, is measured very subtly. Also, the manner of victory says much about a Goa'uld's standing. Overcoming a rival System Lord and vanquishing his forces would yield considerable prestige; leading that System Lord into a cunning trap and causing loss of face would grant even more. In addition, the defeated System Lord – even if it was not a major victory or loss – would lose considerable face in the process.

This shifting of prestige – or counting coup – is the cornerstone of Goa'uld society. It explains the steps they take in affairs and dictates their responses in situations. An attack by an enemy that captures a world is one matter... the loss of face to the other System Lords is an even worse loss and must be dealt swiftly. No one is more familiar with the concept of Goa'uld prestige than the people of the Tauri. Through their recent efforts a number of blows – both small and large – have been dealt to several System Lords. For this reason Apophis has made it his primary goal to crush the Tauri. By destroying the Earth, Apophis in one stroke would avenge his losses and gain substantial standing by removing the foes that killed Ra. (The fact that Apophis benefited directly from the death of Ra is inconsequential in this matter; such an affront is an affront to all Goa'uld, not just one of them.)

Among the System Lords the bartering of prestige is also a common occurrence. A System Lord that requires a quantity of larval Goa'uld may arrange to receive some from another in exchange for some prestige. This can range from the swearing an oath of thanks, the acknowledgement of a debt of gratitude, or even compensation on the field of battle – the Goa'uld have no compunction against sending their Jaffa to their deaths in a meaningless and hopeless battle in order to allow another System Lord to benefit.

SHOCK & AWE

The numbers of the Goa'uld are measured in the hundreds; even at the peak of the Goa'uld Dynasties, adequate hosts has always been in short supply. After the discovery of the Tauri and their use as the host of choice, Goa'uld numbers have been artificially limited by the availability of symbiotes. Thus the reliance of the System Lords upon their shock troops, the Jaffa.

To keep such a large number of forces in line the System Lords have created a series of checks and balances to ensure loyalty. Foremost is the Jaffa dependency on larval Goa'uld – even the strongest Jaffa warrior is nothing without the symbiote that provides him life. Next is the imposition of a nearly endless series of Dark Ages; entire generations without the ability to read or write, technological stagnation, the inability to devise any culture or progress of their own. What little technology the Jaffa are allowed to use is supplied the Goa'uld and so advanced as to be akin to magic.

This philosophy is brought through all manner of Goa'uld structures and weapons. Basic temples and accommodations are grand in appearance and design, decadent by all standards. While the average Jaffa toils in poverty, his god sits upon a throne of gold in a temple the size of the greatest of pyramids. Some Jaffa live and die in these pursuits, never knowing life beyond the shackles of a laborer.

Goa'uld vessels are similarly designed: grand in scope and overwhelming in force. The appearance of a ha'tak is a sight to behold, striking fear into those that face it. Devastating armaments can obliterate entire cities from orbit and wave upon wave of death gliders fly from their bays, raining down death and destruction. Energy shields afford near-invulnerability from conventional attack. Entire legions of Jaffa troops reside on these vessels, deploying a mighty army in a matter of hours to scour and control the countryside. Assault vessels and light bombers fly overhead while energy weapon emplacements provide fire support. Even the common weapon of the Jaffa warrior – the staff weapon – is built for the express purpose of breeding fear and awe.

Heroism is rewarded by status and rank, most Jaffa striving to one day catch the eye of their lord and perhaps be promoted in charge of a battalion, or even become a First Prime. Such warriors – by Jaffa standards – are lavishly rewarded; afforded their own private homes, a small parcel of land, even the ability to take a mate. These honors are closely guarded and offspring are taught not to dismiss the honor of a Jaffa's family that has taken years to garner.

Goa'uld justice is equally swift and unforgiving, turning Jaffa upon Jaffa to jockey for the best of positions. Great prestige can be had by ending the life of a shol'va or by great deeds on the field of battle against a lord's hated enemy. The Goa'uld do not give second chances; a warrior that fails and lives does not deserve to serve a god any longer. In the most generous of situations, a System Lord may afford the warrior one last opportunity to die with honor, typically granting a boon of a suicide attack. Only those coming from a Jaffa family of great honor are afforded such an opportunity; most are killed outright, or tortured to death publicly. The ritual crushing of a Jaffa's symbiote is considered the most heinous method of death and also the most painful. The Goa'uld save these special sentences for those Jaffa that have greatly earned their ire.

Above all, the life under the oppressive boot of a Goa'uld – be it slave or Jaffa – is one of constant fear and uncertainly. Such is how the Goa'uld desire it.

TACTICS

The System Lords employ a number of common tactics on the field of battle. As outlined below, these serve as an example of how the Goa'uld conduct their battles on a grand scale. Such engagements are dictated at the most superficial level; in-depth details at a ship or squad level are nearly always left to underlords or loyal Jaffa. Failure carries dire consequences.

BOMBARDMENT

Bombardment, as the name suggests, deals with using overwhelming force to destroy a planet from space. All ha'tak vessels have enough firepower to bombard a world, leaving it a smoldering remnant without having to send a single warrior to the planet's surface.

Orbital bombardment uses polarized energy cannons and plasma generators to envelop and destroy entire cities. These blasts can wipe out several million people in a matter of minutes. By coordinating efforts with other vessels, a handful of ha'taks can literally scour a world bare in a matter of days. Such bombardment always affects the geosphere and hydrosphere, in most cases irradiating the planet. Climates will change drastically and acid rain will pour from the sky, killing whatever life remains. Burrowing underground affords little protection in most cases; a ha'tak's weapons can penetrate nearly a quarter-mile beneath the surface.

When bombarding or assaulting a world with a Stargate, the Goa'uld always dial that world's Stargate. Even if the Goa'uld do not send troops through, they can prevent anyone from leaving through it. It serves as a poignant reminder that one cannot escape the fury of a god.

OCCUPATION

The Goa'uld rarely occupy a world unless it contains something of particular value that they desire. In most cases bombardment and obliteration is the preferred method (see above). However, when the need arises the System Lords are more than capable of bending a world to their will. Frequently the Goa'uld will conduct a light bombardment, destroying a large number of cities and swathing the skies with their death gliders, instilling fear and uncertainty in the populace. Afterwards, ground troops are then deployed to capture the major structures and installations necessary to keep the governments in line. Any leaders that can be identified will be rounded up, and if not to coerced into submission then publicly executed.

In most cases after achieving control the Goa'uld will leave the indigenous population alive, with Jaffa oversight, of course. This frequently includes a Goa'uld underlord to take control and administer the world in his god's name. Uprisings are dealt with swiftly and without mercy; the cost for disobeying the Goa'uld is dire. Many times entire cities will be obliterated to demonstrate a point. Innocents are often rounded up and publicly executed to enforce Goa'uld leadership. If enough resources are available, a ha'tak may be left behind as a symbol of the System Lord's power. This is used as a command post from which to rule the world. On particularly useful worlds — such as those with naquadah resources — a Stargate may be set up if one does not already exist.

Overcoming such Goa'uld aggression is never easy. Often the only way to escape Goa'uld control is through happenstance or good fortune; it is not uncommon for the System Lords to become complacent with a world and liter-

ally forget about it once it has served its needs. In the case of the Tauri, for example, the Goa'uld focused their attentions on other concerns and left insufficient numbers behind to quell a local resistance. Once the Stargate was buried, the world was not considered important enough to send a ha'tak to reclaim.

SPACE BATTLES

Goa'uld tactics in space are equally direct, preferring to rely on overwhelming force and surprise rather than tactical genius. However, the System Lords – known for cunning and deceit – love to spring traps or strike from the shadows. Once a battle has been joined, the outcome will quickly be determined; the difference is the Goa'uld that dictates how and where the battle takes place. The majority of all space engagements take place against other Goa'uld – only the Asgard are a formidable enemy in the coldness of space.

Surprise: By far, the System Lords prefer surprise. Using misdirection and false intelligence, the Goa'uld will attempt to keep the numbers and locations of their forces secret, frequently moving them around to prevent counter-detection. Once an enemy fleet is found, most System Lords will use the opportunity to launch a surprise strike, or at the very least, a probing attack. Such attacks are alarmingly common among the Goa'uld and serve to heighten tension amongst the System Lords. However, they are expected if not outright demanded by the Goa'uld — by keeping their forces in a constant state of battle readiness, the System Lords as a whole remain more powerful.

Traps: The tried-and-true favorite of the Goa'uld, a clever trap is one of the most satisfying tactics of the species. Cloaked mines or Jaffa strike teams are the preferred favorites, although on more than one occasion false intelligence reports can lead forces into a particularly deadly ambush. A favorite tactic of the System Lord Ba'al includes the falsification of galactic coordinates, leading his enemies into a system with a nearby black hole. Cornered between the crushing gravity well and Ba'al's forces, more than a few Goa'uld have met a swift end.

Stellar Objects: Perhaps the largest weakness of Goa'uld vessels are their limited sensors. While ha'taks have overwhelming weapons they are not good at detecting small vessels. This lends itself well to hiding fleets on the periphery of systems or near the corona sphere of a sun. Cronus led a bold attack against Heru-ur several centuries ago by literally burying a squadron of death gliders on a small moon, then launching them in a flanking maneuver to pin Heru-ur's fleet. While the Gliders were ultimately destroyed, the sacrifice turned the course of battle and inflicted heavy losses.

Sacrifice: With such loyal troops as the Jaffa, it is inevitable that the use of suicidal attacks would become the mainstay of Goa'uld tactics. Surprisingly, they have fallen into disfavor over the past few centuries, more so out of the waning number of symbiotes and naquadah resources than any great love for the Jaffa. But occasionally, in engagements where the stakes are significantly high, it is not unheard of for entire ha'taks to ram one another in attacks of mutual destruction. Apophis in particular will happily sacrifices his pawns if it means securing victory.

CHAPTER TWO

PERTINENT NPCs

This chapter contains information on the various NPCs portrayed in the first season of *Stargate SG-1*. The first section, "Feature NPCs," includes background on major characters and those intended to play large roles in your campaign. The second section, "Supporting NPCs," contains information on characters who either play a more limited role, or who have died in the course of Season One.

All the information in this chapter is considered current as of *Within the Serpent's Grasp* at the conclusion of Season One. Developments from subsequent seasons will be included in the appropriate Season book.

FEATURE NPCs

Feature NPCs are those who have played a major role in the series, or who are intended as large parts of a *Stargate SG-1* campaign. In most cases, they receive three sets of stats, to better reflect the power levels in your particular campaign. Goa'uld characters, however, only receive one set of stats, due to their long lives and unique nature as recurring villains (further details will appear in the upcoming *System Lords* sourcebook). The title in parenthesis indicates the first *Stargate SG-1* episode in which that character appeared, or (in the case of NPCs created specifically for this book), the episode most pertinent to them.

APOPHIS (CHILDREN OF THE GODS)

Goa'uld System Lord

No Goa'uld is as personally hated by the members of the SGC as Apophis. While all Goa'uld can be cruel, violent, and aggressive, the list of crimes which he has perpetrated against the SGC make him especially loathed. The feeling is entirely mutual, as Apophis's repeated attacks on Earth and the members of the SGC bear out.

A rival of Ra, supreme System Lord of the Goa'uld, Apophis rose to power after the Sun God's death at the hands of the first Stargate team on Abydos. He immediately expanded his territory to include Ra's former territories, and took steps to secure his position among the other System Lords — including collecting hosts from worlds that formerly belonged to Ra. This move resulted in the kidnapping of potential hosts from both the SGC and Abydos, which first brought him to the attention of the SGC. In the ensuing conflict, both the wife and brother-in-law of Daniel Jackson were taken as hosts by Apophis's mate Amaunet and son Klorel, earning him the enmity of the SGC on a personal as well as military level. SG-1's contact with his First Prime, Teal'c, also gave the Jaffa the opportunity to defect, which angered Apophis beyond all reason. He has since dedicated himself to destroying the upstart Tauri and the renegade Jaffa who betrayed his trust so grievously.

Apophis is a typical System Lord in many ways: vain, arrogant, and obsessed with power. He styles himself the "Serpent God," and his Jaffa all wear helmets and armor patterned on a serpent motif. He can be quite cunning when he wishes, and remains a tenacious foe even in defeat. More on Apophis will appear in the upcoming *System Lords* sourcebook.

Apophis

Specialty: Goa'uld Noble
Rank: System Lord
Class: Pointman
Level: 15

Strength:	8	Dexterity:	14
Constitution:	10	Intelligence:	14
Wisdom:	11	Charisma:	20

Vitality:	97	Wounds:	10

Defense: 18 (+6 class, +2 Dex)
Initiative Bonus: +8 (+6 class, +2 Dex)
Speed: 30

Fort: +9	Ref: +9	Will: +9

Special Qualities: +4 to Bluff and Innuendo threat ranges, assistance (¼), cross-class ability 2 more, (bonus combat feat, damage reduction 1/–, uncanny dodge (Dex bonus)), dominated body, *generous,* immunity to disease, inherited memory, lead 7/session, long life, radiation resistance, serendipity 1/session, strategy 1/session, tactics 3/session (+2 bonus), versatility (Appraise, Computers, Concentration, Cultures, Disguise, Gather Information, Innuendo, Intimidate, Listen, Sense Motive, Spot).

Skills: Appraise +6, Bluff +20, Bureaucracy +18, Concentration +9, Computers +6, Cultures +7, Diplomacy +22, Disguise +10, Gather Information +18, Innuendo +9, Intimidate +16/+22, Knowledge (Replicators) +6, Knowledge (System Lords) +12, Listen +10, Sense Motive +8, Spot +10.

Feats: Advanced Skill Mastery (Persuasive), Armor Group Proficiency (Light, Medium), Grand Skill Mastery (Persuasive), Great Fortitude, The Look, Naquadah Sense, Persuasive, Political Favors, Political Clout, Weapon Focus (Kara Kesh), Weapon Group Proficiency (Melee, Handgun, Rifle).

Attacks

Unarmed	+10	1d3–1 (subdual)
Kinetic Blast	+13	2d6+2 and 2d6+2 subdual

Gear: Kara kesh, sarcophagus (aboard ha'tak).

Bra'tac (Bloodlines)
Jaffa Revolutionary

In his prime, Master Bra'tac was considered the greatest Jaffa warrior of all time. Even now, as he nears the end of his days, few who see him in action doubt. He did not become that warrior by trusting blindly in the gods; indeed, by the time he was named First Prime of Apophis, he no longer believed they were gods at all.

The second father to dozens of Jaffa, including Teal'c and his son Rya'c, never knew his own father. From the time he can remember, he was told he should be proud that his father died with honor in the service of his god. Yet the boy and his mother were left dependent on the charity of her brother, with nowhere to go but a crowded set of quarters in the city of Chulak. Bra'tac's right to the Prim'ta – the ceremony entrusting him with an infant Goa'uld that would one day take its place among the gods – and to a warrior's training was guaranteed by his father's honorable fate, however, which provided a mean of escape. In his uncle's house he was an interloper, looked down upon by his cousins. On the training field he was a force to be feared.

Never the largest or strongest apprentice, he quickly became the wiliest. A Jaffa's strength is forged in hardship, and his master Shek'nar, seeing his promise, never stood between him and the bullies who foolishly considered him an easy target. By the age of fifteen he regularly bested older boys nearly ready to go to war. In a few short years he surpassed Shek'nar himself, but would always regard the old warrior as his true father, holding dear the lesson of self-reliance and later instilling it in his own apprentices.

At seventeen he saw battle for the first time: Jaffa killing Jaffa for the glory of their gods. Even then his sharp mind could not help but question its purpose, but he had been taught that the gods' reasons were unknown and unknowable, and for a time that was enough. As he rose through the ranks, though, the doubts returned. Why did gods need armies or ships? Why did they taunt one another like spoiled children? Why did they demand such constant loyalty from "inferior" beings like the Jaffa? Finally, not long after his promotion to the honor guard attending Apophis himself, Bra'tac was required to carry his grievously wounded and obviously terrified lord to the sarcophagus to be reborn. This was no god.

If their divinity was a sham, though, the Goa'ulds' power was all too real; the Jaffa had no choice but to kill and die for them. But Bra'tac's rank gave him power too, if only to lessen by a fraction the destruction of his master's endless wars. That power increased when Apophis named him First Prime. Each life he saved became a victory, for Bra'tac as well as for the few trusted apprentices in whom he secretly cultivated that precious seed of doubt. He learned how to disguise merciful behavior as loyalty to his lord, always ready with a quick explanation to cover things up. He also knew when to accept reality and do his master's bidding when there was no other choice. Despite his benevolent nature, he has performed countless atrocities in Apophis's service. Each one haunts him to this day, but his actions also solidified the System Lord's trust in him. Always, he waited for the day when he could defy his master and strike down the false divinity of the Goa'uld. As he grew older, he began to realize that such a day might never come.

That is, until his finest apprentice Teal'c – who replaced him as Apophis's First Prime – struck back against the Serpent God and took up arms with the members of SG-1. Teal'c, has convinced his master that freedom for all Jaffa is not a dream for some far-off future, but a goal to fight for today. Having seen SG-1 in action, Bra'tac has little cause for doubt. Outwardly he mocks Teal'c's high opinion of his Tauri comrades – as he would with his own apprentices, lest they become overconfident – but he is impressed by their accomplishments... and by their potential to achieve so much more. O'Neill is headstrong, like all great leaders in the making, and the woman and the scholar are young and rash, but their hearts are true. With such as these beside him, Teal'c may yet realize his dream. Bra'tac has resolved to aid them – and the rest of the SGC – however he can.

LOW-LEVEL BRA'TAC

Specialty: Jaffa Serpent Guard
Rank: N/A
Class: Guardian/Prime
Level: 5/1

Strength:	16	**Dexterity:**	12
Constitution:	15	**Intelligence:**	12
Wisdom:	14	**Charisma:**	12

Vitality:	63	**Wounds:**	17

Defense: 15 (+4 class, +1 Dex)
Initiative Bonus: +4 (+3 class, +1 Dex)
Speed: 30

Fort: +6   **Ref:** +2   **Will:** +7

Special Qualities: Death squad +1, Enforcer (Basic), *prepared,* radiation resistance, soak 1/session, *unbreakable.*

Skills: Balance +3, Bluff +3, Climb +4, Concentration +7, First Aid +4, Hide +3, Intimidation +16/+14, Jump +5, Knowledge (Goa'uld) +4, Move Silently +3, Pilot +5, Spot +6, Survival (Desert) +7.

Feats: Armor Group Proficiency (Light, Medium, Heavy), Enforcer, Iron Will, Speed Trigger, Stone Cold, Symbiote (Long Life), Toughness, Weapon Focus (Staff Weapon), Weapon Group Proficiency (Handgun, Hurled, Melee, Rifle, Tactical).

ATTACKS

Unarmed	+8	1d3+3 (subdual)
Staff weapon	+5	6d6 (normal, error 1-2, threat 18-20, range 75 ft., qualities and mods AP, AK)

Gear: Staff weapon, Jaffa armor (chain).

MID-LEVEL BRA'TAC

Specialty: Jaffa Serpent Guard
Rank: N/A
Class: Guardian/Prime/Grunt
Level: 5/4/3

Strength:	16	**Dexterity:**	12
Constitution:	16	**Intelligence:**	12
Wisdom:	15	**Charisma:**	12

Vitality:	114	**Wounds:**	18

Defense: 17 (+6 class, +1 Dex)
Initiative Bonus: +7 (+6 class, +1 Dex)
Speed: 30

Fort: +13   **Ref:** +5   **Will:** +13

Special Qualities: Alpha-strike, death squad +1, Enforcer (Basic), *prepared,* overkill (+1d8, 1/session), radiation resistance, ring of death 1/session, second prime, soak 2/session, *unbreakable,* uncanny dodge (Dex bonus).

Skills: Balance +5, Bluff +4, Climb +5, Concentration +10, First Aid +6, Hide +5, Intimidation +24/+22, Jump +8, Knowledge (Goa'uld) +5, Listen +6, Move Silently +3, Pilot +7, Profession (Jaffa Military) +4, Spot +7, Survival (Desert) +12.

Feats: Armor Group Proficiency (Light, Medium, Heavy), Endurance, Enforcer, Iron Will, Martial Arts, Speed Trigger, Staff Basics, Stone Cold, Symbiote (Long Life), Toughness, Weapon Focus (Staff Weapon), Weapon Group Proficiency (Handgun, Hurled, Melee, Rifle, Tactical).
5 base + Toughness + Enforcer + Stone Cold = bonus guardian + bonus grunt

ATTACKS

Unarmed	+14	1d6+3 (subdual)
Staff weapon	+11	6d6 (normal, error 1-2, threat 18-20, range 75 ft., qualities and mods AP,AK)

Gear: Staff weapon, Jaffa armor (chain).

HIGH-LEVEL BRA'TAC

Specialty: Jaffa Serpent Guard
Rank: N/A
Class: Guardian/Prime/Grunt
Level: 5/6/5

Strength:	16	Dexterity:	12
Constitution:	17	Intelligence:	12
Wisdom:	15	Charisma:	12
Vitality:	159	Wounds:	19

Defense: 20 (+9 class, +1 Dex)
Initiative Bonus: +10 (+9 class, +1 Dex)
Speed: 30

Fort: +15   **Ref:** +6   **Will:** +15

Special Qualities: Alpha-strike, death squad +1, Enforcer (Basic), fire team, forced march, *prepared,* overkill (+1d8, 2/session), radiation resistance, ring of death 1/session, second prime, soak 2/session, *unbreakable,* uncanny dodge (Dex bonus), true warrior, voice of the masters.

Skills: Balance +6, Bluff +4, Climb +6, Concentration +14, First Aid +9, Hide +6, Intimidation +35/+33, Jump +10, Knowledge (Goa'uld) +5, Listen +9, Move Silently +3, Pilot +8, Profession (Jaffa Military) +6, Spot +9, Survival (Desert) +15.

Feats: Armor Group Proficiency (Light, Medium, Heavy), Endurance, Enforcer, Iron Will, Martial Arts, Speed Trigger, Staff Basics, Staff Mastery, Stone Cold, Symbiote (Long Life), Toughness, Weapon Focus (Staff Weapon), Weapon Group Proficiency (Handgun, Hurled, Melee, Rifle, Tactical).

6 base + Enforcer + Stone Cold + Toughness + staff basics + bonus Guardian

Attacks

Unarmed	+17	1d3+3 (subdual)
Staff weapon	+14	6d6 (normal, error 1-2, threat 18-20, range 75 ft., qualities and mods AP,AK)

Gear: Staff weapon, Jaffa armor (chain).

LANGFORD, DR. CATHERINE (THE TORMENT OF TANTALUS)

Scholar and Archaeologist

Dr. Catherine Langford was born into the depression of Germany following the aftermath of World War I. Her mother died from complications resulting from a second birth and her father, Prof. Paul Langford did his best to raise Catherine by himself. Unable to bear the memories surrounding them, Prof. Langford used what few contacts he had to gather enough money to travel to Egypt where the German government had arranged for him to start a new dig at the Giza plateau. To Catherine, this was a dream come true; all her short life she had been fascinated with Egyptian culture and the Giza dig was the realization of that love. Gradually she and her father settled down in Egypt where Prof. Langford began his digs. After many unsuccessful finds, they uncovered perhaps the greatest artifact in human history: the Stargate.

They thought the find would be their life's work, but when the Nazis came to power, Catherine and her father were forced to move to America, leaving the Stargate in German hands. The new life was completely unknown to her, but she soon became fond of her new home, thanks to her keen mind and gifted ability with languages. She thought the Stargate was out of her life forever; her father, however, never gave up on it. When the war began, he convinced the Roosevelt administration to try to retake the alien device, and they finally succeeded in 1944 *(see page 41)*. Prof. Langford was placed in charge of the operation, and while Catherine was unable to directly participate, her burning intellect helped fuel her father's inquiries.

It also introduced her to Prof. Langford's assistant, Dr. Ernest Littlefield. The two soon fell deeply in love and planned to marry. Fate, however, had other things in mind. Ernest was reportedly killed in a lab fire and the Stargate program was shut down as a result of the accident. Her father died shortly after the end of the war, and a grief-stricken Catherine tried to forget about that part of her life, turning her attentions to her teaching and research into ancient cultures.

Despite that, the Stargate never entirely receded from her memory, and a chance encounter in 1969 helped rekindle her interest. She was approached by the son of one of her father's colleagues from Germany. The young man knew a great deal about the Stargate, and while his hints were quite vague, he intimated that it might be possible to get it working. She was intrigued by his words and promptly set about reestablishing her father's experiments. Gradually, after much hard work and patience, Catherine managed to renew research in the Stargate.

Initial progress was slow; despite years of effort from her brilliant staff, several key aspects remained frustratingly out of reach. Realizing that she and the other researchers were stuck, she went to a lecture given by Dr. Daniel Jackson. After listening to his theories – and watching most of the scholars leave in disgust – she understood he had a unique perspective needed to unlock the secrets on the Stargate. With Jackson's help, the Stargate was finally opened, and the first mission to Abydos took place soon thereafter.

The inability to dial any other addresses led to the mothballing of the project, which Catherine – now quite elderly – did not fight. That changed again three years later, when she was informed that new addresses had been uncovered and the SGC was now a thriving operation. She accompanied SG-1 to Heliopolis, where her "long dead" fiancé Dr. Littlefield was found alive and well. The experience rejuvenated her, and while she happily returned to retirement with her reunited love, she was secure in the knowledge that her father's work had finally come to fruition.

Dr. Langford is quite spry for her age and the years have not diminished her intelligence in the least. While she distrusts the U.S. military, she is reasonably satisfied that the SGC's goals are benevolent and supports their activities however she can. She rarely travels to Cheyenne Mountain any more, but team members are always welcome in her home and she will gladly answer any questions they have for her. He knowledge of archaeology is world-class and she was working on the Stargate program before most of the SGC was born.

LOW-LEVEL DR. CATHERINE LANGFORD

Specialty: Civilian Specialist
Rank: None
Class: Scientist
Level: 6

Strength:	8	Dexterity:	10
Constitution:	9	Intelligence:	20
Wisdom:	14	Charisma:	14

Vitality:	25	Wounds:	9

Defense: 15 (+5 class)
Initiative Bonus: +2 (+2 class)
Speed: 30

Fort: +1   **Ref:** +2   **Will:** +7

Special Qualities: +2 to education checks, brilliant +1, improvise +3, learned, Ph.D. (Knowledge (Archaeology)), *professor*, research (Persuasive), take 10 (Knowledge (Archaeology), Profession (Archaeologist)).

Skills: Balance +1, Bluff +5, Bureaucracy +4, Computers +4, Concentration +7, Cryptography +9, Cultures +13, Diplomacy +10, Electronics +6, First Aid +6, Gather Information +4, Intimidate +2/+5, Jump +1, Knowledge (Archaeology) +22, Knowledge (History) +16, Languages +16, Listen +5, Profession (Archaeologist) +11, Search +15, Sense Motive +5, Spot +10, Survival (Desert) +6, Swim +0, Tumble +2.

Feats: Alertness, Armor Group Proficiency (Light), Charmer, Old School, Persuasive, Scholarly, Weapon Group Proficiency (Handgun, Melee), World Traveler.

ATTACKS

Unarmed   +2   1d3-1 (subdual)

Gear: None.

MID-LEVEL DR. CATHERINE LANGFORD

Specialty: Civilian Specialist
Rank: None
Class: Scientist
Level: 12

Strength:	9	Dexterity:	10
Constitution:	9	Intelligence:	22
Wisdom:	15	Charisma:	14

Vitality:	51	Wounds:	9

Defense: 20 (+10 class)
Initiative Bonus: +5 (+5 class)
Speed: 30

Fort: +3   **Ref:** +4   **Will:** +10

Special Qualities: +4 to education checks, brilliant +3, improvise +6, know it all 1/mission, learned, Ph.D. (Knowledge (Archaeology), Knowledge (History)), *professor*, research (Inspiration 2/session, Persuasive), take 10 (Knowledge (Archaeology), Knowledge (History), Profession (Archaeologist)).

Skills: Appraise +8, Balance +1, Bluff +5, Bureaucracy +6, Computers +10, Concentration +11, Cryptography +17, Cultures +19, Diplomacy +14, Electronics +10, First Aid +7, Gather Information +6, Intimidate +3/+6, Jump +1, Knowledge (Archaeology) +29, Knowledge (History) +24, Languages +22, Listen +5, Profession (Archaeologist) +16, Search +19, Sense Motive +7, Spot +14, Survival (Desert) +8, Swim +0, Tumble +2.

Feats: Advanced Skill Mastery (Scholarly), Alertness, Armor Group Proficiency (Light), Charmer, Extra Support, Old School, Persuasive, Scholarly, Weapon Group Proficiency (Handgun, Melee), World Traveler.

ATTACKS

Unarmed   +5   1d3-1 (subdual)

Gear: None.

HIGH-LEVEL DR. CATHERINE LANGFORD

Specialty: Civilian Specialist
Rank: None
Class: Scientist
Level: 18

Strength:	9	Dexterity:	10
Constitution:	9	Intelligence:	24
Wisdom:	16	Charisma:	14

Vitality:	75	Wounds:	9

Defense: 24 (+14 class)
Initiative Bonus: +7 (+7 class)
Speed: 30

Fort: +5   **Ref:** +6   **Will:** +14

Special Qualities: +5 to education checks, 10-second solution 1/mission, brilliant +5, improvise +9, Inspiration 2/session, Persuasive), know it all 1/mission, learned, Ph.D.

(Knowledge (Archaeology), Knowledge (History)), *professor,* research (Grand Skill Mastery (Scholarly), take 10 (Knowledge (Archaeology), Knowledge (History), Profession (Archaeologist)).

Skills: Appraise +15, Balance +1, Bluff +7, Bureaucracy +9, Computers +14, Concentration +14, Cryptography +19, Cultures +22, Diplomacy +16, Electronics +11, First Aid +8, Gather Information +9, Intimidate +2/+5, Jump +1, Knowledge (Archaeology) +34, Knowledge (History) +27, Languages +24, Listen +8, Profession (Archaeologist) +21, Search +23, Sense Motive +11, Spot +19, Survival (Desert) +12, Swim +3, Tumble +2.

Feats: Advanced Skill Mastery (Scholarly), Alertness, Armor Group Proficiency (Light), Charmer, Extra Support (x2), Grand Skill Mastery (Scholarly) Iron Will, Old School, Persuasive, Scholarly, Weapon Group Proficiency (Handgun, Melee), World Traveler.

ATTACKS

Unarmed   +8   1d3-1 (subdual)

Gear: None.

MAKEPEACE, COLONEL ROBERT (THE BROCA DIVIDE)

Team Commander, SG-3

Duty, honor, commitment – the values that Robert Makepeace holds dear were instilled in him at an early age. With his father a Marine staff sergeant, he grew up surrounded by the ethos of the Corps, and no one was surprised when he chose service to his country as a career. His capacity for leadership was immediately recognized at Annapolis, and he was directed into a key role within his group after basic training. His career almost ended just as it began.

Makepeace's Paris Island drill instructor was a cruel man who reveled in his power over his charges, inflicting punishments bordering on sadism and criminal assault. During Makepeace's rotation, the instructor crossed that border. One of Makepeace's fellow recruits could not complete a lengthy series of exercises on the obstacle course, and the sergeant laid into the exhausted soldier with a near-fatal physical barrage. Makepeace intervened, and may have saved the young recruit's life when he knocked his drill instructor unconscious. The inquiry that followed could have thrown him out of the Marines. Instead it proved his potential value to the Corps, and taught him a lesson he has kept throughout his career: don't be afraid to do what is right.

Progressing quickly through the ranks, Major Makepeace was assigned to a Special Forces groups working behind the lines in Iraq in the weeks leading up to Operation Desert Storm. Primarily providing support and security during meetings with rebel factions within southern Iraq, he helped gather contacts and intel that would later prove vital to combat rescue missions. Though not one to identify with the local population, Makepeace saw that these freedom fighters were desperate for the help the coalition forces promised to give. This made their abandonment after the war a stronger shock than Makepeace

expected. He vowed to never again let political dictates cost lives or jeopardize the safety and security of the United States if he could do anything about it.

Still, a good Marine pushes on, as he did during the conflict in Yugoslavia. Again he distinguished himself on search and rescue missions behind hostile lines. This brought him to the attention of General Hammond during the initial formations of the SG teams. Hammond wanted someone who worked well in a field support capacity, and who shared his conviction of "no one left behind."

Once Makepeace was on board as commander of SG-3, he helped fill out the team roster with a few hand-picked men from his duty tours. Though he sometimes makes fun of the "flyboys" – the Air Force personnel comprising the bulk of the SGC – it's only good-natured inter-branch ribbing. Makepeace long ago gained respect for the pilots who routinely risked being shot down and had to trust to fate to safely return from a bail-out. He has no problem working under the Air Force's command while on this assignment, and would gladly give his own life to save a fellow SG team member. Only one thing bothers him about his current posting: the way Hammond allows the President and other politicians to micromanage certain situations. Seeing the General talking on the red phone in his office reminds Makepeace of the allies he made in the desert once, and how he was forced to abandon them when they needed help the most. He hopes that history does not repeat itself.

LOW-LEVEL ROBERT MAKEPEACE

Specialty: Marine Officer
Rank: Lt. Colonel (O-5)
Class: Soldier
Level: 3

Strength:	15	Dexterity:	13
Constitution:	14	Intelligence:	10
Wisdom:	10	Charisma:	12
Vitality:	35	Wounds:	15

Defense: 12 (+1 class, +1 Dex)
Initiative Bonus: +5 (+3 class, +1 Dex, +1 specialty)
Speed: 30

Fort: +4   Ref: +2   Will: +3

Special Qualities: *Accurate,* damage reduction 1/-.

Skills: Climb +4, Demolitions +6, Intimidate +6/+5, Jump +4, Profession (Military) +2, Spot +3, Survival (Desert) +2, Tumble +2.

Feats: Armor Group Proficiency (Light, Medium, Heavy), Explosives Basics, Perfect Stance, Point Blank Shot, Precise Shot, Promotion, Weapon Group Proficiency (Handgun, Hurled, Melee, Rifle, Tactical).

Backgrounds: Vow (2).

ATTACKS

Unarmed	+5	1d3+2 (subdual)
FN P90	+3	1d10+1 (normal, error 1-2, threat 19-20, range 30 ft., qualities and mods AP, BP, RG)

Gear: SG team bundle, other bundles as needed (by mission).

MID-LEVEL ROBERT MAKEPEACE

Specialty: Marine Officer
Rank: Colonel (O-6)
Class: Soldier
Level: 7

Strength:	15	**Dexterity:**	13
Constitution:	15	**Intelligence:**	10
Wisdom:	10	**Charisma:**	12
Vitality:	67	**Wounds:**	17

Defense: 14 (+3 class, +1 Dex)
Initiative Bonus: +9 (+6 class, +1 Dex, +2 specialty)
Speed: 30

Fort: +6   **Ref:** +3   **Will:** +5

Special Qualities: *Accurate,* armor use +1, damage reduction 1/-, weapon specialization (grenades).

Skills: Balance +5, Bureaucracy +1, Climb +5, Demolitions +7, Intimidate +7/+6, Jump +4, Profession (Military) +3, Spot +5, Survival (Desert) +6, Tumble +2.

Feats: Armor Group Proficiency (Light, Medium, Heavy), Coolness Under Fire, Double Tap, Explosives Basics, Lay Down Fire, Perfect Stance, Point Blank Shot, Precise Shot, Promotion, Weapon Group Proficiency (Handgun, Hurled, Melee, Rifle, Tactical).

Backgrounds: Vow (2).

ATTACKS

Unarmed	+9	1d3+2 (subdual)
FN P90	+7	1d10+1 (normal, error 1-2, threat 19-20, range 30 ft., qualities and mods AP, BP, RG)

Gear: SG team bundle, other bundles as needed (by mission).

HIGH-LEVEL ROBERT MAKEPEACE

Specialty: Marine Officer
Rank: Colonel (O-6)
Class: Soldier
Level: 12

Strength:	15	**Dexterity:**	14
Constitution:	16	**Intelligence:**	10
Wisdom:	10	**Charisma:**	12
Vitality:	123	**Wounds:**	20

Defense: 17 (+5 class, +2 Dex)
Initiative Bonus: +16 (+10 class, +2 Dex, +4 specialty)
Speed: 30

Fort: +10   **Ref:** +9   **Will:** +9

Special Qualities: *Accurate,* armor use +2, damage reduction 2/-, portable cover (¼ cover), weapon specialization (grenades, pistols, SMGs).

Skills: Balance +6, Bureaucracy +3, Climb +6, Concentration +5, Demolitions +9, Intimidate +9/+8, Jump +6, Profession (Military) +5, Spot +7, Survival (Desert) +7, Tumble +5.

Feats: Armor Group Proficiency (Light, Medium, Heavy), Blind-Fight, Career Operative, Coolness Under Fire, Double Tap, Explosives Basics, Lay Down Fire, Lightning Reflexes, Perfect Stance, Point Blank Shot, Promotion, Speed Trigger, Weapon Focus (FN P90), Weapon Group Proficiency (Handgun, Hurled, Melee, Rifle, Tactical).

Backgrounds: Vow (2).

ATTACKS

Unarmed	+14	1d3+2 (subdual)
FN P90	+13	1d10+3 (normal, error 1-2, threat 19-20, range 30 ft., qualities and mods AP, BP, RG)

Gear: SG team bundle, other bundles as needed (by mission).

MAYBOURNE, COLONEL HARRY (ENIGMA)

Pentagon Intelligence Division – Special Operations, NID Operative

Colonel Maybourne is perhaps the deadliest threat to the continued success and operation of the Stargate Command. An intelligence operative recruited in 1974 by the CIA, Harry Maybourne served a short but eventful career in a variety of intelligence and counter-intelligence capacities before accepting special assignment to the Air Force as part of the newly-formed National Intelligence Department (NID). As one of the original founding members of the NID, Maybourne helped craft many of the strategic and operational procedures that the organization still uses today. The broad scope and monitoring authority of the NID has allowed him to keep tabs on a number of intelligence operations throughout the US, including "black bag" missions that appear on no official accounting. Of these operations, the Stargate Command has become one of the most prominent.

At the Pentagon, Major Bert Samuels was eventually promoted outside his role of Pentagon/NID liaison and Stargate Mission Analysis. Colonel Maybourne stepped in to gain more direct access to the SGC's records and research. At this time he is tasked with the responsibility of analyzing and prioritizing the data recovered by the SGC via the Stargate for use in the defense of the nation. However, the NID's lack of oversight and clandestine nature gives him and his fellows extraordinary latitude. Using the facilities found at Area 51 (which store and study the Stargate and new technologies brought back through it), Colonel Maybourne essentially runs his own rogue organization, determined to harness the resources of the Stargate for his own political ends. The real nature of who pulls the strings at the NID – and who exactly Maybourne answers to – remains a mystery to this day.

Maybourne's manner is haughty and self-righteous, eager to take charge of a situation and exert his authority. This has caused no small amount of friction between himself and the officers of the SGC, particularly General Hammond and Colonel O'Neill. Maybourne's ruthlessness and desire for information was best exemplified by his efforts to detain the Tollan fugitives rescued by SG-1 and sequester them indefinitely for purposes of interrogation and research. Alarmingly, the Colonel was able to gain just such permission via his channels at the Pentagon until SG-

1 successfully blocked his maneuver by helping the Tollans escape. He remains a wily opponent and a potential political threat to any SG team.

LOW-LEVEL HARRY MAYBOURNE

Specialty: NID Officer
Class: Pointman
Level: 5

Strength:	10	**Dexterity:**	11
Constitution:	12	**Intelligence:**	13
Wisdom:	13	**Charisma:**	13
Vitality:	46	**Wounds:**	12

Defense: 14 (+2 class, +2 specialty)
Initiative Bonus: +2 (+2 class)
Speed: 30

Fort: +4 **Ref:** +3 **Will:** +6

Special Qualities: Assistance (½), *generous,* lead 2/session, tactics 1/session, versatility (Computers, Cryptography, Electronics, Forgery, Gather Information, Hide, Listen, Search, Surveillance)

Skills: Bluff +5, Bureaucracy +6, Computers +5, Cryptography +4, Diplomacy +4, Electronics +4, First Aid +3, Forgery +3, Gather Information +8, Hide +2, Listen +3, Move Silently +1, Profession (Spycraft) +3, Search +5, Sense Motive +3, Surveillance +8, Survival (Urban) +2.

Feats: Armor Group Proficiency (Light, Medium), Flawless Identity, Political Favors, Traceless, Weapon Group Proficiency (Handgun, Melee, Rifle).

ATTACKS

Unarmed	+3	1d3 (subdual)

Gear: None.

MID-LEVEL HARRY MAYBOURNE

Specialty: NID Officer
Rank: Colonel (O-6)
Class: Pointman/Field Analyst
Level: 6/4

Strength:	10	**Dexterity:**	11
Constitution:	12	**Intelligence:**	13
Wisdom:	13	**Charisma:**	14
Vitality:	84	**Wounds:**	12

Defense: 18 (+5 class, +3 specialty)
Initiative Bonus: +4 (+4 class)
Speed: 30

Fort: +5 **Ref:** +7 **Will:** +7

Special Qualities: Assistance (½), cross-class ability (bonus combat feat), evidence analyst (Analyst, Advanced), *eye for detail,* favor for a favor 1/session, *generous,* lead 2/session, leap of logic 1/session, shutterbug, tactics 1/session, versatility (Computers, Cryptography, Electronics, Forgery, Gather Information, Hide, Listen, Search, Surveillance, 1 skill).

Skills: Bluff +8, Bureaucracy +10, Computers +10, Cryptography +5, Cultures +3, Diplomacy +7, Driver +2, Electronics +4, First Aid +3, Forgery +3, Gather Information +14, Hide +2, Knowledge (Stargate Program) +5, Languages +3, Listen +6, Move Silently +1, Profession (Spycraft) +5, Search +12, Sense Motive +4, Spot +5, Surveillance +12, Survival (Urban) +3.

Feats: Advanced Skill Mastery (Analyst), Alertness, Analyst, Armor Group Proficiency (Light, Medium), Flawless Identity, Mark, Point Blank Shot, Political Favors, Traceless, Weapon Group Proficiency (Handgun, Melee, Rifle).

ATTACKS

Unarmed   +7   1d3 (subdual)

Gear: Surveyor bundle.

HIGH-LEVEL HARRY MAYBOURNE

Specialty: NID Officer
Rank: Colonel (O-6)
Class: Pointman/Field Analyst
Level: 9/6

Strength:	10	**Dexterity:**	11
Constitution:	12	**Intelligence:**	14
Wisdom:	13	**Charisma:**	14
Vitality:	124	**Wounds:**	12

Defense: 23 (+9 class, +4 specialty)
Initiative Bonus: +6 (+6 class)
Speed: 30

Fort: +7   **Ref:** +9   **Will:** +9

Special Qualities: Assistance (½), cross-class ability (bonus combat feat, research (Advanced Skill Mastery (Alertness))), evidence analyst (Analyst, Advanced, Grand), *eye for detail,* favor for a favor 1/session, *generous,* lead 4/session, leap of logic 1/session, shutterbug, tactics 2/session (+2 bonus), versatility (Computers, Cryptography, Electronics, Forgery, Gather Information, Hide, Listen, Search, Surveillance, Survival (Urban), 1 skill).

Skills: Bluff +11, Bureaucracy +12, Computers +16, Cryptography +7, Cultures +6, Diplomacy +9, Driver +2, Electronics +6, First Aid +4, Forgery +4, Gather Information +17, Hide +5, Knowledge (Stargate Program) +10, Languages +6, Listen +10, Move Silently +1, Profession (Spycraft) +9, Search +15, Sense Motive +6, Spot +7, Surveillance +16, Survival (Urban) +6.

Feats: Advanced Skill Mastery (Alertness, Analyst), Alertness, Analyst, Armor Group Proficiency (Light, Medium), Extra Supplies, Extra Support, Flawless Identity, Grand Skill Mastery (Analyst), Mark, Point Blank Shot, Political Favors, Traceless, Weapon Group Proficiency (Handgun, Melee, Rifle), World Traveler.

ATTACKS

Unarmed   +10   1d3 (subdual)

Gear: Surveyor bundle.

NARIM (ENIGMA)

Tollan Scientist

A recent graduate of the Tollan Advanced Science Institute, Narim has garnered a well-deserved reputation as a thoughtful and approachable member of the scientific corps. Specializing in particle physics, he always had a love and wonder of zoology. Since most animals on Tollan died out before his lifetime, Narim spent the majority of his study going through the historical archives. Particle physics (a fairly mundane Tollan field for the most part mastered decades ago), has not kept him particularly engaged or interested despite excelling at it. So when the call went out for new members of the Tollan Expeditionary Forces he vigorously pursued a position – he couldn't resist the chance to travel to other planets and discover strange and exotic life forms.

Narim was assigned to the 22nd Expeditionary Force, under the leadership of Omoc; a highly-respected Tollan scientist and explorer. While many found Omoc's personality abrasive, Narim was able to see him for who he truly was: a patriot and scientist of the highest caliber. The younger scientist's curiosity placed him in trouble on more than one occasion but his knowledge of xenobiology quickly became unparalleled. In short order Omoc appointed Narim as second in command of the 22nd Expeditionary Force.

Narim and the 22nd were not on Tollan at the time of the Sartian explosion that devastated the two worlds. Returning from a neighboring system on an archeological mission, Narim observed his homeworld from space and was moved to tears by the great swaths of destruction he saw. Rivers of lava flowed across the landscape and dark clouds of basaltic ash covered significant portions of the atmosphere, blocking out the sun and turning the blue skies black. Even in this bleak moment, Narim wept for the Sartians and their shortsightedness – a shortsightedness that looked to doom two worlds as one.

His eternal optimism and desire to find the good in people was of paramount importance when Omoc's team was rescued by the people of Earth. There Narim befriended Captain Samantha Carter and helped to persuade Omoc that, like the Sartians, not everyone from Earth should be condemned because of the actions of a select few. Narim left his new friends on Earth with a great sadness but one day hopes to see them again. He has since regularly petitioned the Curia to open diplomatic channels with the Tauri at some point and has even solicited himself as an envoy.

He currently lives in the Palisade Quarters on Tollana with his adopted feline, Schrödinger.

Low-Level Narim

Specialty: Advanced Society Near Human
Class: Scientist
Level: 3

Strength:	10	**Dexterity:**	11
Constitution:	10	**Intelligence:**	14
Wisdom:	12	**Charisma:**	14

Vitality:	16	**Wounds:**	10

Defense: 13 (+3 class)
Initiative Bonus: +1 (+1 class)
Speed: 30

Fort: +1 **Ref:** +1 **Will:** +4

Special Qualities: +1 species bonus to Computers and Electronics, improvise +2, learned, *professor,* PhD (Knowledge (zoology)).

Skills: Bluff +5, Computers +7, Concentration +4, Cryptography +3, Cultures +5, Diplomacy +9, Electronics +8, First Aid +3, Intimidate +3/+5, Knowledge (Xenobiology) +10, Knowledge (Zoology) +9, Listen +4, Mechanics +6, Profession (Expeditionary Forces) +3, Search +5, Sense Motive +6, Spot +4, Survival (Arctic) +3, Xeno-Languages +6.

Feats: Armor Group Proficiency (Light), Charmer, False Start (Knowledge (Zoology), Persuasive, Scholarly, Weapon Group Proficiency (Handgun, Melee).

Attacks

Unarmed	+4	1d3 (subdual)

Gear: Tollan recall device, phase device, survival gear.

Mid-Level Narim

Specialty: Advanced Society Near Human
Class: Scientist
Level: 8

Strength:	10	**Dexterity:**	11
Constitution:	11	**Intelligence:**	16
Wisdom:	12	**Charisma:**	14

Vitality:	43	**Wounds:**	11

Defense: 16 (+6 class)
Initiative Bonus: +3 (+3 class)
Speed: 30

Fort: +2 **Ref:** +2 **Will:** +7

Special Qualities: +3 species bonus to Computers and Electronics, brilliant +1, improvise +4, learned, *professor,* PhD (Knowledge (zoology)), research (Grease Monkey, versatility (Bluff, Intimidate)).

Skills: Bluff +6, Computers +17, Concentration +7, Cryptography +8, Cultures +6, Diplomacy +12, Electronics +15, First Aid +5, Intimidate +4/+6, Knowledge (Xenobiology) +15, Knowledge (Zoology) +19, Listen +6, Mechanics +10, Profession (Expeditionary Forces) +5, Search +8, Sense Motive +7, Spot +6, Survival (Arctic) +5, Xeno-Languages +8.

Feats: Armor Group Proficiency (Light), Charmer, False Start (Knowledge (Zoology), Grease Monkey, Mathematical Genius, Persuasive, Scholarly, Weapon Group Proficiency (Handgun, Melee).

Attacks

Unarmed	+4	1d3 (subdual)

Gear: Tollan recall device, phase device, survival gear.

High-Level Narim

Specialty: Advanced Society Near Human
Class: Scientist
Level: 13

Strength:	10	**Dexterity:**	11
Constitution:	12	**Intelligence:**	18
Wisdom:	12	**Charisma:**	14

Vitality:	81	**Wounds:**	12

Defense: 20 (+10 class)
Initiative Bonus: +5 (+5 class)
Speed: 30

Fort: +5 **Ref:** +4 **Will:** +9

Special Qualities: +4 species bonus to Computers and Electronics, brilliant +3, improvise +7, know it all 1/mission, learned, *professor,* PhD (Knowledge (Xenobiology), Knowledge (Zoology)), research (Alertness, Grease Monkey, versatility (Bluff, Intimidate)).

Skills: Bluff +7, Computers +23, Concentration +13, Cryptography +13, Cultures +7, Diplomacy +14, Electronics +22, First Aid +7, Intimidate +5/+7, Knowledge (Xenobiology) +25, Knowledge (Zoology) +25, Listen +11, Mechanics +13, Profession (Expeditionary Forces) +9, Search +13, Sense Motive +11, Spot +11, Survival (Arctic) +7, Xeno-Languages +13.

Feats: Advanced Technology, Alertness, Armor Group Proficiency (Light), Charmer, False Start (Computers, Knowledge (Zoology), Grease Monkey, Mathematical Genius, Persuasive, Scholarly, Weapon Group Proficiency (Handgun, Melee).

ATTACKS

Unarmed	+6	1d3 (subdual)

Gear: Tollan recall device, phase device, survival gear.

SUPPORTING NPCS

Supporting NPCs are those whose presence on the show was limited (usually appearing only in a single episode or two), those who were killed during Season One, and new NPCs created specifically for this sourcebook. Each includes a single set of statistics.

ABU (EMANCIPATION)

Chieftain's Son

Abu is the son of Moughal, chieftain of the Shavadai. Though not highly skilled as a warrior, he serves his people as needed nonetheless. Among his more significant contributions to the Shavadai is the brewing of medicines such as anesthetics and healing salves. Abu recently married Nya, the daughter of Turghan, chieftain of the Toughai, and he hopes that the union can forge more permanent ties between their peoples.

ABU

Specialty: Primitive Society
Rank: N/A
Class: Native Off-Worlder
Level: 5

Strength:	12	Dexterity:	13
Constitution:	11	Intelligence:	12
Wisdom:	12	Charisma:	13
Vitality:	20	Wounds:	11

Defense: 13 (+2 class, +1 Dex)
Initiative Bonus: +3 (+2 class, +1 Dex)
Speed: 30

Fort: +4	Ref: +4	Will: +4

Special Qualities: Primitive

Skills: Climb +4, Craft (Medicine) +9, Craft (Pottery) +7, First Aid + 4, Handle Animal +4, Search +6, Spot +6, Survival (Forest) +6.

Feats: Advanced Skill Mastery (Ordinary Past), Armor Group Proficiency (Light), Ordinary Past, Weapon Group Proficiency (Hurled, Melee).

ATTACKS

Unarmed	+4	1d3+1 (subdual)
Dagger	+4	1d4 (error 1, threat 20)

Gear: First Aid Kit (2 doses each of anesthetic and healing salve, *see Simarkan Medicines, page 152).*

ALEKOS (BRIEF CANDLE)

Argosian Explorer

Alekos was the first Argosian to meet SG-1 when they first arrived, and one of several who have since left the confines of the village to explore their world. He currently travels with a group of five others and has gone on four different journeys, each extending farther than the last. On his most current trip, Alekos and his companions discovered the cave and doorway that leads to Pelops' lab *(see page 27)*. They were unable to open it, however, and he plans to contact the SGC to tell them of this discovery upon their return to the village. Alekos is married to Thetys, and the two have a young son named Danel (named after Daniel Jackson, who helped deliver the baby).

ALEKOS

Specialty: Primitive Society
Rank: N/A
Class: Native Off-Worlder
Level: 2

Strength:	12	Dexterity:	11
Constitution:	11	Intelligence:	13
Wisdom:	12	Charisma:	13
Vitality:	9	Wounds:	11

Defense: 12 (+1 class, +1 Dex)
Initiative Bonus: +2 (+1 class +1 Dex)
Speed: 30

Fort: +3	Ref: +2	Will: +3

Special Qualities: Primitive

Skills: Climb +2, Craft (Farming) +5, First Aid +2, Listen +3, Profession (Hunting) +4, Search +3, Spot +2, Survival (Forest) +3.

Feats: Ordinary Past.

ATTACKS

Unarmed	+2	1d3+1 (subdual)

Gear: Rope (50 ft. coil).

AMAUNET (CHILDREN OF THE GODS)

Consort of Apophis

Amaunet is the consort of Apophis, a newly-matured queen who has just taken her first host. Apophis went to great lengths to find a proper body for her; she finally settled on the form of the Abydonian girl, Sha're. In the short time they have been together, she and the Serpent God have made ambitious plans; some say they even care for each other. She enjoys her role as near-equal of a powerful System Lord, although some wonder if perhaps she wishes to be more.

AMAUNET

Specialty: Goa'uld Queen
Rank: N/A
Class: Diplomat
Level: 7

Strength:	12	**Dexterity:**	10
Constitution:	14	**Intelligence:**	14
Wisdom:	15	**Charisma:**	17

Vitality:	41	**Wounds:**	14

Defense: 14 (+4 class)
Initiative Bonus: +3 (+3 class)
Speed: 30

Fort: +4   **Ref:** +2   **Will:** +7

Special Qualities: Bluff and Innuendo threat range +2, dominated body, immunity to disease, inherited memory, long life, parasite, produce larva, radiation resistance.

Skills: Bluff +12, Bureaucracy +7, Concentration +4, Cultures +6, Diplomacy +12, Gather Information +7, Innuendo +6, Intimidate +7/+9, Languages +6, Listen +5, Profession (Diplomat) +6, Sense Motive +9, Spot +3, Survival (Desert) +7.

Feats: Armor Group Proficiency (Light), Charmer, Mark, Naquadah Sense, Persuasive, Weapon Group Proficiency (Handgun).

Backgrounds: Lost Love (Daniel Jackson) 4.

ATTACKS

Unarmed	+6	1d3 (subdual)
Kinetic Blast	+5	2d6 and 2d6 (subdual) Psychic Blast Targets within 50 feet must make a Willpower save (DC 20) or be stunned for 2d10 minutes

Gear: Luxurious robes of office, kara kesh.

ANHUR (CHILDREN OF THE GODS)

Goa'uld Underlord

Anhur is one of the mightiest Goa'uld on Chulak who is not a System Lord. His past service to Ra is well known, which is why he has become a rallying figure for those who oppose Apophis, even those who had little love for the now-deceased Sun God. Anhur has accepted this role with good grace, primarily because he feels he has no choice – he must do whatever it takes to avenge the death of his master, whose demise he blames himself for. Anhur is an unusually noble and tragic Goa'uld. He exhibits a strange kind of honor and his loyalty to his destroyed lord is unusual for his kind. Nevertheless, he remains a Goa'uld warmaster, which makes him an implacable enemy of the Tauri.

ANHUR

Specialty: Goa'uld Warmaster
Rank: N/A
Class: Soldier/Pointman/Officer
Level: 6/4/5

Strength:	16	**Dexterity:**	12
Constitution:	15	**Intelligence:**	18
Wisdom:	17	**Charisma:**	15

Vitality:	138	**Wounds:**	15

Defense: 17 (+6 class, +1 Dex)
Initiative Bonus: +11 (+10 class, +1 Dex)
Speed: 30

Fort: +10   **Ref:** +8   **Will:** +16

Special Qualities: +4 to damage, *accurate*, armor use +1, assistance (½), blood of heroes +8, damage reduction 1/–, dominated body, *encouragement*, field logistics, gallantry, immunity to disease, inherited memory, lead 1/session, lead the charge (damage), long life, parasite, radiation resistance, tactics 4/session (+3 bonus), versatility (Listen, 6 skills), weapon specialization (zat'nik'tel).

Skills: Balance +7, Bluff +12, Bureaucracy +6, Climb +9, Concentration +12, Cultures +12, Demolitions +6, Diplomacy +12, Driver +9, Gather Information +12, Innuendo +12, Intimidate +18/+17, Jump +7, Knowledge (Goa'uld) +13, Knowledge (Military Tactics) +16, Listen +15, Pilot +6, Profession (Military) +15, Search +7, Sense Motive +12, Spot +14, Survival (Desert) +10.

Feats: Alertness, Armor Group Proficiency (Light, Medium, Heavy), Coolness Under Fire, Command Decision, Mark, Persuasive, Point Blank Shot, Precise Shot, Surge of Speed, Toughness, Weapon Group Proficiency (Hurled, Melee, Handgun, Rifle, Tactical), Zat Resistance, Zen Focus.

Backgrounds: Dishonored 3, Vow (Avenge Ra's Death) 4.

ATTACKS

Unarmed	+15	1d3+9 (subdual)
Kinetic Blast	+13	2d6+6 normal and 2d6+6 subdual
Psychic Blast		Targets within 50 feet must make a Willpower save (DC 20) or be stunned for 2d10 minutes
Zat'nik'tel	+13	3d6+6

Gear: Kara kesh, zat'nik'tel, robes of office.

ANTEAUS (THE NOX)

Nox

Anteaus is Lya's husband and Nafrayu's father. He is 365 years old and just barely beginning to show signs of aging. During his time traveling the galaxy, Anteaus searched for relics and history related to the Nox's role in the Heliopolis alliance, hoping to learn and understand how the alliance was formed and why it ultimately failed. He remains passionate about protecting his family and the ways of the Nox from outside influence.

ANTEAUS

Specialty: Nox
Rank: N/A
Class: Scout/Nox Wanderer/Explorer
Level: 5/8/4

Strength:	12	**Dexterity:**	11
Constitution:	14	**Intelligence:**	17
Wisdom:	16	**Charisma:**	16
Vitality:	109	**Wounds:**	14

Defense: 21 (+9 class, +2 rough living)
Initiative Bonus: +10 (+10 class)
Speed: 30

Fort: +12   **Ref:** +10   **Will:** +15

Special Qualities: +6 to Intelligence checks, all over the world, bookworm (½), bushmaster (mountain training, side-step), direction sense +3, long life, rough living +2, stalker, total pacifist, *trailblazer,* uncanny dodge (Dex bonus).

Skills: Balance +9, Climb +10, Concentration +12, Cultures +12, First Aid +20, Handle Animal +21, Hide +16, Jump +7, Knowledge (Heliopolis Alliance) +14, Knowledge (Stargate Physics) +13, Listen +17, Move Silently +12, Search +14, Sense Motive +8, Spot +16, Survival (Forest) +20, Survival (Mountain) +16, Swim +6, Xeno-Languages +13.

Feats: Absorb Languages, Advanced Skill Mastery (Outdoorsman), Cloaking, Cloak Objects, Cloak Others, False Start (Outdoorsman), Forest Training, Mountain Training, Outdoorsman, Read Surface Thoughts, Surge of Speed, Ritual of Life, Run, Shifting, Shift Objects, Shift Others, Sidestep, Track, World Traveler.

ATTACKS

None.

Gear: Robes.

ASHIKAGA (EMANCIPATION)

Warlord of Kyoto

Ashikaga is the Goa'uld warlord of Kyoto and second in power only to Raiden. For the time being he is content to serve Raiden loyally, but like nearly all Goa'uld, he has a lust for power and plans for the day when he will strike against Raiden and claim his master's throne.

ASHIKAGA

Specialty: Goa'uld Warmaster
Rank: N/A
Class: Guardian
Level: 5

Strength:	18	**Dexterity:**	15
Constitution:	17	**Intelligence:**	12
Wisdom:	11	**Charisma:**	14
Vitality:	55	**Wounds:**	17

Defense: 15 (+3 class, +2 Dex)
Initiative Bonus: +4 (+2 class, +2 Dex)
Speed: 30

Fort: +7   **Ref:** +3   **Will:** +4

Special Qualities: Accelerated healing, dominated body, enforcer (basic), immunity to disease, inherited memory, long life, parasite, radiation resistance, soak 1/session, *unbreakable.*

Skills: Balance +8, Climb +10, Concentration +6, Escape Artist +8, Hide +8, Intimidate +10/8, Jump +6, Pilot +8, Spot +3, Survival (Forest) +6.

Feats: Armor Group Proficiency (Light, Medium, Heavy), Blood Thirsty, Enforcer, Naquadah Sense, Stone Cold, Surge of Speed, Toughness, Weapon Group Proficiency (Handgun, Hurled, Melee, Rifle, Tactical).

ATTACKS

Unarmed	+9	1d3+6 (subdual)
Kinetic Blast	+7	2d6+2normal,
		2d6 +2 subdual

Gear: Kara kesh.

BELUS (FIRE AND WATER)

Goa'uld Underlord

Belus' history among the Goa'uld is largely uneventful before his invasion of the Ohnes' home world. Until that time, he enjoyed moderate success in battle, serving under the supreme System Lord Ra. He was responsible for a small domain within Ra's kingdom, acting more or less autonomously since his activities had few and minor consequences.

But when Belus located and invaded the Ohnes' home world, his fortune turned. What began as a successful attack yielding thousands of new slaves ended in disaster when the Ohnes turned against him, forcing him to abandon and destroy his vessel. Beyond the loss of his ship and the hundreds of Jaffa on board, Belus also had to return to his home world in disgrace, having been defeated by mere slaves. Then, after the Ohnes learned of Belus' atrocity, they launched a string of attacks against him, destroying most of his fleet and killing more than half of his forces.

This failure prompted Ra to send Belus to Earth to oversee the occupation of Babylon. It was considered a fairly ignominious duty – fitting punishment for his failure – and even there, the Ohnes pursued him. A small team of freedom fighters led by Omoroca arrived within a few years, intent on driving the Goa'uld from the Earth. Their efforts ultimately failed when the Goa'uld killed Omoroca and captured Kel (another freedom fighter), but they inspired the people to fight back. Belus found himself on the verge of defeat again. He ordered his Jaffa to round up what slaves they could and, taking Kel as personal trophy, transported the captured humans to another world that he named Akkad, for the fledgling civilization on Earth.

Upon Belus' return to Goa'uld space, Ra punished him for his continued failings, sentencing him to service under Ishtar, one of Ra's underlings. Ishtar put Akkad under the control of a Goa'uld named Sargon, but allowed Belus to return to his former stronghold, home to a productive naquadah mine.

Within weeks, Kel made another attempt to kill Belus, hoping to gain his freedom and avenge the deaths of his fellow Ohnes. Kel's attempt severely damaged Belus' host, but failed to kill the Goa'uld symbiote. He chose to take Kel as a new host rather than kill him, making the former freedom fighter forever the prisoner of the Ohnes' most hated enemy.

Ra's death presented a new opportunity for Belus, but like so many before it, it ended in failure. With the exception of minor and occasional missions for Ishtar, he has remained confined to his stronghold, a broken Goa'uld, with his only pleasure coming from the knowledge that his Ohnes host has suffered along with him. Ishtar has allowed him to oversee one of his naquadah mines, an operation Belus finds tedious in the extreme but which keeps him too occupied to plot new mischief.

Belus still harbors a strong grudge against the Ohnes, whom he believes are responsible for his current fate. His Jaffa have standing orders to attack on sight and to bring any Ohnes prisoners to him for slow and leisurely torture.

BELUS

Specialty: Goa'uld Noble (Ohnes Host)
Rank: N/A
Class: Explorer
Level: 6

Strength:	16	**Dexterity:**	15
Constitution:	16	**Intelligence:**	14
Wisdom:	11	**Charisma:**	16
Vitality:	55	**Wounds:**	16

Defense: 16 (+4 class, +2 Dex)
Initiative Bonus: +7 (+5 class, +2 Dex)
Speed: 30

Fort: +6	**Ref:** +7	**Will:** +3

Special Qualities: All over the world (advanced), amphibious, bookworm (½) dehydration, direction sense +3, dominated body, immunity to disease, inherited memory, long life, *obsessive*, parasite, radiation resistance, uncanny dodge (Dex Bonus).

Skills: Bluff +9, Cryptography +8, Cultures +6, Diplomacy +6, First Aid +6, Gather Information +11, Innuendo +4, Intimidate +6/+6, Knowledge (Goa'uld) +8, Knowledge (Ohnes) +6, Languages +8, Listen +6, Open Locks +6, Search +8, Spot +6, Swim +9.

Feats: Advanced Skill Master (World Traveler), Armor Group Proficiency (Light), Communicate, Desert Training, Goa'uld Sense, Naquadah Sense, Persuasive, Psychic Blast, Stone Cold, Surge of Speed, Weapon Group Proficiency (Handgun, Melee), World Traveler.

Backgrounds: Defeated (Ohnes) 1, Hunted (Ohnes) 3, Vendetta (Ohnes) 3.

ATTACKS

Unarmed	+7	1d3+3 (subdual)
Kinetic Blast	+6	2d6normal, 2d6 subdual
Psychic Blast		Targets within 50 feet must make a Willpower save (DC 20) or be stunned for 2d10 minutes.

Gear: Kara kesh, hydrator.

CASSANDRA (SINGULARITY)

Hankan Girl

Cassandra was born to live the life of a guinea pig. Nirrti created her people through genetic engineering in the hopes of finding the perfect host for the Goa'uld. She introduced a retro-virus into Cassandra that will one day blossom into psychokinetic powers, and used the girl as a "Trojan horse" to destroy the SGC with a special miniature naquadah bomb implanted into her chest. Fortunately, the people of the SGC do not view life as expendable. SG-1 took Cassandra to Earth from her home on Hanka, where they were able to neutralize the bomb within her.

Before coming to Earth, Cassandra was a normal peasant girl, albeit a fairly clever and perceptive one. The death of her people traumatized her greatly, but she has recovered quite well under the auspices of the SGC, displaying a sense of playfulness typical for girls her age. She is currently under the care of Dr. Fraiser, who plans on adopting her as her own.

CASSANDRA

Specialty: Primitive Society Near Human
Rank: None
Class: Explorer
Level: 1

Strength:	8	Dexterity:	12
Constitution:	13	Intelligence:	12
Wisdom:	11	Charisma:	13
Vitality:	11	Wounds:	13

Defense: 12 (+1 class, +1 Dex)
Initiative Bonus: +2 (+1 class, +1 Dex)
Speed: 30

Fort: +2   **Ref:** +3   **Will:** +1

Special Qualities: All over the world, direction sense +2, *obsessive.*

Skills: Balance +4, Climb +1, Cultures +3, First Aid +3, Handle Animal +3, Hide +3, Jump +2, Languages +3, Listen +2, Move Silently +4, Search +3, Spot +3, Survival (Mountain) +4, Swim +1.

Feats: Armor Group Proficiency (Light), Forest Training, Naquadah Sense, Weapon Group Proficiency (Hurled, Melee), World Traveler.

ATTACKS

Unarmed	–1	1d3–1 (subdual)

Gear: None.

CONNER, LT. MICHAEL (THE FIRST COMMANDMENT)

Team Member, SG-9

Michael Conner is a young Air Force officer whose career began with great promise. Almost immediately upon graduation from the academy, he was singled out for special duties, including several tours as an attaché for staff officers. His superiors had marked him as someone destined to join their ranks one day. Conner appreciated their confidence in him, but was keenly aware that some of his former classmates considered him a pencil-pushing bureaucrat rather than a "real officer." So he pushed himself even harder and honed his piloting and combat skills. He never wanted to fall behind "where he should be" simply because he spent most of his time in the Pentagon rather than out in the field. When the opportunity to join the SGC arose, Conner seized it with gusto. He saw it as the perfect chance to prove himself. Unfortunately, his tour with SG-9 ended disastrously when his commanding officer attempted to impersonate a god *(see The First Commandment, page 21).* In the aftermath of Captain Hanson's death, Conner is still trying to come to grips with what happened. He is serving detached duty with the SGC as a way to atone for his inability to stop Hanson. One day, he hopes to find peace.

MICHAEL CONNER

Specialty: Air Force Officer
Rank: Lieutenant
Class: Pointman
Level: 4

Strength:	15	Dexterity:	12
Constitution:	14	Intelligence:	15
Wisdom:	12	Charisma:	13
Vitality:	36	Wounds:	14

Defense: 13 (+2 class, +1 Dex)
Initiative Bonus: +3 (+2 class, +1 Dex)
Speed: 30
Fort: +4   **Ref:** +3   **Will:** +5

Special Qualities: Assistance (½), generous, lead 1/session, tactics 1/session, versatility (Computers, Concentration, Hide, Languages, Listen, Move Silently, Spot, Survival).

Skills: Bureaucracy +8, Computers +4, Concentration +5, Diplomacy +8, Hide +6, Languages +3, Listen +4, Move Silently +5, Pilot +6, Profession (Military) +5, Sense Motive +6, Spot +4, Survival (Mountain) +5.

Feats: Armor Group Proficiency (Light, Medium), Fortunate, Political Favors, Stealthy, Weapon Group Proficiency (Handgun, Melee, Rifle).

Backgrounds: Dishonored 1, Vow 1.

ATTACKS

Unarmed	+5	1d3+2 (subdual)
FN P90	+3	1d10+1 (normal, error 1-2, threat 19-20, range 30 ft., qualities and mods AP, BP, RG)

Gear: SG team bundle, other bundles as needed (by mission).

DREY'AUC (BLOODLINES)

Jaffa Outcast

Drey'auc is Teal'c's estranged wife, outcast from the Jaffa when her husband betrayed Apophis. From a farm on the Cord'ai Plains, Drey'auc's strength and beauty led her to a position she hardly dared dream of – until her husband's treachery cost her and their son everything. The only girl in several generations of her humble family to pass the tests and be judged worthy of a Prim'ta, she was often chosen to present her community's harvest tribute to the temple. On one of these trips, she caught the eye of the rising warrior Teal'c. With plans for a mighty new generation of Jaffa, the god Apophis himself blessed their union. It would be several anxious years, during which time Teal'c was named First Prime, before Rya'c's birth fulfilled that promise. The boy was strong and hearty, promising to surpass even his father as a Jaffa.

Then came Teal'c betrayal. In an instant, her husband was gone, declared shol'va by Apophis. Drey'auc found herself among society's outcasts, scorned and reviled by all. It was all she could do just to survive. Now, ten years after the birth of her son, she has far less than when she began, and must use all her wits just to feed her growing boy. But he is growing, strengthened by her devotion to him and by the very symbiote his father once carried (*see Bloodlines, page 42.* When Teal'c returned, she began to understand why he did what he did, and her anger towards him has slowly cooled. She has even begun to consider his words – that Apophis is not a god – and strangely, that has provided a new source of strength. It will not be long before her little boy becomes a mighty warrior, and takes his place at Teal'c's side to free his people. The dream seems far away at times, but for outcasts such as her, it is more than enough.

DREY'AUC

Specialty: Jaffa Priest
Rank: N/A
Class: Goa'uld Clergy
Level: 3

Strength:	8	Dexterity:	13
Constitution:	12	Intelligence:	10
Wisdom:	11	Charisma:	14

Vitality:	16	Wounds:	12

Defense: 14 (+3 class, +1 Dex)
Initiative Bonus: +3 (+2 class, +1 Dex)
Speed: 30

Fort: +3	Ref: +2	Will: +2

Special Qualities: Radiation resistance.

Skills: Bluff +4, Concentration +4, Craft (Sewing) +6, First Aid +2, Listen +2, Intimidate +0/+3, Knowledge (Goa'uld) +1, Listen +1, Mechanics +1, Profession (Farming) +3, Sense Motive +4, Spot +2, Survival (Forest) +2.

Feats: Armor Group Proficiency (Light, Medium), Symbiote (Immunity to Disease, Long Life), Weapon Group Proficiency (Hurled, Melee).

ATTACKS

Unarmed	+1	1d3-1 subdual

Gear: Robes.

GAIRWYN (THOR'S HAMMER)

Cimmerian Woman

Gairwyn lives in the village closest to the Stargate on Cimmeria, where she and her husband serve as both warriors and leaders. Wise and knowledgeable in the history of her people and of the gods who protect them, Gairwyn is among the first called when travelers arrive through "the portal" (the Stargate). Though visitors to Cimmeria are rare, she welcomes all who come to her world, expecting that anyone wise enough to use "the portal" must be either gods or akin to gods, and thus worthy of her respect. Though initially friendly to strangers, Gairwyn can be a fierce enemy, willing to die fighting in defense of her world and her people. To those who earn her trust however, Gairwyn is a loyal and helpful friend, often going out of her way to help those she cares for.

Gairwyn would welcome the return of SG-1 or other teams from the SGC, both as a means of gaining new friends, but also as a way to help her new allies in their struggle against the Goa'uld.

GAIRWYN

Specialty: Primitive Society Near Human
Rank: N/A
Class: Native Off-Worlder
Level: 3

Strength:	10	Dexterity:	11
Constitution:	12	Intelligence:	11
Wisdom:	13	Charisma:	12

Vitality:	16	Wounds:	12

Defense: 11 (+1 class)
Initiative Bonus: +1 (+1 class)
Speed: 30

Fort: +4   **Ref:** +2   **Will:** +3

Special Qualities: Primitive.

Skills: Climb +2, Craft (Hut Construction) +5, Diplomacy +3, Handle Animals +3, Listen +4, Profession (Village Mistress) +5, Search +3, Survival (Forest) +4.

Feats: Armor Group Proficiency (Light), Ordinary Past, Weapon Group Proficiency (Melee, Hurled).

ATTACKS

Unarmed	+2	1d3 (subdual)

Gear: Robes.

HANNO (COR-AI)

Byrsa Villager

Long before he led the *Cor-ai* to decide the fate of his father's killer, Hanno distinguished himself among the Byrsa as a young man of great intelligence and promise. He began life with an exceptional role model in his father Himilco, who never allowed himself to be hindered by the loss of his leg to a Jaffa staff weapon, and who was highly respected for his clear thinking and dedication to the good of the whole community.

After Himilco's death at the hands of another Jaffa, eleven-year-old Hanno threw himself into his schooling, all the more determined to honor his father's memory and one day serve as a great Elder. The Byrsa value reason over emotion, but emotion is still acknowledged as human nature, and Hanno's unchildlike stoicism following the tragedy worried his mother and clan. As he grew to manhood, he gave acceptable attention to his apprenticeship in carpentry, but more to gaining proficiency with the kest, the slingshot-shaped crossbow that is the Byrsa's primary weapon. He volunteered as often as possible to remain in the village as a guardian during Goa'uld raids, driven to protect his people as best he could.

When Teal'c returned to Cartago with SG-1, Hanno thought that justice would be served at last. Instead, the testimony of Teal'c's companions – and the Jaffa's own actions – showed him a better way to honor Himilco's memory. He spared Teal'c and gained a valuable ally in the

process. The grieving child he had held inside for so long finally released, Hanno has since become a primary liaison between the Byrsa and the SGC, learning new ways of defending against the Goa'uld and teaching them to others.

HANNO

Specialty: Primitive Society Near Human
Rank: N/A
Class: Scout
Level: 4

Strength:	12	Dexterity:	14
Constitution:	12	Intelligence:	11
Wisdom:	15	Charisma:	13

Vitality:	36	Wounds:	12

Defense: 16 (+2 class, + 2 Dex, +2 natural armor)
Initiative Bonus: +9 (+3 class, +2 Dex, +4 feat bonus)
Speed: 30

Fort: +5   **Ref:** +4   **Will:** +3

Special Qualities: Bushmaster (Forest Training), rough living +2, sneak attack +1d6, stalker, *trailblazer*, vulnerability (extreme cold).

Skills: Balance +5, Climb +4, Concentration +4, First Aid +6, Handle Animal +4, Hide +10, Jump +6, Listen +7, Move Silently +10, Search +4, Spot +7, Survival (Forest) +8, Swim +4.

Feats: Alertness, Armor Group Proficiency (Light, Medium, Heavy), Forest Training, Improved Initiative, Outdoorsman, Stealthy, Weapon Group Proficiency (Handgun, Hurled, Melee, Rifle).

Backgrounds: Byrsa Mandates (3).

ATTACKS

Unarmed	+4	1d3+1 (subdual)
Kest	+4	1d8+1 (normal, error 1-2, threat 20, range 60 ft.)
Staff weapon	+3	6d6 (normal, error 1-2, threat 18-20, range 75 ft., qualities and mods AP, AK)

Gear: Staff weapon, kest.

HANSON, CAPTAIN JONAS (THE FIRST COMMANDMENT)

Leader, SG-9 (deceased)

Jonas Hanson commanded SG-9 during their ill-fated visit to P3X-513. He attempted to impersonate a god, and was subsequently slain by the angered populace when they learned of his duplicity. *More details on him and his death can be found in on page 21.*

JONAS HANSON

Specialty: Air Force Officer
Rank: Captain (O-3)
Class: Soldier
Level: 5

Strength:	12	Dexterity:	15
Constitution:	14	Intelligence:	12
Wisdom:	10	Charisma:	11
Vitality:	57	Wounds:	14

Defense: 14 (+2 class, +2 Dex)
Initiative Bonus: +6 (+4 class, +2 Dex)
Speed: 30

Fort: +5   **Ref:** +3   **Will:** +4

Special Qualities: *Accurate,* armor use +1, damage reduction 1/-.

Skills: Balance +5, Bluff +8, Climb +3, Demolitions +4, Diplomacy +6, Driver +5, First Aid +3, Intimidate +6/+7, Pilot +4, Profession (Military) +3, Spot +4, Survival (Forest) +3.

Feats: Armor Group Proficiency (Light, Medium, Heavy), Coolness Under Fire, Glint of Madness, Point Blank Shot, Stone Cold, Weapon Focus (SMGs), Weapon Group Proficiency (Handgun, Hurled, Melee, Rifle, Tactical).

ATTACKS

Unarmed	+6	1d3+1 (subdual)
FN P90	+6	1d10+3 (normal, error 1-2, threat 19-20, range 30 ft., qualities and mods AP, BP, RG)

Gear: SG team bundle, other bundles as needed (by mission).

HARLAN (TIN MAN)

Android

When the members of SG-1 arrived on Altair, a single sentient being was present to greet them and explain the situation. Harlan, a unique and eccentric android, maintained all of the systems in the underground facility left behind by the Altairans. Much to the surprise of SG-1, he was also capable of operating the machinery left behind by the other Altairan engineers and copied the visitors' minds into android bodies. The well-meaning machine only wanted companionship and assistance running the facility, and had

no ill intentions – even though SG-1 (and Colonel O'Neill in particular) criticized his decision to duplicate them.

Harlan appears to be an older human male in his fifties or sixties, actually an android replica of his former physical body. A round man with sparse white hair on his head and an inquisitive nature, he has an irritating tendency to talk around a subject without ever getting to the point, but he is friendly and naturally willing to assist any who seek his help. Having been abandoned on Altair for thousands of years, he still suffers from the effects of the isolation, and has difficulty communicating ideas clearly or understanding the feelings and motivations of others.

Though Harlan often speaks of his comrades and allies (all gone from the world for thousands of years) he is very focused on the present and is primarily concerned with the preservation and operation of the underground facility of Altair. Visitors arriving after Harlan's encounter with the Tauri will find him friendly and eager to explain his people's history. Unfortunately for scientists and explorers from Earth, his understanding of the engineering that made the facility possible is limited and as a result he can only explain how he operates the various machines, not how they were constructed.

HARLAN

Specialty: Advanced Society Near Human (Android)
Class: Scientist
Level: 7

Strength:	16	Dexterity:	10
Constitution:	17	Intelligence:	21
Wisdom:	10	Charisma:	12
Vitality:	59	Wounds:	11

Defense: 15 (+5 class)
Initiative Bonus: +3 (+3 class)
Speed: 40

Fort: +4   **Ref:** +2   **Will:** +5

Special Qualities: +2 species bonus to Computers and Knowledge (Androids), brilliant +1, improvise +4, learned, limited range, *professor,* PhD (Knowledge (Androids)), research (Mathematical Genius), robot.

Skills: Computers +18, Concentration +3, Craft (Android Building) +16, Cryptography +9, Diplomacy +3, Electronics +15, First Aid +5, Forgery +11, Hobby (Tinkering) +12, Knowledge (Androids) +27, Knowledge (Biochemistry) +9, Knowledge (Cybernetics) +18, Knowledge (Physics) +18, Listen +2, Mechanics +13, Profession (Android Maker) +12, Surveillance +4, Xeno-Languages +9.

Feats: Advanced Skill Mastery (Mathematical Genius, Scholarly), Android Hacker, Armor Group Proficiency (Light), Mathematical Genius, Ordinary Past, Scholarly, Weapon Group Proficiency (Melee, Handgun).

ATTACKS

Unarmed	+3	1d3 (subdual)

Gear: None.

HATHOR (HATHOR)
Goa'uld Queen

An ancient Goa'uld who took on the identity of the goddess of love (as well as fertility, inebriety and music), Hathor's personal history with Stargate Command makes her one of Earth's most tenacious foes. When the pyramid which contained her resting place was finally discovered in 1998, she immediately killed the archaeologists who awakened her. Using Goa'uld technology to locate the nearest source of concentrated naquadah, she trekked more than 1,000 miles to Cheyenne Mountain, where she infiltrated the SGC and attempted to seize control of the base. Her pheromones turned the male SGC members into her willing thralls, forming the basis of what she hoped would become a grand army.

Fortunately, Captain Carter and Captain Fraiser were able to rally the base's women and defeat the ascendant Goa'uld. The men were freed and Hathor's larval brood destroyed. However, Hathor herself managed to escape the SGC to an unknown planet through the Stargate. Her present whereabouts are unknown.

More on Hathor can be found on page 52 and in the upcoming System Lords sourcebook.

HATHOR

Specialty: Goa'uld Queen
Rank: N/A
Class: Pointman/Scientist
Level: 15/2

Strength:	12	Dexterity:	15
Constitution:	14	Intelligence:	16
Wisdom:	15	Charisma:	20

Vitality:	138	Wounds:	14

Defense: 20 (+8 class, +2 Dex)
Initiative Bonus: +9 (+7 class, +2 Dex)
Speed: 30

Fort: +9	Ref: +9	Will: +14

Special Qualities: Assistance (½), bluff & innuendo threat range +4, cross-class abilities (accelerated healing, all around the world, damage reduction 1/-, sneak attack +1d6), dominated body, *generous,* immunity to disease, inherited memory, lead 7/session, learned, long life, parasite, radiation resistance, PhD. (Knowledge (Biochemistry)), serendipity, strategy 1/session, tactics 3/session (+3 bonus), versatility (Cultures, Gather Information, Innuendo, Intimidate, Languages, Listen, Perform, Search, Spot, Xeno-Cultures, Xeno-Languages).

Skills: Appraise +5, Bluff +17, Bureaucracy +8, Computers +5, Concentration +6, Cultures +16, Diplomacy +28, Electronics +4, First Aid +10, Gather Information +17, Innuendo +19, Intimidate +17/+21, Knowledge (Biochemistry) +17, Knowledge (Pheromones) +19, Languages +11, Listen +9, Perform (Dancing) +17, Search +8, Sense Motive +18, Spot +9, Xeno-Cultures +18, Xeno-Languages +15.

Feats: Advanced Skill Mastery (Persuasive), Advanced Technology, Armor Group Proficiency (Light, Medium), Charmer, The Look, Mark, Persuasive, Naquadah Sense, Scholarly, Silver Tongue, Weapon Group Proficiency (Handgun, Melee, Rifle), World Traveler.

ATTACKS

Unarmed	+13	1d3+1 (subdual)
Kinetic Blast	+12	2d6+2 normal, 2d6+2 subdual

Gear: Kara kesh, nish'ta.

JAMALA (THE FIRST COMMANDMENT)
Avnil Cave Dweller

Jamala is a young cave dweller on Avnil, who had been pressed into service by Captain Hanson to build his great temple. From the beginning, he doubted the man's divinity, although he dared not say so for fear of reprisals. Nevertheless, he could not stand by and watch as Hanson and his men brutalized his people for daring to stand up to them. He was beaten badly when he defended another cave dweller being abused by Lieutenant Baker. Shortly thereafter, he fled the temple building site and encountered SG-1. With them, he helped to overthrow Hanson and set things aright on Avnil. Because he was not seen as a toady of the false deity, he has since risen to some prominence among his people. He has begun to explore the surface world and take on other leadership duties. In time, he may show even greater talents – a fact for which the SGC can be grateful.

JAMALA

Specialty: Primitive Society Near-Human
Rank: N/A
Class: Native Off-Worlder/Explorer
Level: 1/1

Strength:	13	Dexterity:	15
Constitution:	13	Intelligence:	13
Wisdom:	14	Charisma:	11

Vitality:	13	Wounds:	13

Defense: 13 (+1 class, +2 Dex)
Initiative Bonus: +3 (+1 class, +2 Dex)
Speed: 30

Fort: +4   **Ref:** +5   **Will:** +4

Special Qualities: +1 to Jump and Survival, all over the world, direction sense +2, evolutionary advantage (radiation resistance as the Jaffa/Goa'uld specialty), *obsessive,* primitive.

Skills: Balance +4, Climb +4, Craft (Rock Carving) +4, First Aid +5, Hide +3, Jump +4, Languages +6, Listen +6, Mechanics +3, Move Silently +3, Profession (Miner) +4, Search +4, Spot +4, Survival (Mountain) +6, Swim +2, Tumble +4.

Feats: Armor Group Proficiency (Light, Medium), Mountain Training, Ordinary Past, Weapon Group Proficiency (Hurled, Melee), World Traveler.

Backgrounds: None.

ATTACKS

Unarmed	+1	1d3+1 (subdual)

Gear: None.

JOHNSON, LIEUTENANT DANIEL (THE BROCA DIVIDE)

Reconnaissance Officer, SG-3

A veteran of the Yugoslav conflict, Lt. Johnson saw action there under Col. Makepeace's command. Seeing firsthand evidence of the terrors inflicted upon different ethnic factions, Johnson came away from that tour with a distrust of other cultures and peoples. He was excited to follow his commanding officer to his new duty assignment on SG-3 as its recon officer. The excitement soon gave way to a sense of awe at the enormous responsibility the SGC shouldered. His old demons came back to haunt him as well,

when he realized that Teal'c was not just a fellow African-American but an actual alien. Johnson had worked with foreign officers before; some had proven themselves capable, but there were always those whose beliefs and ideals Johnson considered incompatible with mission objectives. They at least were human – this "Jaffa" didn't even have that going for him. He felt the alien would have to go much further than simply renouncing his old life before the SCG should trust him.

His chance to work with Teal'c during the mission to P3X-797 ended in disaster. Johnson's natural mistrust manifested itself in violence when Johnson was infected with the Touched Syndrome. After being cured, and learning of the Jaffa's part in his salvation, Johnson felt more than a little ashamed. He has not yet decided if Teal'c has truly proven himself, but clearly the alien is trying to do so. For the moment, Johnson is content with that, though he makes no apologies for his earlier suspicions.

DANIEL JOHNSON

Specialty: Marine Force Reconnaissance
Rank: 1st Lieutenant (O-2)
Class: Scout
Level: 2

Strength:	15	Dexterity:	14
Constitution:	14	Intelligence:	10
Wisdom:	10	Charisma:	11

Vitality:	20	Wounds:	15

Defense: 15 (+1 class, +2 Dex, +2 natural armor)
Initiative Bonus: +4 (+2 class, +2 Dex)
Speed: 30

Fort: +5   **Ref:** +4   **Will:** +0

Special Qualities: Rough Living +2, stalker, *trailblazer.*

Skills: Balance +4, Climb +4, First Aid +2, Handle Animal +4, Intimidate +4/+2, Jump +4, Listen +2, Move Silently +4, Profession (Military) +1, Spot +3, Surveillance +5, Survival (Desert) +5, Swim +4, Tumble +3.

Feats: Armor Group Proficiency (Light, Medium, Heavy), Far Shot, Outdoorsman, Track, Weapon Group Proficiency (Handgun, Hurled, Melee, Rifle).

ATTACKS

Unarmed	+3	1d3+2 (subdual)
FN P90	+2	1d10+1 (normal, error 1-2, threat 19-20, range 45 ft., qualities and mods AP, BP, RG)

Gear: SG team bundle, other bundles as needed (by mission).

KAWALSKY, MAJOR CHARLES (CHILDREN OF THE GODS)

Team Leader, SG-2 (deceased)

In 1972, Charles Kawalsky flunked. It wasn't that he was a bad kid or dumb, but he'd just spent too much time that first semester at college messing around with his friends. He wasn't very interested in school, really, but he'd never intended to fail. Unfortunately, it was a very poor time to have your Education Exemption terminated, and Charles found himself facing a choice: join the military, or be drafted.

He knew what happened to guys who got drafted – they ended up as grunts in the Army – and he didn't like ships, so he signed up for what seemed like the least dangerous service: the US Air Force. It was the right choice. After Basic Training, everyone saw a change in Charles. When he came home on leave he was fitter, more disciplined, and seemed to really care about where he was going. The military life agreed with him. He graduated at the top of his classes and rated the highest scores in his efficiency reports. If you wanted a job done right, Kawalsky was your man. He soon realized his mistake in not finishing college, and completed his education while serving with Air Force Special Ops, gaining a commission as an officer.

After ten years with the Air Force, he had become a consummate professional, highly skilled at his work, so when he was assigned to an operation in East Germany with a fellow named Jack O'Neill, he made a good impression, even if the operation itself was a textbook case of how not to run a black ops job. When O'Neill received a list of potential members for the first Abydos mission, he selected Kawalsky, knowing he could count on him to complete the objective. When the Stargate program was reopened, Kawalsky was given the job of commanding SG-2, the most prestigious assignment of his career. It was to be his last.

During a mission to Chulak, Kawalsky was surprised by a Goa'uld symbiote, which blindsided him and slipped into the back of his neck. At the time the SGC was still ignorant of much about the Goa'uld, so the possession went unnoticed at first. When it was discovered, an experimental procedure was performed to remove the symbiote, but it failed. The alien hijacked Kawalsky's body and attempted to escape through the Stargate, but in the struggle both the alien and Kawalsky were killed. His colleagues don't dwell on his final moments, however; they remember him as a fine officer who did his duty to the very end. He was buried with full military honors in his home town in New York.

CHARLES KAWALSKY

Specialty: Air Force Officer
Rank: Major (O-4)
Class: Soldier
Level: 6

Strength:	15	**Dexterity:**	15
Constitution:	13	**Intelligence:**	11
Wisdom:	11	**Charisma:**	11

Vitality:	46	**Wounds:**	15

Defense: 14 (+2 class, +2 Dex)
Initiative Bonus: +7 (+5 class, +2 Dex)
Speed: 30

Fort: +7	**Ref**: +4	**Will**: +5

Special Qualities: *Accurate,* armor use +1, damage reduction 1/-, weapon specialization (SMGs).

Skills: Balance +4, Bureaucracy +3, Climb +5, Craft (Carving) +2, Demolitions +3, Driver +5, First Aid +3, Intimidate +5/+3, Jump +5, Pilot +6, Profession (Military) +3, Spot +3, Survival (Desert) +3, Swim +4.

Feats: Armor Group Proficiency (Light, Medium, Heavy), By the Book, Coolness Under Fire, "Keep Your Head Down!", Point Blank Shot, Precise Shot, Toughness, Weapon Focus (SMGs), Weapon Group Proficiency (Handgun, Hurled, Melee, Rifle, Tactical).

ATTACKS

Unarmed	+8	1d3+3 (subdual)
FN P90	+9	1d10+3 (normal, error 1-2, threat 19-20, range 30 ft., qualities and mods AP, BP, RG)

Gear: SG team bundle, other bundles as needed (by mission).

KENDRA (THOR'S HAMMER)

Cimmerian Wise Woman

Kendra is a former Goa'uld host who, after arriving on Cimmeria ten seasons past, was sent to the labyrinth and passed through Thor's Hammer – which restored her true self. Originally from the planet Jebanna, she studied in a temple where she was trained with a strong mental discipline. Her will allowed Kendra to actually exert a minor influence on the Goa'uld that controlled her, which she used to lead the Goa'uld to Cimmeria and its eventual destruction at the hands of Thor's Hammer.

Since being freed, Kendra has remained on Cimmeria and honored their ways, adopting their beliefs and faith in Thor and the other Norse Gods. She claims to regularly speak with the gods, who offer her wisdom and counsel when needed, and stands ready to help defend her new home from any who would threaten it.

Kendra lives alone in a small home in the mountains, located a few hours walk from the village nearest the Stargate. She serves as a local healer of sorts for the locals, using the knowledge she gained as a Goa'uld host to help the people of Cimmeria. She is still capable of using Goa'uld technology, though she has yet to use the ribbon device (the memories of it are not pleasant). Kendra's experience with SG-1 helped her confront and overcome deeply-hidden fears regarding her ordeal in the labyrinth. She has since become less and less reclusive, journeying into the local villages from time to time to visit Gairwyn and other friends.

KENDRA

Specialty: Primitive Society Near Human
Rank: N/A
Class: Native Off-Worlder
Level: 5

Strength:	11	**Dexterity:**	12
Constitution:	12	**Intelligence:**	13
Wisdom:	15	**Charisma:**	15
Vitality:	25	**Wounds:**	12

Defense: 13 (+2 class, +1 Dex)
Initiative Bonus: +3 (+2 class, +1 Dex)
Speed: 30

Fort: +5	**Ref:** +5	**Will:** +5

Special Qualities: Former Goa'uld host, primitive.

Skills: Climb +3, Concentration +5, Knowledge (Goa'uld) +4, Profession (Hunter) +8, Profession (Priestess) +8, Spot +7, Search +6, Survival (Mountain) +7.

Feats: Advanced Skill Mastery (Ordinary Past), Armor Group Proficiency (Light), Ordinary Past, Weapon Group Proficiency (Melee, Hurled).

ATTACKS

Unarmed	+3	1d3 (subdual)

Gear: Robes.

KENNEDY, COLONEL MARTIN (THE ENEMY WITHIN)

NID Interrogator

Colonel Martin Kennedy is a United States Air Force officer assigned to the National Intelligence Department as an investigator and interrogator. Indeed, he has spent most of his military career working for the NID, a fact that other officers are quick to remember. Though skilled at his chosen vocation, he is not trusted by regular military personnel. Kennedy returns the favor, showing contempt and disdain for those who regard him as a "spook" – or worse. Nevertheless, Kennedy has managed to make himself invaluable to NID. He is one of the department's resident experts on the SGC and its operations. Even when his assignments go awry, he has come out on top with his superiors, who continue to give him great latitude in his work. Should Colonel Kennedy ever gain greater authority within the NID, there's no end to the trouble he could cause the SGC.

MARTIN KENNEDY

Specialty: NID Interrogator
Rank: Colonel (O-6)
Class: Pointman/Field Analyst
Level: 5/2

Strength:	13	**Dexterity:**	11
Constitution:	12	**Intelligence:**	15
Wisdom:	16	**Charisma:**	14
Vitality:	53	**Wounds:**	12

Defense: 17 (+4 class, +1 Dex, +2 specialty)
Initiative Bonus: +4 (+3 class, +1 Dex)
Speed: 30

Fort: +4	**Ref:** +6	**Will:** +7

Special Qualities: Assistance (½), evidence analysis (Analyst), *eye for detail,* favor for a favor 1/session, *generous,* lead 2/session, tactics 1/session, versatility (Computers, Gather Information, Innuendo, Intimidate, Listen, Search, Spot).

Skills: Bluff +8, Bureaucracy +8, Computers +7, Diplomacy +7, Gather Information +14, Innuendo +7, Intimidate +11/+12, Knowledge (Intelligence Gathering) +9, Listen +9, Profession (NID) +7, Search +11, Sense Motive +10, Spot +10, Surveillance +13.

Feats: Alertness, Analyst, Armor Group Proficiency (Light), Hard Core, Mark, Promotion, Weapon Group Proficiency (Handgun, Melee, Rifle).

Backgrounds: Hunting 1, Long-Term Mission 3.

ATTACKS

Unarmed   +5   1d3+1 (subdual)

Gear: None.

KINSEY, SEN. ROBERT (POLITICS)

Chairman, Senate Appropriations Committee

A graduate of Harvard and political activist during most of his early life, Robert Kinsey made his first bid for national office in 1968 when a seat on the Senate became available. He was narrowly defeated, but the experience gave him a taste for politics, and six years later Kinsey once again made a bid for the Utah seat. This time he succeeded and quickly established himself as a force among the freshman ranks of the Senate. Senator Kinsey's tell-it-as-it-is attitude and unwillingness to suffer fools gladly made him a media favorite and a party hero. In late 1992 Senator Kinsey became the senior member of the Senate Appropriations Committee, and set his sights on the White House soon thereafter. He wisely chose to refrain from making his bid right away, but as of the end of Season One, political experts place the Senator at the top of a short list.

Personally, Kinsey is a practiced Washington insider, with the manners of a gentleman and the savvy of a great white shark. He speaks bluntly and directly, but never foolishly, and his straightforward manner has often been mistaken for political naivete by opponents who soon learn better. Player characters who encounter him are likely to find a dogged and tenacious political foe.

ROBERT KINSEY

Specialty: Civilian Specialist
Rank: N/A
Class: Pointman
Level: 5

Strength:	9	**Dexterity:**	10
Constitution:	11	**Intelligence:**	14
Wisdom:	12	**Charisma:**	14
Vitality:	22	**Wounds:**	11

Defense: 11 (+1 class)
Initiative Bonus: +2 (+2 class)
Speed: 30

Fort: +3   **Ref:** +3   **Will:** +5

Special Qualities: +2 to Education checks, assistance (½), *generous*, lead 1/session, tactics 1/session, take 10 (Knowledge (Politics), Profession (Politician)), versatility (Computers, Forgery, Innuendo, Intimidate, Languages, Perform, 2 skills).

Skills: Bluff +12, Bureaucracy +10, Computers +4, Diplomacy +10, Forgery +5, Innuendo +4, Intimidate +9/+12, Knowledge (Politics) +10, Languages +5, Perform (Public Speaking) +9, Profession (Politician) +9.

Feats: Armor Group Proficiency (Light, Medium), Hard Core, Persuasive, Political Favors, Weapon Group Proficiency (Handgun, Melee, Rifle).

ATTACKS

Unarmed   +2   1d3-1 (subdual)

Gear: Professional bundle.

KLOREL (CHILDREN OF THE GODS)

Son of Apophis

Klorel is the son and heir of the Serpent God. His father places great trust in him and hopes that he will prove an invaluable asset in his plans for conquest. For that reason, Apophis chose as his son's host the most perfect specimen he could find: the Abydonian youth Skaara, who not only possessed a strong body, but a keen mind as well. The young Goa'uld is eager to please his father, but sometimes wonders if he can maintain control over so strong-willed a host. Only time will tell if there is any basis for his doubts.

KLOREL

Specialty: Goa'uld Warmaster
Rank: N/A
Class: Wheelman/Ace
Level: 5/3

Strength:	13	**Dexterity:**	14
Constitution:	15	**Intelligence:**	13
Wisdom:	13	**Charisma:**	11
Vitality:	77	**Wounds:**	15

Defense: 16 (+4 class, +2 Dex)
Initiative Bonus: +7 (+5 class, +2 Dex)
Speed: 30

Fort: +4   **Ref:** +11   **Will:** +4

Special Qualities: +2 to damage, *battle born, custom ride* (6 GPs), daredevil, dominated body, familiarity +1, fancy flying (hardness), immunity to disease, inherited memory, kick start 1/session, long life, *lucky*, parasite, radiation resistance, taking wing (Aviator, Advanced).

Skills: Balance +6, Boating +5, Demolitions +4, Disguise +2, Driver +8, Electronics +3, Handle Animal +4, Intimidate +7/+6, Jump +3, Knowledge (Aircraft) +6, Mechanics +8, Pilot +16, Profession (Fighter Pilot) +8, Spot +15, Surveillance +3, Survival (Desert) +7.

Feats: Advanced Skill Mastery (Aviator), Armor Group Proficiency (Light, Medium), Aviator, Combat Instincts, Firm Hand, Lightning Reflexes, Naquadah Sense, Offensive Driving, Oversteer, Surge of Speed, Weapon Group Proficiency (Melee, Handgun, Rifle, Tactical), Wind Rider.

Backgrounds: Fear (failure) 4.

ATTACKS

Unarmed	+9	1d3+3 (subdual)
Kara kesh	+10	2d6+2 regular and 2d6+2 subdual

Gear: Elegant noble's attire, kara kesh.

Note: Klorel's class abilities provide the following benefits:

Lucky: Klorel may spend 1 action die to add 2 dice to a vehicle-related skill check instead of 1. (Core.)

Custom Ride: Klorel has 5 resource points with which he may requisition a vehicle or vehicular improvements at the start of each mission (Core.)

Daredevil: Klorel may daredevil-only maneuvers during a chase. (Chase rules will appear in the upcoming *Unexplored Worlds* sourcebook.)

Kick Start: Once per session, Klorel may change a failed Mechanics skill check to a success.

Familiarity: Klorel gains a +1 competence bonus with Driver, Mechanics, Pilot, and maneuver checks made using any specific vehicle with which he has spent at least 20 days around. He also gains this bonus with attack checks made firing the vehicle's weapons.

Battle Born: Whenever Klorel spends 1 action die to increase an attack check result or damage roll when using an aircraft- or spacecraft-mounted weapon, he rolls 2 dice instead of one, adding the sum of both to his result. (Core ability.)

Taking Wing: Klorel gains a virtual basic skill feat called "Aviator," which grants a +2 bonus with Knowledge (Aircraft), Pilot, and Spot checks, and increases his threat range with these skills to 19-20. He has the Advanced Skill Mastery feat for this.

Fancy Flying: The hardness of any aircraft or spacecraft Klorel controls is increased by +5.

Full details on the Wheelman class and Ace prestige class can be found online (www.alderac.com), and in the upcoming *Unexplored Worlds* sourcebook.

KUR (COLD LAZARUS)
Goa'uld System Lord

Lord Kur is the Unity warrior currently impersonating a System Lord in an effort to avenge his people's death. *See Cold Lazarus, page 30 for more information.*

KUR

Specialty: Unity Warrior
Rank: N/A
Class: Soldier/Scout/Grunt
Level: 5/3/3

Strength:	14	**Dexterity:**	16
Constitution:	14	**Intelligence:**	15
Wisdom:	13	**Charisma:**	10

Vitality:	127	**Wounds:**	15

Defense: 19 (+4 class, +3 Dex, +2 rough living)
Initiative Bonus: +11 (+9 class, +2 Dex)
Speed: 30

Fort: +10	**Ref:** +7	**Will:** +11

Special Qualities: +4 to attack checks, *accurate,* alpha-strike, armor use +1, bushmaster (Desert Training), damage reduction 1/-, electromagnetic field, *hot-blooded,* long life, overkill (+1d8, 1/session), radioactive, rough living +2, shapeshifter, stalker, telepathy.

Skills: Balance +8, Climb +6, Concentration +7, Cultures +4, Demolitions +10, Driver +11, First Aid +5, Gather Information +3, Hide +6, Innuendo +2, Intimidate +7/+5, Jump +4, Listen +6, Move Silently +6, Profession (Infiltrator) +8, Search +5, Spot +12, Survival (Forest) +8, Survival (Desert) +8.

Feats: Advanced Energy Blast, Armor Group Proficiency (Light, Medium, Heavy), Coolness Under Fire, Desert Training, Electromagnetic Adaptation, Electromagnetic Control, Endurance, Energy Blast, Forest Training, Iron Will, Mind Scan, Outdoorsman, Speed Trigger, Blast Lance Basics, Weapon Group Proficiency (Melee, Hurled, Handgun, Rifle, Tactical).

ATTACKS

Unarmed	+16	1d3+2 (subdual)
Kara kesh	+17	2d6+2 regular and 2d6+2 subdual
Staff weapon	+17	6d6 (normal, error 1-2, threat 18-20, range 75 ft., qualities and mods AP,AK)

Gear: Elegant noble's attire, kara kesh, staff weapon.

Kynthia (Brief Candle)

Argosian Woman

Kynthia approached O'Neill during SG-1's initial visit to Argos, offering him a marriage cake. True to her invitation, she stayed with O'Neill as much as he would allow her during his time on Argos. Her love of life and desire to cherish each day helped O'Neill come to grips with the change inflicted upon him before he and the rest of SG-1 freed the Argosians from Pelops' nanocytes. Kynthia's innocence reflected the beliefs of all the Argosians, who truly believed they were the Chosen and that Pelops would forever protect them. The loss of that innocence came as a considerable blow, but she proved quite capable of handling it.

Now she helps to lead her people in their new lives: gathering supplies, organizing the construction of new buildings and learning all that she can about the world around her. She has recently taken up stargazing, in the hopes of understanding more about the worlds beyond the night sky.

Kynthia

Specialty: Primitive Society Near Human
Rank: N/A
Class: Native Off-Worlder
Level: 1

Strength:	8	Dexterity:	10
Constitution:	9	Intelligence:	13
Wisdom:	12	Charisma:	15
Vitality:	5	Wounds:	9

Defense: 10 (+0 class)
Initiative Bonus: +0 (+0 class)
Speed: 30

Fort: +1	Ref: +1	Will: +2

Special Qualities: Primitive.

Skills: Craft (Basket Weaving) +2, Craft (Cooking) +2, Hobby (Starwatching) +2, Listen +2, Search +2, Survival (Forest) +2, Swim +0.

Feats: Ordinary Past.

Attacks

Unarmed	+0	1d3-1 (subdual)

Gear: None.

Langford, Professor Paul (The Torment of Tantalus)

Archaeologist (deceased)

Prof. Langford was the first person in thousands of years to gaze upon the Stargate when he found it buried at the Giza plateau in 1928. Before that, he was a university professor in Berlin where he lived with his young daughter Catherine. But after his discovery, he understood that nothing could ever be the same for the people of Earth. Try as he might, however, he could never fully understand the workings of the Stargate. It was left to his daughter to finish the work he began after he died of a heart attack in 1947.

Paul Langford

Specialty: Civilian Specialist
Rank: None
Class: Scientist
Level: 11

Strength:	10	Dexterity:	10
Constitution:	11	Intelligence:	18
Wisdom:	14	Charisma:	14
Vitality:	51	Wounds:	11

Defense: 19 (+9 class)
Initiative Bonus: +4 (+4 class)
Speed: 30

Fort: +3	Ref: +3	Will: +9

Special Qualities: +3 to Education checks, brilliant +2, improvise +6, know it all 1/mission, learned, Ph.D. (Knowledge (Archaeology), Knowledge (History)), *professor*, research (inspiration 2/session), take 10 (Knowledge (Chemistry), Knowledge (History), Knowledge (Physics), Profession (Archaeologist).

Skills: Appraise +12, Bluff +4, Bureaucracy +6, Concentration +11, Cryptography +8, Cultures +18, Diplomacy +8, First Aid +5, Gather Information +8, Handle Animal +3, Knowledge (Archaeology) +27, Knowledge (History) +21, Languages +20, Listen +8, Profession (Archaeologist) +16, Search +20, Spot +15, Survival +10, Swim +2.

Feats: Advanced Skill Mastery (Scholarly), Alertness, Armor Group Proficiency (Light), Extra Supplies, Political Favors, Scholarly, Weapon Group Proficiency (Handgun, Melee), World Traveler.

Attacks

Unarmed	+5	1d3 (subdual)

Gear: None.

LITTLEFIELD, DR. ERNEST (THE TORMENT OF TANTALUS)

Marooned Scientist

Dr. Ernest Littlefield had a fairly ordinary life as a physics professor until he was brought on to the Stargate project in 1945. His curiosity and desire for understanding drove him to obsession, a condition cured only upon meeting with Prof. Langford's daughter Catherine at a supper at the professor house.

It was not long afterwards that the Stargate was finally opened and a wormhole created. Understanding that nothing put into the Stargate could return unless it had intelligence to try and find a way back, Ernest volunteered to be the first to step through. The Stargate closed behind him, cutting off the air supply to his diving suit and leaving him stranded on the other side. When Ernest did not return, Prof. Langford broke the news with a lie to Catherine.

Ernest, alone on Heliopolis, made do as best he could. But 50 years of solitude had an adverse effect on his mind, and he began to believe that Catherine had gone through the Stargate with him. Over time, his delusion grew deeper as he imagined an entire life for he and his love on the planet. His reality came to a shattering end when SG-1, accompanied by Catherine, found him on Heliopolis. The ordeal shook him to the core, but he emerged with a greater appreciation of life's gifts and the knowledge not try to reach too far for something that may be unattainable.

Ernest returned to Earth with SG-1 and now lives happily with Catherine, whom he finally married; the two are trying to make up for 50 years of lost time.

DR. ERNEST LITTLEFIELD

Specialty: Civilian Specialist
Rank: None
Class: Scientist/Explorer
Level: 4/8

Strength:	10	**Dexterity:**	11
Constitution:	15	**Intelligence:**	15
Wisdom:	12	**Charisma:**	12
Vitality:	103	**Wounds:**	17

Defense: 18 (+8 class)
Initiative Bonus: +8 (+8 class)
Speed: 30

Fort: +9	**Ref:** +7	**Will:** +11

Special Qualities: +4 to Education checks, all over the world (advanced), bookworm ½, direction sense +4, improvise +2, learned, Ph.D. (Knowledge (Physics)), *professor*, research (Alertness), take 10 (Knowledge (Chemistry), Knowledge (History), Knowledge (Physics)), uncanny dodge (can't be flanked, Dex bonus).

Skills: Appraise +4, Balance +2, Bluff +3, Boating +2, Bureaucracy +3, Climb +2, Concentration +6, Craft (Primitive Weapons) +7, Cryptography +6, Cultures +8, Diplomacy +5, Driver +1, Electronics +12, First Aid +6, Jump +2, Knowledge (Chemistry) +7, Knowledge (History) +7, Knowledge (Physics) +10, Languages +11, Listen +10, Mechanics +16, Profession (Physicist) +6, Search +12, Sense Motive +3, Sport (Running) +4, Spot +16, Survival (Forest) +11, Swim +5.

Feats: Advanced Skill Mastery (Grease Monkey), Alertness, Armor Group Proficiency (Light), Forest Training, Grease Monkey, Great Fortitude, Iron Will, Scholarly, Toughness (×2), Weapon Focus (Spear), Weapon Group Proficiency (Handgun, Melee), World Traveler

ATTACKS

Unarmed	+8	1d3 (subdual)
Spear	+8	1d8+2

Gear: None.

LOM'AC (BLOODLINES)

Tolv'al Mercenary

As a young warrior in the service of Apophis, Lom'ac thought the gods (particularly his) smiled on him. That changed after his first battle. On a planet controlled by Heru-ur's forces, he took part in an attack to destroy a key shipyard. The defenders responded with stunning ferocity, and Lom'ac was one of the few who made it back to Chulak alive. Every man had been injured and some were dying, yet all Apophis noticed was their failure. He had them all killed where they stood, but on a whim, the god decided to spare Lom'ac as a warning to others. Forced to live as a kresh'taa outside the city, and with no one to tend to his wounds, it took weeks for his symbiote to fully heal him.

Not long ago a young acolyte approached the fallen warrior with an offer of employment. Though loath to degrade himself further, several years as kresh'taa had taught him to do what was needed to survive. Lom'ac was not ready to die when his symbiote matured in a few years, and when the time came, this ambitious priest Mal'ic might be in a position to do something about that. So Lom'ac agreed, and now performs the distasteful acts that the priest of Cronus believes will propel him into the center of his cult.

LOM'AC

Specialty: Jaffa Kresh'taa
Rank: N/A
Class: Guardian
Level: 5

Strength:	18	Dexterity:	12
Constitution:	16	Intelligence:	9
Wisdom:	11	Charisma:	10
Vitality:	59	Wounds:	18

Defense: 14 (+3 class, +1 Dex)
Initiative Bonus: +3 (+2 class, +1 Dex)
Speed: 30

Fort: +7   **Ref:** +2   **Will:** +4

Special Qualities: Accelerated healing, enforcer (Basic), soak 1/session, radiation resistance, *unbreakable*.

Skills: Balance +3, Bluff +2, Climb +5, Concentration +2, Hide +4, Intimidation +7/+3, Jump +6, Knowledge (Goa'uld) +2, Move Silently +4, Spot +3, Survival (Forest) +2, Tumble +3

Feats: Alertness, Armor Group Proficiency (Light, Medium, Heavy), Enforcer, Martial Arts, Rapid Healing, Symbiote (Immunity to Disease), Toughness, Weapon Group Proficiency (Handgun, Hurled, Melee, Rifle, Tactical).

ATTACKS

Unarmed	+9	1d6+4 (subdual)
Dagger	+8	1d4+4 (normal, error 1, threat 19-20, range 5 ft.)

Gear: Dagger, robes.

LYA (THE NOX)

Nox

Lya is Anteaus' husband and Nafrayu's mother. At 300 years, she has traveled the galaxy extensively, but since the birth of Nafrayu 10 years ago, she has spent more time at home than traveling. Friendly and more curious than many of her race, Lya has taken on role of liaison of sorts between the SGC and the Nox, and between the Nox and the Tollan, a group whom she helped rescue from the NID *(see Enigma, page 62)*. Lya finds other species – humans in particular – fascinating, and since the first encounter with SG-1 has quietly studied the Tauri and their ways. On more than one occasion Lya has discovered SG teams on different worlds, but remained hidden so as to observe them discreetly. Thus far her observations support SG-1's claims of Tauri benevolence, though their willingness to employ violence confirms that the humans are still very young and have much to learn.

LYA

Specialty: Nox
Rank: N/A
Class: Explorer/Nox Wanderer
Level: 9/7

Strength:	10	Dexterity:	13
Constitution:	12	Intelligence:	17
Wisdom:	15	Charisma:	17
Vitality:	90	Wounds:	14

Defense: 20 (+9 class, +1 Dex)
Initiative Bonus: +13 (+12 class, +1 Dex)
Speed: 30

Fort: +10   **Ref:** +9   **Will:** +17

Special Qualities: +6 to Intelligence checks, all over the world (basic, advanced), bookworm (½), danger sense (melee), direction sense +4, long life, *obsessive*, total pacifist, uncanny dodge (Dex Bonus, can't be flanked).

Skills: Balance +5, Climb +6, Cultures +23, Electronics +13, First Aid +23, Gather Information +21, Handle Animal +21, Jump +4, Knowledge (Astronomy) +15, Knowledge (Physics) +13, Languages +7, Listen +11, Mechanics +13, Search +13, Sense Motive +8, Spot +18, Survival (Arctic) +8, Survival (Forest) +8, Tumble +3, Xeno-Cultures +13, Xeno-Languages +12.

Feats: Absorb Language, Advanced Skill Mastery (World Traveler), Alertness, Charmer, Cloaking, Cloak Objects, Cloak Others, Control Device, Control Stargate, Forest Training, Grease Monkey, Read Surface Thoughts, Ritual of Life, Shifting, Shift Objects, Shift Others, Sidestep, Stargate Explorer, World Traveler, Xeno-Studies.

ATTACKS
None.

Gear: Robes.

MASLIH (COR-AI)

Chief Elder of the Byrsa

Maslih has served as an Elder for over twelve years, and became Chief Elder two years ago. As a master stoneworker, she is also one of those responsible for maintenance of the kaleo, and for passing the trade to the next generation. Many of those duties are now performed by those she taught as adolescents, but Maslih still finds time to lend a hand or a word of advice when it is needed.

Always pragmatic and direct, she became even more so following the death of her husband Mago in a Goa'uld raid fifteen years ago. As an Elder, she must employ a certain amount of tact and diplomacy, but many of the Byrsa value her bluntness equally highly. Visitors from Earth, too, have learned to respect it; they always know where they stand with her, and appreciate the clarity with which she approaches a problem. She has worked closely with them, both in her capacity as Chief Elder and as one of the craftsmen participating in the improvements to the Hiding. She has selected two of the most promising senior apprentices to study directly with the SGC engineers, to learn the new skills that the visitors possess.

MASLIH

Specialty: Primitive Society Near Human
Rank: N/A
Class: Respected Elder
Level: 6

Strength:	8	Dexterity:	9
Constitution:	10	Intelligence:	12
Wisdom:	17	Charisma:	14
Vitality:	16	Wounds:	10

Defense: 14 (+5 class, –1 Dex)
Initiative Bonus: +3 (+4 class, –1 Dex)
Speed: 30

Fort: +2   **Ref:** +2   **Will:** +7

Special Qualities: Specialty (Sense Motive), vulnerability (extreme cold).

Skills: Bluff +10, Bureaucracy +8, Concentration +9, Diplomacy +10, Gather Information +8, Listen +8, Profession (Stone Worker) +7, Sense Motive +11, Spot +7.

Feats: Alertness, Armor Group Proficiency (Light,), Charmer, Forest Training, Ordinary Past, Persuasive, Weapon Group Proficiency (Hurled, Melee).

Backgrounds: Byrsa Mandates (3).

ATTACKS

Unarmed   +2   1d3–1 (subdual)

Gear: Stoneworkers' tools (primitive).

MEHEN (SOLITUDES)

Goa'uld Underlord

Mehen actually once challenged the power of Apophis, hoping to usurp the System Lord's place as the serpent god. After a crushing defeat, he entered the service of his former foe as many conquered Goa'uld do. Following his change of allegiance, Mehen began to work tirelessly in order to improve Apophis' standing among the System Lords and was a primary coordinator of the fight against Ra. At present, he believes that since he could not defeat Apophis then his best hope of achieving power and influence is to aid the System Lord in achieving total dominance over all the Goa'uld.

Mehen inhabits the body of a human male that was taken from Earth millennia ago. The host, originally a slave laborer from northern Africa, is bald-headed and muscular with ebony skin and a sharply trimmed goatee. Mehen has always been a hands-on leader and prefers hosts with physical strength and capability. His voice is deep and he speaks slowly, drawing out his words like a snake slithering through reeds. When his ire is raised, however, Mehen becomes a coiled whip and the crack of his voice commands immediate obedience and servitude.

Mehen commands the Serpent Guards used by Apophis, but occasionally commands more devotion than even the System Lord. He rewards the Jaffa that serve him well with riches and comfort, and his First Prime lives in a palace almost as large as those of other Goa'uld. The Jaffa warriors see Mehen as an example of greatness in their own path; the underlord trains in combat from time to time among the Jaffa, demonstrating his prowess and solidifying their loyalty.

MEHEN

Specialty: Goa'uld Noble
Rank: N/A
Class: Soldier/Grunt
Level: 7/8

Strength:	13	Dexterity:	15
Constitution:	14	Intelligence:	15
Wisdom:	13	Charisma:	16
Vitality:	140	Wounds:	14

Defense: 18 (+6 class, +2 Dex)
Initiative Bonus: +13 (+11 class, +2 Dex)
Speed: 30

Fort: +10   **Ref:** +6   **Will:** +16

Special Qualities: +4 species bonus to damage, *accurate,* alpha-strike, armor use +1, damage reduction 1/–, dead to rights, dominated body, fire team, forced march, *hot-blooded,* immunity to disease, improved iron will, inherited memory, long life, overkill (+2d8, 3/session), parasite, radiation resistance, weapon specialization (staff weapon).

Skills: Balance +6, Climb +5, Concentration +14, Demolitions +14, Driver +16, First Aid +7, Intimidate +19/+20, Jump +7, Profession (Military) +19, Spot +15, Survival (Desert) +9.

Feats: Armor Group Proficiency (Light, Medium, Heavy), Confident Charge, Coolness Under Fire, Coordinate Fire, Endurance, Extreme Range, Far Shot, Iron Will, "Keep Your Head Down!", Naquadah Sense, Point Blank Shot, Precise Shot, Speed Trigger, Staff Weapon Basics, Staff Weapon Mastery, Surge of Speed, Weapon Group Proficiency (Hurled, Melee, Handgun, Rifle, Tactical).

ATTACKS

Unarmed	+16	1d3+5 (subdual)
Kinetic Blast	+17	2d6+6 normal and 2d6+6 subdual
Staff Weapon	+15	6d6+6 (normal, error 1-2, threat 18-20, range 75 ft., qualities and mods AP, AK)

Gear: Kara kesh, staff weapon.

MOUGHAL (EMANCIPATION)

Shavadai Chieftain

Moughal is the chieftain of the Shavadai, and the oldest and wisest of all the tribal leaders of his land. He is more progressive in this thinking than most of his counterparts, and realizes that the old laws and old ways no longer serve the people of Simarka. Moughal was injured years ago in battle against the Toughai, long before Turghan became chieftain of that tribe. He walks with a limp and uses a cane, and his days as an effective warrior have long since ended. But he remains an imposing leader nonetheless, and his people adore him for his practical and farsighted policies.

MOUGHAL

Specialty: Primitive Society Near Human
Rank: N/A
Class: Scout/Pointman
Level: 3/2

Strength:	10	Dexterity:	7
Constitution:	12	Intelligence:	12
Wisdom:	14	Charisma:	15

Vitality:	37	Wounds:	12

Defense: 12 (+2 class, –2 Dex, +2 Rough Living)
Initiative Bonus: +2 (+4 class, –2 Dex)
Speed: 30

Fort: +6   **Ref:** +2   **Will:** +8

Special Qualities: Assistance (½), bushmaster (Forest Training), rough living +2, stalker, *trailblazer,* versatility (6 skills).

Skills: Concentration +7, Diplomacy +6, First Aid +6, Handle Animal +8, Hide +3, Knowledge (Ancient Law) +8, Listen +8, Search +8, Sense Motive +6, Spot +8, Survival +12.

Feats: Armor Group Proficiency (Light), Forest Training, Outdoorsman, Track, Weapon Group Proficiency (Hurled, Melee).

Backgrounds: Political Enemy (Turghan) 4.

ATTACKS

Unarmed	+4	1d3 (subdual)
Dagger	+4	1d4 (error 1, threat 19-20)
Sword	+4	1d8 (error 1, threat 19-20)

Gear: Walking stick.

NAFRAYU (THE NOX)

Nox

At 10 years old, Nafrayu is the youngest of the Nox encountered by SG-1. The son of Lya and Anteaus is very curious and inquisitive (like his mother) but innocent in the ways of others. He has yet to master the use of Nox technology, spending his days near his family's hut and the nearby forest.

NAFRAYU

Specialty: Nox
Rank: N/A
Class: Nox Wanderer
Level: 2

Strength	11	Dexterity:	9
Constitution:	10	Intelligence:	15
Wisdom:	15	Charisma:	14

Vitality:	6	Wounds:	10

Defense: 10 (+1 class, –1 Dex)
Initiative Bonus: +0 (+1 class, –1 Dex)
Speed: 30

Fort: +3   **Ref:** +0   **Will:** +5

Special Qualities: +2 to Intelligence checks, long life, total pacifist.

Skills: Climb +1, First Aid +6, Handle Animal +4, Hide +3, Knowledge (The Forest) +3, Knowledge (Botany) +3, Move Silently +0, Sense Motive +3, Spot +3, Survival (Forest) +3, Survival (Swamp) +3, Xeno-Languages +4.

Feats: Absorb Languages, Forest Training, Ritual of Life.

ATTACKS

None.

Gear: Robes.

NEM (FIRE AND WATER)

Ohnes Scholar

Nem was the mate of Omoroca before she traveled to Earth and was killed by Belus. A scholar and scientist by profession, he has since lived alone in a small outpost near the Stargate, meeting visitors to the Ohnes' home world and ever hopeful that Omoroca would one day return. In ensuing four thousand years ,Nem studied the Goa'uld and their history and has become an expert in the subject. After learning that Belus killed Omoroca *(see page 45)*, he vowed revenge, and is currently traveling from world to world, seeking information that can lead him to Belus.

Nem is a noble soul, but very intense and driven by his desire to avenge his love. He sometimes make rash decisions, and is not above hurting other people to get what he desires – especially if he believes that they are aiding the Goa'uld. He is well disposed towards the SGC, however, and might approach teams wearing recognizable insignia with offers of aid or requests for information about his foe.

NEM

Specialty: Ohnes Scholar
Rank: N/A
Class: Scientist
Level: 7

Strength:	15	**Dexterity:**	11
Constitution:	14	**Intelligence:**	17
Wisdom:	13	**Charisma:**	12
Vitality:	55	**Wounds:**	14

Defense: 16 (+6 class)
Initiative Bonus: +3 (+3 class)
Speed: 20

Fort: +4   **Ref:** +2   **Will:** +6

Special Qualities: Amphibious, brilliant +1, dehydration, +2 bonus to Education checks, improvise +4, learned, *professor,* Ph.D, research (Versatility).

Skills: Computers +9, Concentration +9, Electronics +10, First Aid +8, Gather Information +7, Intimidate +9/7, Knowledge (Goa'uld) +10, Mechanics +10, Profession (Scientist) +9, Search +8, Sense Motive +7, Spot +8, Surveillance +6, Survival (Aquatic) +8, Swim +8, Xeno-Languages +6.

Feats: Armor Group Proficiency (Light), Clear Mind, Communicate, Goa'uld Sense, Psychic Blast, Scholarly, Weapon Group Proficiency (Handgun, Melee).

Backgrounds: Hunting (Belus) 3, Vendetta (Belus) 4.

ATTACKS

Unarmed	+5	1d3+2 (subdual)
Blaster Pistol	+3	3d4 (error 1-2, threat 19-20, range 30 ft., qualities)
Psychic Blast		Targets within 50 feet must make a Willpower save (DC 20) or be stunned for 2d10 minutes

Gear: Hydrator *(see page 151)*.

OHPER (THE NOX)

Nox

Ohper is the oldest of the Nox SG-1 encountered during their mission to Gaia, and indeed one of the oldest Nox currently in existence. He sat on the council of Elders years ago, but has long since relinquished such duties for the peace and serenity of the forest. He still makes himself available to the current leaders for advice and guidance, and his family monitors the Stargate for any sign of outsider intruders. Beyond that, he spends his days deep in the forest, communing with the unity of life.

OHPER

Specialty: Nox
Rank: N/A
Class: Nox Wanderer/Respected Elder
Level: 10/8

Strength:	11	**Dexterity:**	9
Constitution:	13	**Intelligence:**	19
Wisdom:	18	**Charisma:**	17
Vitality:	26	**Wounds:**	14

Defense: 22 (+12 class)
Initiative Bonus: +9 (+9 class)
Speed: 30

Fort: +9   **Ref:** +7   **Will:** +18

Special Qualities: +6 to Intelligence checks, long life, specialty (Gather Information), total pacifist.

Skills: Bluff +15, Bureaucracy +15, Concentration +12, First Aid +18, Gather Information +18, Handle Animal +17, Hide +7, Knowledge (Botany) +13, Knowledge (The Forest) +13, Listen +14, Move Silently +7, Sense Motive +21, Spot +19, Survival (Forest) +17, Survival (Swamp) +17, Xeno-Languages +18.

Feats: Absorb Language, Advanced Skill Mastery (Ordinary Past), Alertness, Charmer, Cloaking, Cloak Objects, Cloak Others, Forest Training, Ordinary Past, Read Surface Thoughts, Ritual of Life, Shifting, Shift Objects, Shift Others.

ATTACKS

None.

Gear: Robes.

OMOC (ENIGMA)

Tollan Expeditionary Team Leader

A calm and unassuming man, Omoc's stoic nature conceals wisdom beneath a thick layer of mistrust. On Tollan, he was an influential leader, advising the Curia on several matters of state and political affairs. Omoc's conservative position helped temper the Tollan desire for space exploration and contact with other species; he was one of the strongest opponents to the Curia's agreement to begin trade relations with the Sartian Government.

As a scientist, Omoc is a skilled exobiologist and astrophysicist, and wrote a number of dissertations on alien cultural development patterns, as observed by his years of study in the field. While never one to shrink from duty, his first love has always been Tollan and its people. As a high ranking member of the Tollan Expeditionary Forces, he led a number of cultural and scientific surveys to neighboring worlds. After the destruction of Sartian and the cataclysm that erupted on Tollan, Omoc was quick to take charge. The Expeditionary Forces were called into action quickly in order to evacuate as many personnel as possible from Tollan. In this defining moment, he was able to recommend a world suitable for settlement by his people. Located outside the Stargate network, it would require the use of every Tollan space vessel to transport the survivors there. Because of their vulnerability – even the Tollan had run afoul of the Goa'uld on more than one occasion – it was deemed necessary to bury the Tollan Stargate to ensure that no one could follow his people or mistakenly gate to their dying world.

Omoc and the other members of his team returned to Tollan to bury the gate but succumbed to the ash and sulfur in the atmosphere before completing their objective. It was shortly thereafter that they were rescued by the Tauri and eventually transported to their new home, Tollana. Since then, Omoc has been nominated for a position on the High Council and now seeks to guide his people into a new era. Sometimes, he thinks about slowing down, but the drive to serve his people always overcomes his desire to rest... no matter how well-deserved it may be.

OMOC

Specialty: Advanced Society Near Human
Class: Scientist/Explorer
Level: 3/3

Strength:	10	**Dexterity:**	11
Constitution:	11	**Intelligence:**	14
Wisdom:	15	**Charisma:**	9
Vitality:	31	**Wounds:**	11

Defense: 15 (+5 class)
Initiative Bonus: +4 (+4 class)
Speed: 30

Fort: +3	**Ref:** +4	**Will:** +9

Special Qualities: All over the world, bookworm (½), direction sense +2, improvise +2, learned, *professor,* PhD (Knowledge (Exobiology)).

Skills: Appraise +3, Computers +7, Concentration +6, Cultures +11, Demolitions +3, Diplomacy +2, Disguise +1, Electronics +8, First Aid +6, Gather Information +2, Hide +2, Knowledge (Astrophysics) +11, Knowledge (Exobiology) +14, Listen +4, Mechanics +5, Profession (Expeditionary Forces) +9, Search +5, Sense Motive +8, Spot +7, Surveillance +7, Survival (Desert) +3, Survival (Urban) +3, Xeno-Cultures +8, Xeno-Languages +11.

Feats: Advanced Technology, Armor Group Proficiency (Light), Extra Support, Iron Will, Mark, Scholarly, Weapon Group Proficiency (Handgun, Melee), World Traveler, Xeno-Studies.

ATTACKS

Unarmed	+3	1d3 (subdual)

Gear: Tollan recall device, inverted phased communicator, phase device, survival gear.

PELOPS, THE GIVER OF DAYS (BRIEF CANDLE)

Goa'uld System Lord

Pelops is a relatively minor Goa'uld in terms of political power, but his experiments in nanotechnology have earned himself a place among the vilest of all the System Lords. From his home world of Sparta, he continues to research applications of nanotechnology, and is unaware that the Argosians are no longer under the influence of his nanocytes. Should he learn otherwise he would likely return to reinstate his experiment on Argos with a more forceful presence.

More on Pelops can be found on page 28, and in the upcoming System Lords sourcebook.

PELOPS

Specialty: Goa'uld Warmaster
Rank: N/A
Class: Scientist
Level: 9

Strength:	13	Dexterity:	12
Constitution:	14	Intelligence:	19
Wisdom:	15	Charisma:	14
Vitality:	62	Wounds:	14

Defense: 18 (+7 class, +1 Dex)
Initiative Bonus: +5 (+4 class, +1 Dex)
Speed: 30

Fort: +5	**Ref:** +4	**Will:** +8

Special Qualities: Brilliant +2, dominated body, immunity to disease, long life, improvise +5, inherited memory, parasite, radiation resistance, learned, *professor*, PhD (Mechanics), research (Grease Monkey, Advanced Skill Mastery (Grease Monkey)).

Skills: Appraise +9, Bureaucracy +4, Computers +15, Concentration +11, Craft (Nanotechnology) +16, Cryptography +12, Diplomacy +8, Driver +6, Electronics +19, First Aid +9, Gather Information +6, Intimidate +5/+6, Knowledge (Nanotechnology) +19, Languages +9, Listen +7, Mechanics +22, Profession +7, Search +10, Sense Motive +10, Spot +8, Surveillance +10, Survival (Swamp) +6.

Feats: Advanced Skill Mastery (Grease Monkey), Armor Group Proficiency (Light, Medium), Grease Monkey, Mathematical Genius, Naquadah Sense, Scholarly, Silver Tongue, Surge of Speed, Talented (Mechanics), Training, Weapon Group Proficiency (Handgun).

ATTACKS

Unarmed	+5	1d3 +3 (subdual)
Kinetic Blast	+5	2d6 +2 normal, 2d6+2 subdual

Gear: Kara kesh.

RAIDEN, GOD OF THUNDER (EMANCIPATION)

Goa'uld System Lord

Raiden is the Goa'uld who brought the Simarkans' ancestors to that planet centuries ago. He abandoned the planet after the rebellion in which the Temple of the Sholmoses *(see page 17)* was destroyed and the Stargate rendered inoperable. Since that time Raiden has found numerous worlds with populations from which to draw upon for slaves and hosts. He rarely leaves the flagship of his fleet, which is most often found in orbit above Kyoto.

More on Raiden can be found on page 17.

RAIDEN

Specialty: Goa'uld Warmaster
Rank: N/A
Class: Pointman
Level: 7

Strength:	17	Dexterity:	15
Constitution:	14	Intelligence:	16
Wisdom:	14	Charisma:	16
Vitality:	65	Wounds:	14

Defense: 15 (+3 class, +2 Dex)
Initiative Bonus: +5 (+3 class, +2 Dex)
Speed: 30

Fort: +6	**Ref:** +6	**Will:** +7

Special Qualities: Assistance (½ time), cross-class ability (accelerated healing), dominated body, *generous*, immunity to disease, inherited memory, lead (3/session), long life, parasite, radiation resistance, tactics (1/session), versatility (Concentration, Hide, Intimidate, Listen, Pilot, Spot, 2 skills).

Skills: Bluff +12, Bureaucracy +11, Concentration +10, Diplomacy +13, First Aid +10, Hide +10, Intimidate +13/+13, Listen +12, Pilot +11, Sense Motive +12, Spot +12.

Feats: Armor Group Proficiency (Light, Medium), Command Decision, Glint of Madness, Hard Core, Naquadah Sense, Surge of Speed, Weapon Group Proficiency (Handgun, Melee, Rifle).

ATTACKS

Unarmed	+8	1d3+5 (subdual)
Kinetic Blast	+7	2d6+2 normal, 2d6+2 subdual

Gear: Kara kesh.

RUAX (THOR'S HAMMER)

Goa'uld Prisoner (Deceased)

Trapped in the labyrinth of Cimmeria for a long period of time, the possessed Unas that confronted O'Neill and Teal'c was an aggressive and dangerous warrior: a Goa'uld underlord named Ruax. He was formerly one of the chief henchmen of the System Lord Sokar and part of a council of four underlords tasked with carrying out their master's will. Ruax was a fearsome warrior – regarded by most as a true demon – and was primarily responsible for assassinating the System Lord's enemies. On one particular mission, he became so obsessed with hunting down his target that he followed her blindly through an open Stargate. When the pair emerged on the other side, Ruax was teleported into the labyrinth by Thor's Hammer and his prey escaped to fight another day.

While Ruax bided his time within the labyrinth, waiting for someone to come along and help free him, turmoil broke out among Sokar's forces, who began to fight amongst themselves for the coveted position at the System Lord's right hand. As of the end of Season One, Sokar has not chosen to intervene on behalf of one minion or another, and as a result there is currently a small war taking place between several factions of underlords. Ruax was finally slain in the labyrinth by members of SG-1.

RUAX

Specialty: Goa'uld Warmaster
Rank: N/A
Class: Soldier
Level: 10

Strength:	18	Dexterity:	13
Constitution:	18	Intelligence:	11
Wisdom:	14	Charisma:	10
Vitality:	104	Wounds:	20

Defense: 15 (+4 class, +1 Dex)
Initiative Bonus: +9 (+8 class, +1 Dex)
Speed: 40

Fort: +9   **Ref:** +4   **Will:** +9

Special Qualities: +2 species bonus to damage, *accurate*, armor use +2, damage reduction 1/-, dominated body, immunity to disease, inherited memory, long life, parasite, portable cover (¼ cover), radiation resistance, regeneration, sarcophagus incompatible, weapon specialization (unarmed strike, zat'nik'tel).

Skills: Balance +7, Climb +12, Concentration +8, Driver +3, First Aid +6, Intimidate +17/+13, Jump +12, Profession (Military) +6, Spot +6, Survival (Mountain) +7, Swim +6, Tumble +4.

Feats: Armor Group Proficiency (Light, Medium, Heavy), Chi Strike, Combat Instincts, Confident Charge, Increased Speed, Naquadah Sense, Surge of Speed, Toughness, Weapon Focus (Unarmed Strike), Weapon Group Proficiency (Hurled, Melee, Handgun, Rifle, Tactical), Zat Resistance.

3 base + 4 soldier

ATTACKS

Unarmed	+14	1d3+8 (subdual)

Gear: None.

RUSSO, COLONEL DOUGLAS (THE BROCA DIVIDE)

USAMRIID Team Commander

Unlike his three brothers, Douglas Russo saw the Army only as a means to put himself through medical school, not as a career. But in the process of fulfilling his commitments, he discovered his true calling. Soon after medical school, during a stint at Fort Detrick's USAMRIID labs, Russo was thrust into the front lines of the 1989 Ebola crisis in Reston, Virginia. Though serious consequences were avoided, the incident crystallized the dangers lurking undiscovered in the world. As travel times decreased and the number of travelers increased, there was a growing risk of such chaos being visited on the U.S. That risk drove Russo to join the fight to prevent it. Coming from an Army family, he had long felt the pressure to follow in their footsteps and protect the country. Now he would be following the family tradition, but in a new way.

The young captain joined one of the field research teams as a junior member, and took his fight across the globe. In an average year he might spend time in Zaire tracing the origins of Ebola, the American Southwest treating a resurgence of the Hanta virus, or the South American jungle in search of new potential cures. He had a knack for working with the local populace, no matter where he was sent, and was always on the lookout for early signs of a new strain in the local media. These efforts did not go unnoticed, and within a few years he was leading entire teams of researchers. Promotions followed, and when the time came to overhaul the teams and their methods, Russo's experience was put to good use.

When his promotion to colonel came, he was mainly directing the actions of multiple teams from Fort Detrick, overseeing both the field research and the laborious work of identifying and cataloging the pathogens from the field.

His background made him an ideal choice when the SGC underwent its quarantine review following the infection from the Land of Light *(see page 18)*. Though not given full disclosure on the reasons behind the review, Russo recognized that Cheyenne Mountain was yet another front line in the same war he had been fighting for years. So when the team investigating the parasitic virus confronted him with their suspicions of its extraterrestrial nature, he knew that he had to get involved. It could prove to be the most important battlefield of all.

When the true nature of the SGC was revealed to him, Russo did not hesitate to take up his old field position once again. After helping test the mountain's isolation lab upgrades, and spending a little political capital, Russo took command of his most far-ranging field assignment on P3X-797. There he remains, researching Land of Light's unique virus and hoping to apply what he has learned to a wide array of other maladies.

(**Note**: individual campaigns set on P3X-797 may wish to replace Russo with one of the player characters instead.)

DOUGLAS RUSSO

Specialty: Army Infectious Disease Field Agent
Rank: Colonel (O-6)
Class: Scientist
Level: 4

Strength:	12	**Dexterity:**	14
Constitution:	15	**Intelligence:**	16
Wisdom:	13	**Charisma:**	10
Vitality:	31	**Wounds:**	15

Defense: 15 (+3 class, +2 Dex)
Initiative Bonus: +4 (+2 class, +2 Dex)
Speed: 30

Fort: +5   **Ref:** +3   **Will:** +5

Special Qualities: Improvise + 2, learned, PhD (Knowledge (Disease)), *professor,* research (Inspiration 1/session).

Skills: Bureaucracy +5, Computers +9, Concentration +8, Cultures +10, Diplomacy +6, First Aid +10, Knowledge (Disease) +20, Knowledge (Medicine) +12, Languages +7, Profession (Doctor) +8, Sense Motive +5, Spot +7, Survival (Jungle) +7.

Feats: Armor Group Proficiency (Light), Great Fortitude, Promotion, Weapon Group Proficiency (Handgun, Melee), Scholarly, World Traveler.

ATTACKS
Unarmed	+3	1d3+1 (subdual)
FN P90	+3	1d10+1 (normal, error 1-2, threat 19-20, range 30 ft., qualities and mods AP, BP, RG)

Gear: SG team bundle, other bundles as needed (by mission).

RYA'C (BLOODLINES)
Jaffa Outcast

R'yac is the son of Teal'c, some ten years old at the end of Season One. More one him can be found under the heading of his mother, Drey'auc *(see page 99)*.

RYA'C

Specialty: Jaffa Kresh'taa
Rank: N/A
Class: Guardian
Level: 1

Strength:	7	**Dexterity:**	12
Constitution:	10	**Intelligence:**	10
Wisdom:	10	**Charisma:**	10
Vitality:	12	**Wounds:**	10

Defense: 12 (+1 class, +1 Dex)
Initiative Bonus: +1 (+0 class, +1 Dex)
Speed: 30

Fort: +2   **Ref:** +1   **Will:** +1

Special Qualities: Enforcer (Basic), radiation resistance, *unbreakable.*

Skills: Climb +1, Concentrate +3, Hide +2, Hobby (Scrounging) 1, Intimidate +1/+3, Listen +3, Move Silently +3, Profession (Jaffa Military) +1, Search +2, Spot +4.

Feats: Alertness, Enforcer, Symbiote (Immunity to Disease).

ATTACKS
Unarmed	-1	1d3-2 subdual

Gear: Robes.

SAMUELS, MAJOR (LATER LT. COLONEL) BERT (CHILDREN OF THE GODS)
Pentagon Liaison

Assigned to Stargate Command as General Hammond's Executive Officer during the shutdown of the Stargate program, Major Samuels was a beneficiary of the gate's reactivation, as it suddenly made his post an important position in a major Air Force operation. He was determined to squeeze every advantage out of the opportunity, but the other officers at the SGC, notably Hammond and O'Neill, intensely disliked Samuels' naked ambition. When the man was transferred to the Pentagon, they breathed a sigh of relief, but it wasn't the last they would see of him.

At the Pentagon, Samuels attached himself to the coattails of Senator Kinsey, a powerful politician looking to score points by making a major cut to the military budget.

Samuels offered him an enormous sacrificial lamb in the form of the SGC, and in doing so earned himself a promotion to Lt. Colonel. He served as liaison between the SGC and the Pentagon for a time, but was reassigned after his cowardice was revealed during a Goa'uld attack. Since then, Samuels has worked behind the scenes to support the Senator's efforts to control the SGC or remove the Stargate to an agency more under Kinsey's control. He has shown himself to be a self-centered, unscrupulous weasel with a strong grudge against Stargate Command and everyone associated with it.

BERT SAMUELS

Specialty: Air Force Officer
Rank: Major (O-4) (later Lt. Colonel (O-5))
Class: Soldier/Pointman
Level: 1/3

Strength:	10	**Dexterity:**	11
Constitution:	11	**Intelligence:**	13
Wisdom:	11	**Charisma:**	12
Vitality:	24	**Wounds:**	11

Defense: 11 (+1 class)
Initiative Bonus: +2 (+2 class)
Speed: 30

Fort: +3   **Ref:** +2   **Will:** +5

Special Qualities: Assistance (½), *generous,* lead 1/session, versatility (Computers, Diplomacy, Forgery, Innuendo, Gather Information, 2 skills).

Skills: Balance +1, Bluff +6, Bureaucracy +12, Computers +3, Concentration +2, Demolitions +3, Diplomacy +5, Driver +3, First Aid +2, Forgery +3, Gather Information +3, Innuendo +2, Intimidate +4/+5, Pilot +3, Profession (Office Administration) +3, Spot +3.

Feats: Armor Group Proficiency (Light, Medium, Heavy), Persuasive, Point Bank Shot, Political Favors, Silver Tongue, Weapon Group Proficiency (Handgun, Hurled, Melee, Rifle, Tactical).

ATTACKS

Unarmed   +3   1d3 (subdual)

Gear: Professional bundle.

SHAK'L (THE NOX)

Jaffa Serpent Guard (Deceased)

Shak'l was a Jaffa in the service of Apophis, a loyal soldier who had the wondrous opportunity to die for his god. Raised on tales of Jaffa heroics, he strove each day to be worthy of joining their ranks. The day he succeeded was the happiest of his life, for he knew that his god smiled upon him. His original duties placed him under Teal'c, then the First Prime of Apophis, and he was greatly impressed by the elder warrior's prowess. When Teal'c betrayed Apophis,

Shak'l took it as a personal slight. The Serpent God was all that mattered for him; he lived and died at the Goa'uld's command That Teal'c would throw that all away and remain alive was a grave insult.

Apophis soon took notice of Shak'l's devotion and strength; after several successful missions, he was promoted to Second Prime, and hoped to advance even further by hunting down and slaying Teal'c. Unfortunately for him, Teal'c proved his superior when they finally met again: the renegade slew Shak'l before he could harm more innocents. As a Jaffa, Shak'l was everything a Goa'uld could hope for: fanatic, merciless, and utterly obedient to his god. His strength and ability were a sad testament to how much potential the Jaffa have wasted under the yoke of their masters.

SHAK'L

Specialty: Jaffa Serpent Guard
Rank: N/A
Class: Guardian
Level: 4

Strength:	16	**Dexterity:**	14
Constitution:	15	**Intelligence:**	13
Wisdom:	12	**Charisma:**	10
Vitality:	49	**Wounds:**	15

Defense: 14 (+2 class, +2 Dex)
Initiative Bonus: +8 (+2 class, +2 Dex, +4 feat)
Speed: 30

Fort: +6   **Ref:** +3   **Will:** +5

Special Qualities: Enforcer (Basic) , soak (1/session), radiation resistance, toughness, *unbreakable.*

Skills: Balance +4, Climb +5, Concentration +5, Escape Artist +4, First Aid +4, Hide +6, Intimidate +13/+10, Move Silently +5, Pilot +4, Spot +6, Survival (Forest) +6, Tumble.

Feats: Armor Group Proficiency (Light, Medium, Heavy), Enforcer, Improved Initiative, Quick Draw, Stone Cold, Symbiote (Long Life), Toughness, Weapon Group Proficiency (Handgun, Hurled, Melee, Rifle).

Unarmed	+7	1d3+3 (subdual)
Gauntlet Knife	+7	1d4+3 (normal, error 1, threat 20)
Staff Weapon	+2	6d6 (normal, error 1-2, threat 18-20, range 75 ft., qualities and mods AP, AK)

Gear: Gauntlet knife, staff weapon, Jaffa armor.

SKAARA (CHILDREN OF THE GODS)
Abydonian Youth

Born on Abydos under the rule of the Goa'uld Ra, Skaara led a harsh existence into his teen years. His father, Kasuf, was the leader of their people, but Skaara had no wish to take his father's place. Like all boys, he longed for adventure and change, even if his inexperience would not let him articulate exactly what that was. His sister, Sha're, cautioned him to cover the flame in his heart, lest it shine too brightly and call the attention of Ra. Skaara understood. Ra was an evil god, and his might was absolute. There could be no change on Abydos, not now or ever.

Then came O'Neill.

The Tauri were unlike any Abydonians Skaara had ever met. Their eyes did not lower to the ground at the mention of Ra's name. They held their heads high, without fear. Skaara was in awe. He wanted to understand O'Neill, grasp what it was that gave him such inner strength. Was he also a god? No. The Tauri denied their divinity... and Ra's as well, with words that Ra must surely hear and strike them down for. Indeed Ra did return, but the Tauri did not supplicate themselves before the evil god. They fought!

Skaara's spirit burned with shame at his lifetime of cowardice, and he convinced his friends that the Tauri were showing them the path to freedom. With a fierce determination born of years of oppression and hidden anger, they assisted O'Neill and his men, and helped them to destroy the Goa'uld System Lord. Skaara knew that his life would never be the same. After the death of Ra, Daniel Jackson decided to remain behind on Abydos and marry Sha're, but O'Neill journeyed back through the *chaapa'ai*. Skaara missed him, but life on Abydos was lighter, full of promise like never before. Daniel taught him the language of the Tauri, writing, new ways to build things, and many secrets of the heavens. It was as he had always dreamed, but soon it was to become a nightmare.

One year after the defeat of Ra, the chaapa'ai sprang to life once more. Soon O'Neill returned with foreboding news: another evil god had appeared, perhaps seeking revenge for the death of Ra. Skaara stood watch over the chaapa'ai personally, but was captured along with his sister when the Goa'uld Apophis appeared with a formation of Serpent Guards. They were taken to Chulak, where they subsequently became hosts for Apophis' son, Klorel, and Queen, Amaunet *(see the entry on Klorel for more information)*. As of the end of Season One, he remains enthralled to the Goa'uld... but O'Neill has taught him to be strong and such lessons are not easily forgotten. If anyone can fight such a nightmare, it is he.

SKAARA

These stats reflect Skaara's standing just before his possession.

Specialty: Primitive Society Near Human
Rank: N/A
Class: Native Off-Worlder
Level: 3

Strength:	10	Dexterity:	12
Constitution:	12	Intelligence:	10
Wisdom:	12	Charisma:	11
Vitality:	16	Wounds:	12

Defense: 12 (+1 class, +1 Dex)
Initiative Bonus: +2 (+1 class, +1 Dex)
Speed: 30

Fort: +4	Ref: +3	Will: +3

Special Qualities: Primitive.

Skills: Climb +2, Craft (Primitive Weapons), +4, Hide +3, Move Silently +3, Profession (Herding) +6, Spot +4, Search +3, Survival (Desert) +4.

Feats: Armor Group Proficiency (Light), Ordinary Past, Weapon Group Proficiency (Hurled, Melee).

ATTACKS

Unarmed	+2	1d3 (subdual)
Spear	+2	1d8 (error 1, threat 20)

Gear: Weapon, robes.

TUPLO (THE BROCA DIVIDE)
High Councilor of the City of the Land of Light

Tuplo's family is one of several that have ruled the City of the Land of Light as far back as their records reach — over forty generations. As was the tradition, he spent his youth in an ordinary profession, among the people, learning what it was to be one of the Untouched without the privileges of his inevitable position. Tuplo spent the years as a craftsman, learning the art and business of metalworking, and raising a family. When he was in his mid-thirties, the previous High Councilor, Chapin, became Touched by the *heelksha* and was banished to the Land of the Dark, requiring Tuplo to replace his uncle. Shortly thereafter he lost his wife, Nara, to the heelksha as well.

Though tragic, it was an all-too-common occurrence which Tuplo could not allow to interfere with his new position. In place of his devotion to his wife, Tuplo doted on his daughter Melosha, and was proud of the accomplishments she made in her chosen profession of storyteller. His hopes for her were all but shattered when she was captured by the Touched as well. Tuplo hid his emotions, even for his daughter. This is how the Councilors are expected to behave. So it is a testament to his true feelings that he organized a small band of friends, including fellow Councilors, to track Melosha and attempt a rescue.

Fortunately the team from Earth helped free Melosha, and later cured her and others of the curse of the Touched. As the ranks of the Untouched swelled with the newly cured, Tuplo led the other Councilors in welcoming their new friends, and pledged whatever aid and hospitality they could offer in return. He gladly approved the SGC's request for a base in the Land of the Dark, realizing that there were still more of the Touched to cure. Having their friends close by is the first gesture of a grateful population, and a measure of protection in case the heelksha returns.

TUPLO

Specialty: Primitive Society Near Human
Rank: N/A
Class: Native Off-Worlder/Diplomat
Level: 3/2

Strength:	10	Dexterity:	11
Constitution:	12	Intelligence:	10
Wisdom:	12	Charisma:	14

Vitality:	27	Wounds:	12

Defense: 12 (+2 class)
Initiative Bonus: +2 (+2 class)
Speed: 30

Fort: +4   **Ref:** +2   **Will:** +6

Special Qualities: Dependency (Sunlight), Primitive, Reduced Sleep Need.

Skills: Bluff +7, Bureaucracy +3, Climb +2, Craft (Metalworking) +5, Cultures +2, Diplomacy +6, Gather Information +3, Innuendo +2, Intimidate +4/+6, Languages +1, Listen +4, Profession (Diplomat) +4, Profession (Hunting) +5, Search +3, Sense Motive +3, Spot +3, Survival (Forest) +4.

Feats: Armor Group Proficiency (Light), Ordinary Past, Persuasive, Weapon Group Proficiency (Hurled, Melee).

ATTACKS

Unarmed	+3	1d3+2 (subdual)
Sling	+3	1d4 (normal, error 1, threat -, range 20 ft.)

Gear: Symbol of office (headgear), robes.

TURGHAN (EMANCIPATION)

Toughai Chieftain

Turghan is the leader of the Toughai, the People of the Forest. He is a ruthless warrior and the fiercest chieftain on Simarka, commanding the loyalty of twenty two tribes. He believes that aggressiveness keeps his people strong, and while he has little desire for personal glory, he will not hesitate to launch an attack if he feels the Toughai will benefit from it. The marriage of his daughter to Abu of the Shavadai has improved relations with them, though considerable tensions still remain.

TURGHAN

Specialty: Primitive Society
Rank: N/A
Class: Soldier
Level: 6

Strength:	16	Dexterity:	15
Constitution:	15	Intelligence:	12
Wisdom:	12	Charisma:	14

Vitality:	56	Wounds:	17

Defense: 14 (+2 class, +2 Dex)
Initiative Bonus: +7 (+ 5 class, +2 Dex)
Speed: 30

Fort: +5   **Ref:** +4   **Will:** +6

Special Qualities: *Accurate,* armor use +1, damage reduction 1/-, weapon specialization (sword).

Skills: Balance +6, Climb +7, Diplomacy +4, Intimidate +10/+9, Move Silently +5, Search +5, Spot +6, Survival (Mountain) +5, Tumble +6.

Feats: Armor Group Proficiency (Light), Combat Instincts, Mountain Training, Power Attack, Stone Cold, Toughness, Track, Weapon Group Proficiency (Hurled, Melee).

Backgrounds: Political Enemy (Moughal) 3, Political Enemy (Abu) 1.

ATTACKS

Unarmed	+9	1d3+3 (subdual)
Dagger	+9	1d4+3 (error 1, threat 20)
Sword	+9	1d8+5 (error 1, threat 18-20)

Gear: sword, bow, 20 arrows.

VRITRA (THE ENEMY WITHIN)

Goa'uld System Lord

Vritra is the System Lord who controls the planet Prakiti, having driven out its previous lord, Indra. Though a warrior at heart, he also understands the value of scientific investigation and technological development. He is obsessed with obtaining Ancient devices, which is why he raids worlds rather than seizing them outright. Despite all the setbacks he has encountered thus far, he remains convinced that Prakiti is home to a large cache of Ancient technology and will stop at nothing to obtain it.

VRITRA

Specialty: Goa'uld Noble
Rank: N/A
Class: Soldier/Scientist
Level: 10/4

Strength:	16	Dexterity:	12
Constitution:	16	Intelligence:	13
Wisdom:	9	Charisma:	13
Vitality:	137	Wounds:	16

Defense: 15 (+4 class, +1 Dex)
Initiative Bonus: +13 (+8 class, +1 Dex, +4 Improved Initiative)
Speed: 30

Fort: +8   **Ref:** +4   **Will:** +6

Special Qualities: *Accurate,* armor use +2, damage reduction 1/-, dominated body, immunity to disease, improvise +2, inherited memory, learned, long life, parasite, portable cover (¼) radiation resistance, research (World Traveler), weapon specialization (Kara Kesh, Unarmed).

Skills: Appraise +6, Balance +7, Climb +8, Computers +7, Concentration +3, Cryptography +5, Cultures +3, Diplomacy +4, Driver +4, Electronics +5, First Aid +2, Intimidate +12/+10, Jump +6, Knowledge (Ancients) +5, Languages 3*, Listen +4, Pilot +6, Profession (Military) +4, Search +8, Spot +8, Surveillance +2, Survival (Forest) +3, Tumble +6, Xeno-Cultures +4, Xeno-Languages +2.

 * can only be used untrained – no skill ranks

Feats: Armor Proficiency Group (Light, Medium, Heavy), Bloodthirsty, Combat Instincts, Command Decision, Improved Initiative, Martial Arts, Naquadah Sense, Open Stance, Persuasive, Scholarly, Stone Cold, Surge of Speed, Warrior's Grace, Weapon Proficiency Group (Hurled, Melee, Handgun, Rifle, Tactical), World Traveler.

Backgrounds: Hunting 4, Long-Term Mission 3.

ATTACKS

Unarmed	+16	1d6+5 (subdual)
Kara kesh	+14	2d6+2 and 2d6+2 (subdual)

Gear: Kara kesh, extravagant military attire.

WARNER, DR. WILLIAM (THE ENEMY WITHIN)

Chief Surgeon, SGC

Dr. William Warner is Stargate Command's Chief Surgeon. He acquired his position due to the recommendation of Chief Medical Officer Dr. Janet Fraiser, who recognized his talents, particularly in the field of microsurgery. Dr. Fraiser believed – quite rightly it turned out – that Warner's unique specialty would make him an ideal member of her staff. Since joining the SGC, he has saved the lives of many personnel who've suffered injuries that might otherwise have killed them. He has perfected many techniques that have the potential to one day save countless lives in the outside world. Warner's greatest regret is that he failed to remove the Goa'uld larva that possessed Major Charles Kawalsky, especially after so such a seemingly successful operation. He continues to hone his skills, hoping one day to make up for the failure.

WARNER, DR. WILLIAM

Specialty: Air Force Officer
Rank: Major
Class: Scientist
Level: 3

Strength:	11	Dexterity:	12
Constitution:	14	Intelligence:	17
Wisdom:	13	Charisma:	12
Vitality:	24	Wounds:	14

Defense: 14 (+3 class, +1 Dex)
Initiative Bonus: +2 (+1 class, +1 Dex)
Speed: 30

Fort: +3   **Ref:** +2   **Will:** +5

Special Qualities: Improvise +2, learned, *professor,* Ph.D (Knowledge (Medicine)).

Skills: Bureaucracy +5, Computers +9, Concentration +9, Cultures +6, Diplomacy +4, Driver +5, Electronics +8, First Aid +9, Knowledge (Goa'uld) +11, Knowledge (Medicine) +11, Languages +6, Mechanics +7, Pilot +3, Profession (doctor) +7, Profession (Military) +3, Search +6, Sense Motive +4.

Feats: Armor Group Proficiency (Light), False Start (Knowledge (Medicine)), Fortunate, Scholarly, Weapon Proficiency (Melee, Handgun), World Traveler.

Backgrounds: Vow (perfect Goa'uld removal technique) 2.

ATTACKS

Unarmed	+1	1d3 (subdual)

Gear: SG medical bundle (off-world missions only).

This chapter contains a variety of new character options, classes, rules updates, and the like. Where pertinent, episode references have been included to direct you to the specific mission log from which the rule stems.

New Human Specialties

These specialties are normally limited to Earth-bound humans, usually attached to the SGC or another branch of the military.

Army Medical Corps

(New Army specialty)

The US Army Medical Research Institute for Infectious Diseases (USAMRIID), located at Fort Detrick, MD, is one of the foremost research institutes in the world for high-risk biological material. Accordingly, medical specialists from it and similar facilities are at the forefront of the SGC's efforts to identify, contain, and investigate outbreaks of infectious diseases both at the base and on other worlds. While seldom assigned to initial exploration missions, Army Medical Corps personnel are often called in to help clean up problems that occur and to prevent recurring outbreaks in the future. Their foremost priority is to ensure that no biohazard returns to Earth, or, failing that, escapes the SGC. Army Medical Corps personnel also serve the SGC in a variety of other life sciences and medical assignments.

Special Talents

- +1 Specialty bonus with Knowledge (Biology) and Profession (Doctor) skill checks. This bonus increases by an additional +1 at 4th level and every 4 levels thereafter. In addition, these are always class skills for the character.

- *Pay Grade:* The character may choose to be paid as either an officer or a specialist.

- *Bonus Feat:* World Traveler. All prerequisites for this feat – including skill ranks – are waived.

NID Interrogator

(New National Intelligence Department (NID) Specialty)

The National Intelligence Department has as its mission (among other things) the acquisition of as much knowledge about the enemies of the United States as possible. Such knowledge is obtained in many ways, including tried and true methods of interrogation, as well as more sophisticated techniques that some would say border on the unethical. To the NID, such concerns are of no consequence; the defense and continued survival of the United States of America trumps all other considerations. For that reason, NID interrogators are not well regarded by other characters of the US government. Even within the NID, interrogators have an unsavory reputation as necessary evils. Interrogators rarely acknowledge the true nature of their mission, lest their reputations interfere with their ability to do their jobs.

SPECIAL TALENTS

- +1 specialty bonus to Gather Information and Intimidate checks. This bonus increases by +1 every 4 character levels gained thereafter.

- Pay Grade: The character is paid as an officer *(see Stargate SG-1 core rulebook, page 284).*

- Bonus Feat: Mark. All prerequisites for this feat – including skill ranks – are waived.

NEW ALIEN SPECIALTIES

These specialties are intended for characters not native to Earth, as specified in their entry. Characters from each of these specialties receive the shared special talents of their race.

GOA'ULD QUEEN

(New Goa'uld Specialty)

Goa'uld queens are are responsible for the creation of new larvae that are then implanted into Jaffa hosts until they mature. Without queens, the Goa'uld would eventually die out. More information about Goa'uld queens can be found on page 111 of the *Stargate SG-1* core rulebook.

SPECIAL TALENTS

- +2 Charisma.

- Bluff and Sense Motive are always class skills for the Goa'uld. Further, the queen's threat range with these skills is increased by 1 (e.g. a threat range of 19-20 becomes 18-20). This bonus increases by 1 at 5th level and for every 5 levels gained thereafter.

- Special Quality: Produce Larvae. The Goa'uld queen can produce large numbers of larvae in a short period of time. To do so, she requires a DNA sample of the race intended as hosts for the larvae. Once she has obtained the sample, the queen joins it with her own DNA to create a brood of 8 to 10 larvae. These larvae must be birthed in a warm liquid environment when they are ready to come forth, approximately 24 hours after the queen joins her DNA with that of the intended host.

- Bonus Feat: Persuasive. All prerequisites for this feat – including minimum skill ranks – are waived.

DRAGON GUARD

(New Jaffa Specialty)

The dragon guards are fierce warriors loyal to the System Lord Kur. They are known to fight past impossible odds and for their unnatural savagery in battle.

SPECIAL TALENTS

- +2 Strength.

- 4 extra vitality points at 1st level, and one additional vitality point at each additional level.

- Bonus Feat: Two-Weapon Fighting. All prerequisites for this feat – including ability scores – are waived.

JAFFA CLERGY

(New Jaffa Specialty)

Jaffa priests are charged with enforcing the will of their gods in Jaffa society. They are thus afforded great respect and power, though they are also in closer proximity to their gods (and therefore more closely scrutinized).

SPECIAL TALENTS

- +2 Wisdom.

- +1 Species bonus with Concentration and Sense Motive checks. This bonus increases by an additional +1 at 4th level and for every 4 character levels gained thereafter. Priests must perform complex and sometimes exhausting rituals, where a tiny mistake can bring down the wrath of a displeased Goa'uld.

- Bonus Feat: Symbiote. To join the priesthood, the Jaffa must have been chosen by one of the children of the gods, and been implanted with a Goa'uld larva. Choose one symbiote ability *(see the Stargate SG-1 core rulebook, page 265).*

KRESH'TAA

(New Jaffa Specialty)

The outcasts of Jaffa society, whether due to their own actions or those of a relative, these Jaffa are forced to live apart from the mainstream. While the others live in their cities of stone and wood, the kresh'taa must make do with the scraps left over – old sheets for tents, worn clothing thrown away, and whatever food can be scrounged. This has bred more than a little discontent with the status quo the Goa'uld maintain over the Jaffa, though there is little talk of rebellion, in the hopes that one day and outcast can be redeemed and rejoin the very society that shuns them. It has also made the ones who survive into cautious and stealthy scavengers.

SPECIAL TALENTS

- +0 Constitution. This replaces the standard +2 bonus gained by all Jaffa characters *(see the Stargate SG-1 core rulebook, page 147)*, +2 Dexterity, +2 Intelligence. The cast out kresh'taa must live by their wits.

- +1 species bonus with Hide and Sleight-of-Hand checks. This bonus increases by an additional +1 at 4th level and for every 4 character levels gained thereafter. Kresh'taa are used to having to acquire what they need to survive surreptitiously.

- Bonus Feat: Alertness. All prerequisites for this feat – including minimum skill ranks – are waived.

UNAS AS GOA'ULD HOSTS (THOR'S HAMMER)

If an Unas is taken as a host for a Goa'uld, create character stats for the Goa'uld as normal but with the following modifications to the Goa'uld Macro-Species:

- *Ability Scores:* Strength +4, Dexterity -2.

- *Regeneration:* A Goa'uld that takes an Unas as a host gains the ability to take advantage of their natural regenerative abilities. The character recovers 1 vitality point per minute and 1 wound point per 5 minutes. Further, the character always automatically stabilizes whenever injured, even when reduced to negative wounds (so long as he or she does not die).

- *Sarcophagus Incompatible:* Goa'uld that take Unas as hosts may not use the sarcophagus device to heal their host body.

- *Species Feats:* Goa'uld that inhabit Unas bodies may select level-based feats from the species feat tree *(see the Stargate SG-1 core rulebook page 283)*. Additionally, the character may select feats from the species feat tree that list Unas as a species prerequisite, as well as those that are for Goa'uld only.

ABYDONIANS

(New Near-Human Species/Specialty)

The residents of Abydos are descended from humans taken from Ancient Egypt to work in the naquadah mines of Ra. They have since been freed by the SGC and are now staunch allies of Earth. This is a near-human species with a primitive society *(as per the Stargate SG-1 core rulebook, pages 148-151)*.

SPECIAL TALENTS

- +2 Constitution, -2 Intelligence. Abydonians are much hardier than their Earth counterparts, but while not necessarily less intelligent, they lack the rudiments of education that all Earth humans take for granted.

- +1 Species bonus with any skill check made in the following skills: Handle Animal, Survival.

- Languages: Ancient Egyptian is the native language of the Abydonians.

- Pay Grade: While working with the SGC, the character is paid as an enlisted soldier or specialist *(see the Stargate SG-1 core rulebook, page 283)*.

- Primitive Society Bonus Feat: Abydonians automatically receive the Desert Training feat for free. All prerequisites for this feat – including minimum skill levels – are waived.

ARGOSIANS

(New Near-Human Species/Specialty)

The residents of Argos are descended from humans taken from Ancient Greece to be used as guinea pigs in one of Pelops' nanotechnology experiments. This is a near-human species with a primitive society *(as per the Stargate SG-1 core rulebook, pages 148-151)*.

SPECIAL TALENTS

- +2 Charisma, -2 Strength. While Argosians have an almost unnatural attractiveness, their all but carefree existence left them little need for physical exertion.

- Evolutionary Advantage: Genetically Engineered (+2 to Constitution).

- Evolutionary Disadvantage: (Shortened Lifespan 100 days) or Gene Pool Deficiency (-2 to Intelligence).*

- Species Feats: Argosians may take species feats as a Near Human Primitive Society.

  Languages: Ancient Greek is the native language of the Argosians.

- +2 species bonus with Disposition checks. This bonus increases by an additional +1 at 4th level and for every 4 character levels gained thereafter.

- Pay Grade: While working with the SGC, the character is paid as an enlisted soldier or specialist (*see the Stargate SG-1 core rulebook, page 283*).

- Bonus Feat: The Look. All prerequisites for this feat — including minimum skill levels — are waived.

*Prior to SG-1's arrival on Argos, Argosians had the Shortened Lifespan Evolutionary Disadvantage. After the events of *Brief Candle*, they have the Gene Pool Deficiency Evolutionary Disadvantage.

BYRSA

(New Near-Human Species/Specialty)

The residents of Byrsa are descended from humans taken from ancient Carthage. Though they are not directly ruled by any Goa'uld, they remain vulnerable to slaving raids and other attacks from the System Lords. This is a near-human species with a primitive society (*as per the Stargate SG-1 core rulebook, pages 148-151*).

SPECIAL TALENTS

- Evolutionary Advantage – Skill Enhancement (Hide, Move Silently): For generations the Goa'uld have used Cartago as a favored source of new hosts. Having no way to directly fight them, the Byrsa developed the uncanny knack to almost fade from sight to avoid being taken. These techniques are taught from the time a Byrsa can walk, and are practiced daily. As a result, all Byrsa are considered to have the Stealthy Feat (*see the Stargate SG-1 core rulebook, page 261*). All prerequisites for this feat — including minimum skill levels — are waived.

- Evolutionary Disadvantage – Vulnerability (Extreme Cold): The Byrsa descend from stock that developed in Earth's equatorial regions, and they have lived in similar environments since being relocated by the Goa'uld. Given Cartago's mild weather, they have almost no experience with genuine cold. If a Byrsa is exposed to temperatures below 0°F for a full round, the character suffers 1d6 normal damage at the end of that round, and all subsequent rounds, until the exposure ceases.

- Languages: Ancient Phoenician is the native language of the Byrsa.

- Pay Grade: While working with the SGC, the character is paid as an enlisted soldier or specialist (*see the Stargate SG-1 core rulebook, page 283*).

- Primitive Society Bonus Feat: All Byrsa receive the Forest Training Feat. All prerequisites for this feat — including minimum skill levels — are waived.

NEW BACKGROUND: BYRSA MANDATES (3)

Taught to live by a code of honor that places high value on the harmony of the community, the Bysra hold themselves to the highest standards of conduct at all times, even when provoked or threatened. Should a Byrsa commit an unjustified act, either out of anger or fear or hate, that action stains both that individual and the entire clan. The shame continues (manifested as a -2 circumstance bonus in interactions with other Byrsa) until an apology is offered to the victim, and the offender is forgiven. If the victim will not forgive, the shame is ongoing (additional offenses do not produce a stacking bonus).

THE UNTOUCHED

(New Near-Human Species/Specialty)

The Untouched are residents of the Land of Light, descended from humans taken from ancient Minos. This is a near-human species with a primitive society (*as per the Stargate SG-1 core rulebook, pages 148-151*).

SPECIAL TALENTS

- Evolutionary Advantage – Reduced Need for Sleep: Due to the fact that they live in the area always in sunlight, the Untouched have adapted their melatonin cycles to be independent of light/dark periods. Though they still require sleep, their biochemical make-up allows them to go for up to a week without rest and suffer no ill effects. The normal individual sleeps an average of four out of every 60 hours.

- Evolutionary Disadvantage – Dependency: Perhaps due to the same changes lessening the need for sleep, the Untouched require regular exposure to direct sunlight or begin to fall ill. If the individual does not spend at least one hour out of every 24 exposed to direct sunlight (or an alternate full spectrum light source), they suffer a -2 species penalty to all attack, education, inspiration and skill checks until that condition is fulfilled. (Note: This dependency does not apply to individuals suffering from the Touched virus.)

- Languages: Ancient Greek is the native language of the Untouched.

- Pay Grade: While working with the SGC, the character is paid as an enlisted soldier or specialist (*see the Stargate SG-1 core rulebook, page 283*).

- Primitive Society Bonus Feat: All Untouched receive the Forest Training Feat. All prerequisites for this feat — including minimum skill levels — are waived.

DISPLACED NEAR-HUMAN

(Near-Human Society Option)

The System Lords raid many worlds, taking prisoners and slaves and transporting them via the Stargates to their centers of power. There, these near-humans are forced to survive in an environment quite unlike their own. They must learn to adapt to Goa'uld notions of order or suffer the consequences. Some manage to cling to some semblance of their old ways, but most soon realize that they shall never return to their homes.

SPECIAL TALENTS

- +2 Wisdom, –2 Charisma. Displaced near-humans learn that their lives may depend on being quick-witted and aware of one's surroundings. At the same time, it pays to avoid shows of initiative or personal magnetism, lest the Goa'uld become concerned about the possibility of a slave revolt.

- +1 specialty bonus with skill checks made using Bluff and any one of the following skills, per the society from which the displaced near-human came: Craft (any one), Diplomacy, Knowledge (any one), Profession (any one), and Survival. This bonus increases by +1 every 4 character levels gained thereafter.

- Pay Grade: While working with the SGC, the character is paid as an enlisted soldier or specialist *(see the Stargate SG-1 core rulebook, page 283)*.

- Bonus Feat: Any terrain or style feat. The character must still meet all the prerequisites for this feat before choosing it.

NEW RACES

The following new alien macro-species appeared during Season One, or were mentioned elsewhere in this book.

NETJERIANS (MACRO-SPECIES)

The Netjerians are a tall, thin race with purple-black skin and elongated features. They hail from the planet Ta-Netjer, the former throne world of the System Lord Hathor. Since their abandonment by Hathor, they have become virulently opposed to the Goa'uld, having built a high-tech and progressive society through their own efforts. They are by nature peaceful but not pacifistic. They are incensed by injustice and oppression, owing to their own experiences in the distant past. Netjerians are very keen to work with the humans of the SGC, meaning they would make excellent characters for players interested in an alien species.

SHARED SPECIES TRAITS

- +2 Charisma, –4 Constitution. The Netjerians are extremely personable but are not as hardy as other species.

- Strong Willed: The character gains a +1 Species bonus to Will saves made to resist the effects of mental domination or control. This bonus increases by an additional +1 At 2nd level and for every 2 character levels gained thereafter.

- Species Feats: The character may choose level-based feats from the species feat tree *(see the Stargate SG-1 core rulebook, page 264)*. Typically, a character cannot choose feats from the species trees unless he possesses a character option that expressly allows him to do so.

- Pay Grade: While working with the SGC, the character is paid as an officer *(see the Stargate SG-1 core rulebook, page 284)*. Alien characters are often paid in commensurate non-monetary concessions and favors.

- Language: Netjerian is a native language for the character.

NETJERIAN PILOT

The Netjerians are among the best starship pilots to be found among the lesser races of the galaxy. Over the centuries, they have gained a remarkable facility with the piloting of star-faring vessels. This facility is so innate in some Netjerians that they can easily transfer it to vessels with which they have only minimal familiarity. It is this talent that these aliens believe can provide great assistance to the SGC as it battles against the Goa'uld System Lords.

SPECIAL TALENTS

- +2 Dexterity.

- +1 Species bonus with Mechanics and Pilot checks. This bonus increases by an additional +1 at 4th level and for every 4 character levels gained thereafter.

- Bonus Feat: Wind Rider. All prerequisites for this feat – including minimum skill ranks – are waived.

NETJERIAN PROVOCATEUR

The Netjerians frequently send small teams of operatives onto Goa'uld-held worlds in order to sow dissension and rebellion against the System Lords. Because these aliens excel at interpersonal relations, they are also quite effective at swaying opinion against the Goa'uld. In addition, these provocateurs can act as espionage characters and saboteurs should the need arise.

SPECIAL TALENTS

- +2 Wisdom.

- +1 Species bonus with initiative checks. This bonus increases by +1 at 4th level and for every 4 character levels gained thereafter. Netjerian provocateurs have learned to be on their toes at all times, given the danger of the work they typically undertake.

- Bonus Feat: Persuasive. All prerequisites for this feat – including minimum skill ranks – are waived.

Netjerian Soldier

By nature, the Netjerians are not a violent species. They undertake conflict only with great reluctance, such as when faced with overt evil and oppression. Such is the case with the Goa'uld, which is why so many Netjerians have chosen to take up arms and defend not only themselves but all those who suffer at the hands of the System Lords.

Special Talents

- +2 Strength.

- +1 Species bonus with any attack made against a Goa'uld. This bonus increases by an additional +1 at 5th level and for every 5 character levels gained thereafter.

- Bonus Feat: Zen Focus. All prerequisites for this feat are waived.

Playing Nox Characters

Nox characters are extremely powerful, and should most often be used as NPCs only. However, the Gamemaster can allow Nox player characters if he so chooses. Any player choosing a Nox character should be encouraged to play the Nox's pacifistic and non-violent natures to the hilt. The Nox do not compromise on these values, and the Gamemaster should enforce this point. In addition, no Nox would ever permanently join an SG team, given the SGC's willingness to employ violence to solve their problems.

Nox (Macro-Species)

The Nox are an ancient race of beings whose appearance belies their technological capabilities. Primitive in appearance and manner, the Nox are among the most advanced species in the galaxy. Nox are universally committed to a philosophy they call the Journey of Life – a metaphor which describes the path they follow throughout their lives, as they seek to learn, experience, and teach the wisdom that comes with age.

Special Talents

- +2 Intelligence, +2 Wisdom, -2 Strength, -2 Constitution. The Nox possess an almost unnatural intellect and willpower, but their peaceful existence leaves them little need for physical exertion.

- +2 species bonus with Intelligence checks and Will saving throws. This bonus increases by an additional +1 at 4th level and for every 4 character levels gained thereafter.

- Total Pacifists: The Nox's base attack bonus never increases beyond +0, regardless of class bonuses.

- Languages: Nox is the native language of the Nox

- Long Life: The Nox live an average of 500 years.

- Bonus Feat: Forest Training. All prerequisites for this feat – including skill ranks – are waived.

Ohnes (Macro-Species)

An ancient (by Earth standards) race dedicated to fighting the Goa'uld across the galaxy, the Ohnes are an amphibious species with extremely long life spans. The SGC has thus far made only occasional contact with the Ohnes since SG-1's first encounter on P3X-866, but such contact has yielded promising results. It is hoped that one day the Ohnes will become a more permanent ally in the fight against the System Lords.

Shared Species Talents

- +2 Strength, -2 Dexterity, -2 Charisma. The Ohnes gain physical strength from living under the oceans of their worlds, but they are not especially quick or dexterous and their matter-of-fact attitude make them less than personable.

- Speed: The character has a base speed of 20. When swimming, the Ohnes' speed increases to 30.

- Amphibious: Ohnes breathe equally well in air and water.

- Dehydration: Ohnes must spend at least three hours each day submerged in water or they begin to suffer from dehydration. After an Ohnes character has gone 2 days without being either submerged in water or sprayed or hosed down, he must begin making Fortitude saves every hour (DC 10 + 1 for each previous check), suffering 1d6 damage from dehydration for each failed save. An Ohnes suffering damage from dehydration is fatigued (see the Stargate SG-1 core rulebook, page 378). The Ohnes have developed a device called a hydrator that allows them to remain out of water for prolonged periods of time (see page 151).

- Species Feats: The character may choose level-based feats from the species feat tree (see the Stargate SG-1 core rulebook, page 264). Further, the Ohnes may take the Naquadah Sense feat. Typically, a character may not choose feats from the species tree unless he possesses a character option that expressly allows him to do so.

- Pay Grade: While working with the SGC, the character is paid as an enlisted soldier (see the Stargate SG-1 core rulebook, page 283). Alien characters are often paid in commensurate non-monetary concessions and favors.

TABLE 3.1: NEW SPECIALTY MODIFIERS

SPECIALTY	ABILITY ADJUSTMENTS	BONUS FEAT
US Army (Macro-Specialty)	As core rulebook	As core rulebook
Medical Corps	None	World Traveler
NID (Macro-Specialty)	As core rulebook	As core rulebook
NID Interrogator	None	Mark

SPECIES	ABILITY ADJUSTMENTS	BONUS FEAT
Goa'uld (Macro-Species)	As core rulebook	As core rulebook
Goa'uld Queen	+2 Charisma	Persuasive
Jaffa (Macro-Species)	As core rulebook	As core rulebook
Dragon Guard	+2 Strength	Two-Weapon Fighting
Jaffa Clergy	+2 Wisdom	Symbiote
Kresh'taa	+0 Constitution, +2 Dexterity, +2 Intelligence	Alertness
Near-human (Macro-Species)	As core rulebook	As core rulebook
Abydonian	+2 Constitution, −2 Intelligence	Desert Training
Argosian	+2 Charisma, −2 Strength	The Look
Byrsa	None	Forest Training
Untouched	None	Forest Training
Netjerian (Macro-Species)	+2 Charisma, −4 Constitution	Per sub-specialty
Netjerian Pilot	+2 Dexterity	Wind Rider
Netjerian Provocateur	+2 Wisdom	Persuasive
Netjerian Soldier	+2 Strength	Zen Focus
Nox (Macro-Species)	+2 Intelligence, +2 Wisdom, −2 Strength, −2 Constitution	Forest Training
Ohne (Macro-Species)	+2 Strength, −2 Dexterity, −2 Charisma	Communicate
Ohnes Laborer	+2 Constitution	Aquatic Training
Ohnes Scholar	+2 Intelligence	Clear Mind
Ohnes Warrior	+2 Wisdom	Goa'uld Hunter
The Unity (Macro-Species)	None	Per sub-specialty
Explorer	None	Electromagnetic Adaptation
Pacifist	None	Energy Healing
Vengeance Seeker	None	Improved Energy Blast

- Languages: Ohnes is a native language for the character.

- Bonus Feat: Communicate. The Ohnes possess a variety of psychic abilities, but all of them are capable of basic communication.

OHNES LABORER

Ohnes of the laborer caste comprise the bulk of the Ohnes population, working in various types of duties in underwater cities and settlements. Though most remain on their home world all their lives, in recent years many laborers have joined the freedom fighters, warriors, and scholars battling the Goa'uld across the galaxy.

SPECIAL TALENTS

- +2 Constitution. Extensive time spent under water makes Ohnes laborers hardier than normal.

- +1 species bonus with Fortitude saving throws. This bonus increases by an additional +1 at 3rd level and for every 3 character levels gained thereafter.

- Bonus Feat: Aquatic Training. All prerequisites for this feat – including minimum skill ranks – are waived.

OHNES SCHOLAR

Ohnes of the scholar caste search and explore the galaxy in hopes of uncovering knowledge that will unlock the secrets of the universe and its origins. Ohnes scholars also believe the key to victory against the Goa'uld lies in gathering knowledge, and thus spend considerable time searching for insight that will help their people defeat the System Lords.

SPECIAL TALENTS

- +2 Intelligence. Ohnes scholars spend most of their lives performing some form of research, granting them excellent reasoning abilities.

- +1 Species bonus with education checks. This bonus increases by an additional +1 at 4th level and for every 4 character levels gained thereafter. The Ohnes have amassed a significant body of knowledge over the thousands of years of their civilization.

- Bonus Feat: Clear Mind. All prerequisites for this feat – including minimum skill ranks – are waived.

OHNES WARRIOR

Ohnes of the warrior caste lead the battle against the Goa'uld throughout the galaxy, aiding and assisting other worlds in military and covert action.

SPECIAL TALENTS

- +2 Wisdom. The intense training Ohnes warriors undergo gives them strong willpower.

- +1 species bonus with Willpower saving throws. This bonus increases by an additional +1 at 4th level and for every 4 character levels gained thereafter.

- Bonus Feat: Goa'uld Hunter. All prerequisites for this feat – including minimum skill ranks – are waived.

THE UNITY (MACRO-SPECIES)

An energy-based crystalline life form from P3X-562, the Unity are essentially sentient crystals that have evolved to the point where they can manipulate their physical makeup and transform into exact replicas of other beings. Each Unity is capable of some telepathy and is incredibly dangerous in its crystal form. The Unity were nearly all wiped out by the Goa'uld but have since been rediscovered by the Tauri and have become allies of Stargate Command.

SHARED SPECIES TALENTS

- Abilities: No ability modifiers when mimicking another form (see below). When in crystal form, the Unity possesses the statistics of a Unity Crystal (see Unity Crystal on page 130).

- Shapeshifter: When not taking on the form of another being, the Unity is a small but dangerous crystal (see "Unity Crystal" for statistics while in crystal form). A Unity may regress to this crystal form as a full action.

- Ageless: All Unity are effectively immortal, ignoring all affects of aging.

- Telepathy: All Unity may communicate with any other Unity (including those in crystal form) within 60 feet telepathically as a free action.

- Radioactive: Whenever a Unity dies (-10 wound points or less) the character gives off lethal radiation in a radius of 30 feet. All those entering the area must make a Fortitude save once every ten minutes (DC 20 + 5 for every previous save) or lose 1d4 Constitution points. No further saves need be made once the character leaves the affected area, and Constitution points lost in this manner are regained at a rate of one point per day. The radiation will continue to affect the area for 1d4 days after the death of the Unity.

- Sensitive (Electromagnetic Fields): Certain planets can be lethal to a Unity thanks to their electromagnetic field (see page 154). Whenever a Unity would normally be affected negatively by the electromagnetic field, it may ignore those affects for 4 hours plus a number of hours equal to its Constitution modifier.

- Energy Blast: the Unity can project a blast of energy capable of harming most creatures on contact. By making a successful touch attack against an enemy, you may deal 2d6 points of damage to that opponent. Doing so costs 4 vitality points.

- Species Feats: The Unity may choose level-based feats from the species feats tree. Normally a character may not choose feats from the species tree unless he possesses a character option that expressly allows him to do so.

- Languages: Unity do not speak any languages, unless specifically granted by a character option (such as the Xeno-Languages skill).

UNITY EXPLORER

Some members of the Unity have taken on the physical form of explorers that have come through the Stargate and have begun travelling through the galaxy on their own. The Unity explorers are curious and inquisitive by nature and have always assumed the form of mobile species capable of operating the Stargate.

SPECIAL TALENTS

- +1 Specialty Bonus to Gather Information and Survival checks. This bonus is increased by an additional +1 at 4th level, and for every 4 levels thereafter.

- Bonus Feat: Electromagnetic Adaptation. All prerequisites for this feat – including minimum skill ranks – are waived.

UNITY PACIFIST

The pacifists among the Unity are capable healers and friends of the Tauri. They prefer peaceful solutions to a situation and typically abhor violence in any form. Despite this, these pacifists realize that the System Lords must be stopped in order to keep more innocents (like those of the Unity) slain by the Goa'uld. They prefer to fight the Goa'uld in more indirect ways, stymieing the efforts of the System Lords rather than confronting them militarily.

SPECIAL TALENTS

- +1 Specialty Bonus to Diplomacy and First Aid checks. This bonus is increased by an additional +1 at 4th level, and for every 4 levels thereafter.

- Bonus Feat: Energy Healing. All prerequisites for this feat – including minimum skill ranks – are waived.

Unity Vengeance Seeker

Unlike the pacifists, vengeance seekers think it both just and right to confront the Goa'uld directly. Many launch devastating attacks against the System Lords' Jaffa servants, preferring to strike with the help of other species such as the Tauri. Additionally, the more aggressive Unity from this specialty have become assassins and hunters who seek out the Goa'uld themselves and bypass their main forces.

Special Talents

- +1 Specialty Bonus to touch attack checks. This bonus is increased by an additional +1 at 5th level, and for every 5 levels thereafter.

- Bonus Feat: Improved Energy Blast. All prerequisites for this feat – including minimum skill ranks – are waived.

Unity Crystal

When not mimicking a more mobile species, the Unity revert to a sessile form often mistaken for a simple mineral outcropping.

Unity Crystal, CR (per character): SZ Tiny; v/wp: (per character/5); Init +0; Spd Immobile; Def 7 (+2 size, –5 Dex); Atk: none; Face 1 square; Reach 1 square; SA None; SQ Energy hazard, shapeshifter; SV Fort +4, Ref +0, Will (Per character); Str N/A, Dex N/A, Con 10, Int (per character), Wis (per character), Cha (per character); Skills: per character; Feats: per character.

Special Qualities

All Unity crystals have the following special qualities.

Energy Hazard: Any character that touches a Unity crystal without special protection immediately suffers 4d6 points of standard damage, plus 4d6 subdual damage, and is knocked back 10 feet. The character touching the crystal may make a Reflex save (DC 10) to reduce all damage by half.

Shapeshifter: Unity crystals can shapeshift into almost any form ranging in size from Tiny to Medium. When doing so, they take on the physical form of any being they have encountered before. They gain the physical attributes of that being (Strength, Dexterity, and Constitution), any natural armor or weapons of that creature, and any physical abilities such as water-breathing or low light vision. The Unity retains all class levels, skills, feats, and other abilities even in this form. The transformation process requires a full-round action and costs the Unity 5 vitality points. After the transformation is complete, the Unity suffers a –2 penalty to all attack rolls and saves due to disorientation in the new form for 1 hour.

New Prestige Classes

This section provides a variety of new prestige classes, allowing character to specialize in a variety of techniques.

Grunt

While the soldier represents the zenith of combat flexibility, some characters focus more heavily on one or more narrowly-defined aspects of warfare. The grunt is a master of heavy weaponry and a strong team player in combat situations.

Abilities: The grunt focuses on ranged combat, and is therefore best served by a high Dexterity, but the variety of physical challenges he faces makes Strength quite important as well.

Vitality: 1d12 plus Constitution modifier per level.

Requirements

To become a grunt, a character must meet all of the following requirements.

Character Level: 5+.

Strength: 13+.

Base Attack Bonus: +5 or better.

Feats: Endurance, Iron Will, Weapon Group Proficiency (Tactical).

Special: Jaffa characters need the Weapon Group Proficiency (Rifle) instead of Weapon Group Proficiency (Tactical).

Class Skills

The grunt's class skills and key abilities are:

Class Skill	Key Ability
Concentration	Wis
Craft	Wis
Demolitions	Int
Driver	Dex
First Aid	Wis
Intimidate	Str or Cha
Jump	Str
Listen	Wis
Profession	Wis
Search	Wis
Sport	Str or Dex
Spot	Wis
Survival	Wis
Swim	Str
Tumble	Dex

Skill Points at Each Additional Level: 4 + Int modifier.

CLASS FEATURES

All of the following are class features of the grunt.

Starting Feats: The grunt begins play with the following feats.

Armor Proficiency (Light)
Armor Proficiency (Medium)
Armor Proficiency (Heavy)
Weapon Group Proficiency (Melee)
Weapon Group Proficiency (Handgun)
Weapon Group Proficiency (Rifle)
Weapon Group Proficiency (Tactical)

Hot-Blooded: While the grunt understands the risks of his work, he also gets a thrill from the life-and-death intensity of battle. At the beginning of each combat, the grunt gains two extra action dice of his standard die-type (d4, d6, etc.). He may choose to immediately give one of these dice to a teammate also involved in the battle. If not used by the end of the combat, these action dice are discarded. Gaining these dice produces no experience point award for the grunt or his teammate. This is the grunt's core ability.

Alpha-Strike: When the grunt receives a half action as part of a surprise round, he may use it to attack with a tactical weapon that requires a full round action or perform an autofire, cover fire, strafe, or suppressive fire action.

Bonus Feat: At 2nd level, the grunt may choose one additional feat from the following list: Blast Lance Basics, Flamer Basics, Mortar Basics, Rocket Basics, or SAW Basics.

At 7th level, the grunt receives either the Mastery feat corresponding to the Basics feat he chose at 2nd level (i.e. if he chose Flamer Basics at 2nd level, he gains Flamer Mastery at 7th level), again with the same restrictions.

In both cases, the grunt must meet all prerequisites for the chosen feat before selecting it, including ability score and base attack bonus minimums.

Overkill: The grunt frequently uses tactical weapons to their maximum potential. Beginning at 3rd level, once per session, the grunt may elect to inflict an additional +1d8 damage with a successful attack using any tactical weapon except explosives (including mortars, rocket launchers, flamethrowers, Large-size gadget weapons, and all types of machine guns).

The character may use this ability one additional time per session at 5th level and every two levels thereafter (i.e. 3 times at 7th level and 4 times and 9th level).

At 7th level, the grunt's overkill damage bonus increases to +2d8.

This ability may only be used once per attack. If the grunt uses this ability to boost the damage of an autofire attack with a tactical weapon, the bonus damage is only applied to the first hit.

Fire Team: The grunt is a veteran of squad level tactics and able to establish massed or crossfire situations with ease. At 4th level, the grunt and all teammates present with him in combat gain the benefits of the Coordinate Fire feat, even if they would not normally meet the prerequisites for it. All teammates lose this benefit at the end of the combat (though they regain it at the start of the next combat with the grunt).

Forced March: At 4th level, the grunt's strength is considered 2 points higher when determining his carrying capacity (*see the Stargate SG-1 core rulebook, page 286*), and his speed is considered 10 ft. faster when determining how far he may travel in an hour or a day (*see the Stargate SG-1 core rulebook, page 441*).

At 8th level, this ability is applied to all members of the character's team so long as the grunt packs everyone's gear and supervises the march.

Improved Iron Will: At 6th level, the grunt receives an additional +2 with all Will saves. This bonus stacks with the effects of the Iron Will feat.

Dead to Rights: Starting at 8th level, the grunt no longer needs to spend an action die to activate a critical hit using a tactical weapon.

Battle Cry: Upon reaching 10th level, once per session as a free action, the grunt may unleash a fearsome battle cry. For the next 5 full rounds (i.e. until the grunt's initiative count 5 rounds after his battle cry), any opponent attempting to attack the grunt must immediately make a Will save (DC 25 plus the grunt's Charisma modifier). With success, the attack continues as normal. With failure, the opponent's attack automatically misses (no attack roll is made).

TABLE 3.2: THE GRUNT

LvL	Base Att	Fort Save	Ref Save	Will Save	Def Bon	Init Bon	Gear Picks	Res Pts	Special
1	+1	+1	+0	+2	+0	+1	0	0	Alpha-strike, hot-blooded*
2	+2	+2	+0	+3	+1	+1	0	1	Bonus feat
3	+3	+2	+1	+3	+1	+2	1	1	Overkill (+1d8, 1/session)
4	+4	+2	+1	+4	+2	+2	1	2	Fire team, forced march
5	+5	+3	+1	+4	+2	+3	1	2	Overkill (+1d8, 2/session)
6	+6	+3	+2	+5	+2	+4	2	3	Improved iron will
7	+7	+4	+2	+5	+3	+4	2	3	Bonus feat, overkill (+2d8, 3/session)
8	+8	+4	+2	+6	+3	+5	2	4	Dead to rights, forced march (team)
9	+9	+4	+3	+6	+4	+5	3	4	Overkill (+2d8, 4/session)
10	+10	+5	+3	+7	+4	+6	3	5	Battle cry

* Core Ability — A character only ever gains the core abilities of the first base class and the first prestige class he chooses.

Hazardous Material (HAZMAT) Specialist

Occasionally SGC teams encounter dangerous materials, hostile environments or alien biological or chemical weapons. When this happens, hazardous materials specialists decontaminate the team members, the area around the Stargate, vehicles, etc. These specialists are also called in to identify dangerous agents on other planets and, if possible, remove or neutralize them, making it safe for other SGC teams to explore. At times hazardous materials specialists are even called in to assist medical teams in treating alien races.

Abilities: Constitution is the primary ability of hazardous materials specialists as they need to have very high tolerances to the substances they are sometimes exposed to. Intelligence and Wisdom are also very important as nearly all of the hazardous materials specialist's abilities have one of these as their key ability.

Vitality: 1d12 plus Constitution modifier per level.

Requirements

To become a hazardous materials specialist, a character must meet all of the following requirements:

Character Level: 5+.
Constitution: 13+.
Concentration: 2 ranks.
First Aid: 6 ranks.
Knowledge (Chemistry): 2 ranks.
Search: 6 ranks.
Feats: Mother Hen, NBC Training.

Class Skills

The hazardous materials specialist's class skills and key abilities are:

Class Skill	Key Ability
Bureaucracy	Cha
Computers	Int
Concentration	Wis
Craft	Int
Demolitions	Int
Driver	Dex
Electronics	Int
First Aid	Wis
Knowledge	Int
Listen	Wis
Mechanics	Int
Profession	Wis
Search	Int
Spot	Wis
Survival	Wis

Skill Points at Each Additional Level: 4 + Int modifier.

Class Features

The following are class features of the hazardous materials specialist.

Starting Feats: The hazardous materials specialist gains the following feats at 1st level.
Armor Group Proficiency (Light)
Armor Group Proficiency (Medium)
Weapon Group Proficiency (Handgun)

In Harm's Way: The HAZMAT specialist is used to operating on dangerous ground, working in deadly conditions where the slightest mistake spells disaster. At 1st level, the HAZMAT specialist may continue to take 10 in deadly environments. This is the HAZMAT specialist's core ability.

HAZMAT: The hazardous materials specialist must be able to detect and neutralize NBC agents, if at all possible. At 1st level, the hazardous materials specialist gains a virtual basic skill feat called "NBC Specialist". This feat grants the hazardous materials specialist a +2 bonus with Concentration, First Aid, and Search checks, and increases his threat range with these skills to 19-20.

At 5th level, the hazardous materials specialist gains the False Start feat linked to his NBC Specialist feat.

At 9th level, the time required for the HAZMAT specialist to make First Aid and Search Checks is halved (to a minimum of 1 half action).

Burnout: Few things are as efficient at neutralizing chemical and biological threats as fire. At 2nd level, the HAZMAT specialist gains the Flamer Basics feat. All prerequisites for this feat are waived.

At 7th level, the HAZMAT specialist's teammates gain the benefits of the Flamer Basics feat.

Bonus Feat: At 3rd level, the hazardous materials specialist gains a bonus gear or terrain feat. He must meet all prerequisites for this feat before choosing it.

At 7th level, the hazardous materials specialist receives an additional bonus gear or terrain feat with the same restrictions.

Check Your Partner: The HAZMAT specialist is able to communicate the need for meticulous care for equipment to his teammates. At 4th level, the HAZMAT specialist's teammates gain the benefits of Mother Hen feat.

Tolerance: Through a combination of knowledge and extra care in the presence of toxins, the HAZMAT specialist can avoid the worst dangers of his profession. At 4th level, the HAZMAT specialist gains a +2 circumstance bonus to all saves made to resist the effects of nuclear, biological, and chemical agents. This includes, but is not limited to, diseases, poisons, radioactivity, and gases.

At 8th level, this bonus increases by an additional +2 (to a total of +4).

Superior Metabolism: The HAZMAT specialist keeps himself in top form, to make himself more resistant to the horror he has to combat. Beginning at 6th level, whenever the HAZMAT specialist succeeds with a Fortitude save to suffer reduced damage from any effect (such as poison), he instead suffers no damage.

If the HAZMAT Specialist already has this ability from another class, whenever he fails a Fortitude save to suffer reduced damage from any effect (such as poison), he suffers only ½ damage (rounded down).

Nick of Time: At 8th level, if the HAZMAT specialist has a first aid kit and can act to assist himself or another character as a full action after they have been poisoned, contracted a disease, or been affected by radiation, but before any secondary damage takes effect, that character automatically succeeds on his save(s) against any secondary damage. Further, he immediately recovers from one half (round down) the initial damage received.

Wildfire: There is no one you want on hand more than a veteran HAZMAT specialist when there is a contamination crisis. At 10th level, the first time the HAZMAT specialist enters or is overtaken by a deadly environment each session, he immediately gains 5 action dice. He does not gain XP for these dice and any unused dice are lost when the character leaves the deadly environment or it is neutralized.

VALKYRIE

The Valkyries are the elite combat units of the Asgard and are regarded as great warriors among humankind. Despite their frail build and slight frame, the Valkyries are swift and capable combatants that specialize in analyzing and then overwhelming their enemies. Valkyries use the Asgard's advanced technologies to gain an edge over opponents; they study their enemies' movements, apply mathematical theories and statistical analyses to battle tactics, and formulate plans to overcome their natural physiological handicaps through the application of intelligence and force. They know their weapons (and the technology that powers them) intimately and are able to apply this knowledge in practical situations in order to take their opponents down quickly and efficiently.

Abilities: Intelligence and Dexterity are the most important abilities to the Valkyrie. The Valkyrie's philosophy revolves around the application of scientific theory and statistical probability to combat, making Intelligence key to their tactics. They also make extensive use of the shock spear and other ranged weapons, making Dexterity essential during combat.

Vitality: 1d10 plus Con modifier per level.

REQUIREMENTS

To become a valkyrie, a character must meet all of the following requirements.

Species: Asgard (or GM discretion).
Character Level: 5+.
Intelligence: 13+.
Base Attack Bonus: +5 or higher.
Knowledge (tactics): 8 ranks.
Sense Motive: 4 ranks.
Feats: Far Shot, Goa'uld Hunter, Perfect Stance.

TABLE 3.3: THE HAZMAT SPECIALIST

LvL	Base Att	Fort Save	Ref Save	Will Save	Def Bon	Init Bon	Gear Picks	Res Pts	Special
1	+0	+2	+1	+0	+0	+1	2	1	HAZMAT (NBC Specialist), in harm's way•
2	+1	+3	+2	+0	+1	+1	3	2	Burnout (Basics)
3	+1	+3	+2	+1	+1	+2	3	3	Bonus feat
4	+2	+4	+2	+1	+2	+2	4	4	Check your partner, tolerance +2
5	+2	+4	+3	+1	+2	+3	4	5	HAZMAT (False Start)
6	+3	+5	+3	+2	+2	+4	5	6	Superior metabolism
7	+3	+5	+4	+2	+3	+4	5	7	Bonus feat, burnout (team)
8	+4	+6	+4	+2	+3	+5	6	8	Nick of time, tolerance +4
9	+4	+6	+4	+3	+4	+5	6	9	HAZMAT (½ time)
10	+5	+7	+5	+3	+4	+6	7	10	Wildfire 1/session

* Core Ability — A character only ever gains the core abilities of the first base class and the first prestige class he chooses.

CLASS SKILLS

The valkyrie's class skills and key abilities are:

CLASS SKILL	KEY ABILITY
Balance	Dex
Bluff	Cha
Bureaucracy	Cha
Computers	Int
Concentration	Wis
Craft	Int
Cultures	Wis
Demolitions	Int
First Aid	Int
Hide	Dex
Intimidate	Str or Cha
Listen	Wis
Move Silently	Dex
Pilot	Dex
Profession	Wis
Search	Int
Sense Motive	Wis
Sleight of Hand	Dex
Spot	Wis
Survival	Wis

Skill Points at Each Additional Level: 6 + Int modifier.

CLASS FEATURES

All of the following are class features of the valkyrie.

Class Feats: The valkyrie gains the following feats at 1st level

Weapon Group Proficiency (Melee)
Weapon Group Proficiency (Handgun)
Weapon Group Proficiency (Rifle)

Thunderstrike: Whenever the valkyrie spends an action die to add a damage roll, he may also add the results of that action die to the results of any one skill or attack check made by an ally before the valkyrie's initiative count the following round. This is the valkyrie's core ability.

Favored Foes: At 1st level, the valkyrie may select an alien species (such as Goa'uld, Human, Jaffa, Reetou, Replicators, etc.) or all life forms native to a single planet. The valkyrie gains a +2 competence bonus on all skill checks when using valkyrie class skills against the targeted species or when making checks opposed by the targeted species. Likewise, he gets a +2 competence bonus on all damage rolls against such creatures.

At 5th level and again at 9th level, the valkyrie may select an additional alien species or planet's life forms as his favored foes.

Bonus Feat: At 2nd level, the valkyrie gains a bonus feat from the basic or ranged combat tree. The valkyrie must meet all prerequisites for this feat before choosing it.

At 7th level the valkyrie gains an additional feat from the basic or ranged combat feat trees with the same restrictions.

Weapon Specialization: At 3rd level, the valkyrie chooses one weapon category with which he is proficient (e.g. knives, grappling, shotguns, unarmed, etc.). He is considered to be specialized with this weapon category, inflicting an additional 2 points of damage with each successful hit with any included weapon. If the valkyrie's choice is a ranged weapon category, this bonus applies only when the opponent is within 1 range increment.

At 5th level, and every other level thereafter (7th, and 9th level), the valkyrie may specialize with one additional category of weapon.

In Small Packages: Starting at 4th level, the valkyrie is capable of engaging enemies in close combat despite his smaller stature. In any case where being a size category smaller than an opponent would apply a penalty to his opposed roll or a bonus to his opponent's roll (such as in the case of a grapple action), the valkyrie is considered to be Medium-sized for the purposes of that roll.

Squad Tactics: The valkyrie's expertise in fighting as a group is remarkable. Beginning at 4th level, the valkyrie gains the Wolfpack Basics feat.

At 8th level, all of the valkyrie's teammates gain the benefits of the Wolfpack Basics feat.

Optimal Composure: At 6th level, the valkyrie has mastered the unshakable calm with which many Asgard greet even the gravest of danger. The valkyrie adds his

TABLE 3.4: THE VALKYRIE

LvL	BASE ATT	FORT SAVE	REF SAVE	WILL SAVE	DEF BON	INIT BON	GEAR PICKS	RES PTS	SPECIAL
1	+1	+0	+0	+1	+1	+1	1	1	Favored foes, thunderstrike
2	+2	+0	+0	+2	+2	+1	2	2	Bonus feat
3	+3	+1	+1	+2	+3	+2	3	3	Weapon specialization
4	+4	+1	+1	+2	+3	+2	4	4	In small packages, squad tactics (Wolfpack Basics)
5	+5	+1	+1	+3	+4	+3	5	5	Favored foes, weapon specialization
6	+6	+2	+2	+3	+5	+4	6	6	Optimal composure
7	+7	+2	+2	+4	+6	+4	7	7	Weapon specialization
8	+8	+2	+2	+4	+6	+4	8	8	Optimal damage, squad tactics (team)
9	+9	+3	+3	+4	+7	+5	9	9	Favored foes, weapon specialization
10	+10	+3	+3	+5	+8	+6	10	10	Optimal tactics

* Core Ability — A character only ever gains the core abilities of the first base class and the first prestige class he chooses.

Intelligence bonus to all Concentration checks and Will saves (in addition to his Wisdom modifier) while in combat, and may always take 10 on a Concentration check regardless of his circumstances.

Optimal Damage: At 8th level, the valkyrie is capable of inflicting severe amounts of damage to an opponent using an analysis of that opponent's fighting style and physiology. By taking a full action to study a single target, the valkyrie gains a +4 bonus to his damage rolls against that target for a number of rounds equal to his Intelligence modifier.

Optimal Tactics: At 10th level, the valkyrie is capable of using his superior intellect to make his actions in combat more efficient and effective. When the valkyrie uses the press action *(see the Stargate SG-1 core rulebook, page 357)* to gain an additional half action, his initiative count is reduced by 10 instead of 20.

NEW SKILL USES

This section covers a variety of new uses for previously established skills.

COMPUTER USE (INT)

The following new uses for the Computer Use skill allow a character greater access to the computer-based mind of an android.

Android Disposition Check (1 hour): Whenever a character encounters an android and wishes to change its disposition toward them *(see page 420 of the Stargate SG-1 core rulebook),* the character may make a Computer Use check when directly connected to the android's brain. Make a Computer Use check against a DC equal to 10 + the android's Intelligence score.

With a success on this check, you may change the android's disposition toward you to any other disposition. The android may make a Will save (DC equal to your Computer Use check result) to detect the tampering with its disposition.

Failure on this check means that you do not change the android's disposition. The android may make a Will save (DC equal to your Computer Use check result –10) to detect the tampering with its disposition.

Retry: Yes, assuming the android does not stop you from making another skill check.

Threat: None.

Critical Success: Not only do you change the android's disposition toward you, you may change its disposition toward any one faction or organization as well.

Error: None.

Critical Failure: The android disengages your connection to its computer brain and automatically changes its disposition toward you one level more hostile than it was before you made the Computer Use check.

Android Reprogram Check (4 hours): Whenever you have access to an android's computer brain, you may attempt to reprogram its knowledge centers to grant or remove certain information or skills from its memory.

In doing so, you rearrange the android's skill points as you see fit, transferring them from one skill to another (though never in excess of the android's maximum skill points for any skill). The DC for this check is 10 + the number of skill points to be transferred from one skill to another.

With a success on this check, you may change the android's skill point distribution on two skills by transferring skill points from one to the other. The android may make a Will save (DC equal to your Computer Use check result) to detect the tampering with its memory banks.

Failure on this check means that you do not change the android's skill point distribution. The android may make a Will save (DC equal to your Computer Use check result –10) to detect the tampering with its memory banks.

Retry: Yes, assuming the android does not stop you from making another skill check.

Threat: None.

Critical Success: None.

Error: None.

Critical Failure: The android disengages your connection to its computer brain and all skill points that were to be transferred from one skill to another are considered unspent until a successful check in either of those particular skills are made.

CRAFT (MEDICINE) (INT; TRAINED ONLY)

Brew Check (2 Hours, Complex, Kit): Simarkan medicine men brew medicines using different combinations of local plants. Brewing medicine is a complex skill check, and each type of medicine has an associated DC. The interval for the check is 2 hours. Brewing medicine requires the specific ingredients needed for the medicine being brewed, as well as several tools, including a mortar and pestle (or something to grind ingredients together), a pot, a source of heat, and containers for the completed medicine. Stats for each medicine can be found on page 152.

MEDICINE	DC
Anesthetic Salve	60
Healing Salve	60
Scorpion anti-venom	65
Pit viper anti-venom	65
Malaria cure	80
Yellow Fever cure	100

Retry: If you fail the Craft check, the salve is useless, but you may try again. Further attempts require additional materials.

Threat: None.

CRAFT (POISON) (INT; TRAINED ONLY)

You may handle and prepare poisons, often improvising from common household items.

Create Poison (Variable): You may improvise an effective poison. Each use of this skill produces a single dose of poison. The type of poison you are trying to produce determines the DC of this check.

POISON TYPE	DC
Base save DC 12	10
Increase save DC +3*	+4
Decrease save DC −3	−4
Delivered by Ingestion	+0
Delivered by Contact/Injury	+4
Delivered by Inhalation	+8
d4 ability or d6 vitality damage**	+2
d6 ability or d10 vitality damage**	+3
Momentarily blinded (2d6 rounds)	+4
Temporarily blinded (1d6 minutes)	+6
Lingering blindness (2d6 hours)	+8
Momentarily deafened (2d8 rounds)	+4
Temporarily deafened (1d8 minutes)	+6
Lingering deafness (2d8 hours)	+8
Momentary disorientation † (2d4 rounds)	+6
Temporary disorientation † (2d4 minutes)	+8
Lingering disorientation† (2d4 hours)	+10
Momentary nausea ‡ (2d6 rounds)	+4
Temporarily nausea ‡ (1d6 minutes)	+6
Lingering nausea ‡ (2d6 hours)	+8
Lasting nausea ‡ (4d6 hours)	+10
Momentary paralysis or unconsciousness (1d4 rounds)	+6
Temporarily paralysis or unconsciousness (1d4 minutes)	+8
Lingering paralysis or unconsciousness (1d4 hours)	+10
Lasting paralysis or unconsciousness (3d4 hours)	+12
Each GP or $100 spent on materials Δ	−2

* This option may be chosen up to 6 times (max save DC of 30).

** Initial damage may not exceed secondary damage. This option (or paralyzation/unconsciousness) must be applied separately to both initial and secondary damage. This option may be taken twice for initial or secondary damage.

† Disoriented characters are considered staggered, but do not need to make a Fortitude save each round *(see the Stargate SG-1 core rulebook, page 378-379).*

‡ Nauseated characters are considered entangled, but not anchored round *(see the Stargate SG-1 core rulebook, page 378-379).*

Δ The maximum reduction to the DC from spending BP or cash is −10 (5 BP or $500).

Poison onset time: The time before the poison's secondary damage takes effect acts as a multiplier for the DC modifier for the secondary damage as follows:

SPEED	MULTIPLIER
Instant (1d4 rounds)	×2
Fast (2d6 rounds)	×1.25 (round up)
Standard (1d4 minutes)	×1
Slow (3d6 minutes)	×.75 (round up)
Delayed (2d6 hours)	×1

This does not effect the DC modifier from initial damage.

Initial vs. Secondary Damage: The DC modifier from the initial damage cannot exceed the DC modifier from the secondary damage *(adjusted for onset time, see above).*

Example 1: Fabricating contact poison (injury DC 18, 1d4 Con initial, 2d4 Con secondary/standard onset time) would have a DC of 31 (10+8+4+3(+6×1)).

Example 2: Creating a typical nerve gas (inhaled DC 18, paralyzation initial, 1d6 Con secondary/instant onset time) would have a DC of 42 (10+8+8+8(+4×2)). Better stock up on chemicals before you start!

The more dangerous the poison desired, the longer the character must work and greater the chance of mishap. The time required for this check is a number of minutes equal to one half of the DC (round up). The error range for this check is equal to the DC/10 (round down). All poisons produced in this fashion are assumed to have become inert and been disposed of at the end of the session. Characters with the Improvisation ability may expend one use of that ability to gain a +10 competence bonus to this check.

Threat: None.

Critical: You produce double the number of does or are finished in one half the time (round up).

Error: You accidentally expose yourself to the poison you are creating.

Critical Failure: Any saves you must make from exposing yourself to your poison are at −4.

Special: Characters with this skill may include doses of poison they have created in their personal gear. This poison may have a maximum Craft DC of the character's total Craft (Poison) bonus +10 (+20 if the character has the Poison Basics feat). 3 pre-prepared doses costs 2 gear picks, plus the cost of any materials used to reduce the DC of the check, and remains potent for the duration of the current mission.

First Aid (Wis)

Apply Salve Check (Full Action, Kit Only): You attempt to apply a Simarkan salve to a character's wounds. This check requires the appropriate type of salve (anesthetic, healing, or anti-venom). With a successful First Aid check (DC 15), you properly apply salve to a character's wounds.

Retry: If you fail the check, you may retry only once.

Threat: None.

Critical Success: The salve's effects are enhanced *(see descriptions, below)*.

Error: None.

Critical Failure: Your attempt at applying the salve aggravates the injury. The character suffers 1 wound, and the character is exposed to a moderate infection *(see Table 11.12: Diseases and Poisons on page 440 in the Stargate SG-1 core rulebook)*

Special: If you possess 4 or more ranks in Craft (Medicine), you gain a +2 synergy bonus with First Aid checks made to apply salves.

NEW GEAR FEATS

The following feats are considered part of the gear feat tree *(see Stargate SG-1 core rulebook, page 259)*.

HEALING DEVICE BASICS

You are talented with the use of the Goa'uld healing device and can perform miracles with it.

Prerequisites: Must be capable of using a healing device.

Benefit: When using the healing device, you may increase the amount of vitality or wound points healed per round by one.

POISON BASICS

You are knowledgeable in the creation and use of toxic substances.

Prerequisites: Craft (Poison) skill 5+.

Benefit: You receive a 25% discount on the gear pick or cash cost of any poison or equipment for delivering it (e.g. dart guns). Your error range while handling poisons is reduced by 1 (to a minimum of 0), and you have no chance of poisoning yourself when applying poison to a weapon. You may take 20 when using the Craft Poison skill. Further, you receive a +2 competence bonus to all Fortitude saves you make to resist the effects of poison.

POISON MASTERY

You are highly adept in brewing and using poisons.

Prerequisites: Craft (Poisons) skill 10+, Poison Basics.

Benefit: You receive a 50% discount on the gear pick or cash cost of any poison (this replaces the 25% discount provided by Poison Basics) or equipment for delivering it (e.g. dart guns). In addition, the DC of saves made to resist any poison you use is increased by 3. Finally, the GM must spend an extra action die to activate your critical failures when creating or using poisons.

POISON SUPREMACY

You have worked with toxins until they are virtually in your blood.

Prerequisites: Craft (Poisons) skill 15+, Poison Mastery.

Benefit: The time required for you to prepare a poison is cut in half (round up). You receive a +10 bonus to education checks to identify a poison or drug and its properties. In addition, you receive a +4 competence bonus to all Fortitude saves you make to resist the effects of poison (this bonus replaces the bonus received from Poison Basics).

STARGATE BASICS

You have become intimately familiar with the kind of technology that enables the Stargate network and can apply this knowledge to practical situations.

Prerequisites: Intelligence 13+.

Benefit: You gain a +4 bonus to all Mechanics checks when dealing with a Stargate, DHD, or other related devices (GM's discretion). Further, when using the hasty dialing method for dialing a Stargate address on a DHD *(see the Stargate SG-1 core rulebook, page 400),* the time taken to dial is reduced to 2 half actions. Finally, whenever you roll an action die to add to a skill check involving the Stargate, you may roll 2 dice and add the total of both to your check.

NEW SPECIES FEATS

The following feats are considered part of the species feat tree *(see the Stargate SG-1 core rulebook, page 264).*

Some species feats include an entry for Vitality Point Cost. Use of this ability requires the character to exert himself to such a degree that he suffers a small amount of damage. Characters with insufficient vitality remaining to pay this cost may not use this ability until they recover enough vitality to do so.

ABSORB LANGUAGE

You can learn the spoken languages of other species quickly.

Prerequisites: Nox only.

Benefit: After hearing another language spoken for an hour, you can make a Xeno-Languages (Linguistics) check against a DC based on the language *(see the Stargate SG-1 core rulebook, page 239).* If you succeed, you may speak the language as if it were a native language.

ALTER LARVA

You can alter the genetic structure of the larva you produce in subtle or significant ways.

Prerequisites: Goa'uld Queen sub-species, Wis 13+.

Benefits: You can improve the Goa'uld larvae you produce by altering your body chemistry during the gestation period. Firstly, you may choose the sub-species to which each larvae will belong, including queen, although you may create no more than one queen per brood of larvae. In addition, for every point of your positive Wisdom modifier, you may increase the ability or abilities of your choosing of your larvae, above and beyond whatever bonuses are provided by their sub-species. Thus, if you have a Wisdom modifier of +3, you may add up to 3 points to any of your larva's abilities. This bonus need not be added to a single ability – it can be divided among several – and you need not use every point of bonus available. The bonus applies to as many larvae in a single brood as you wish. You may choose to apply different bonuses (or none at all) to the larvae of other broods.

Alternately, each point of your Wisdom modifier may be exchanged for a +2 competence bonus with a single skill for your larvae. Again, you may stack this bonus if you wish or divide it among several skills. As in the example above, a +3 Wisdom modifier could be used to give your larvae a +2 bonus to three different skills or a +6 bonus to one (or anything in between). All of the other rules apply regarding how you may alter your larvae in this fashion. You may also mix and match between ability bonuses and competence bonuses for skills, so long as you provide no more bonuses than your Wisdom modifier allows.

BACK FROM THE BRINK

You are an exceptionally tough Unas that can live through grievous damage and still return to the fight.

Prerequisites: Unas only, Constitution 13+.

Benefit: You do not die until you reach negative wounds equal to your Constitution. You may continue to take one half action per round until you are reduced below -10 wounds.

Normal: A character is considered dead after reaching -10 wounds.

CLOAKING

You can make yourself invisible.

Prerequisites: Nox only, character level 3+, Hide 4+.

Benefit: As a free action, you can become invisible, giving you total concealment *(see the Stargate SG-1 core rulebook, page 368)*. You may take any actions you desire, including attacking, without revealing yourself.

Special: You cannot maintain the effect of this feat while performing the Ritual of Life feat *(page 140)*.

CLOAK OBJECTS

You can make inanimate objects invisible.

Prerequisites: Nox only, Cloaking.

Benefit: Once per round as a free action, you can make a non-moving, inanimate object within your line of sight invisible, giving the object(s) total concealment *(see the Stargate SG-1 core rulebook, page 368)*. The maximum size of objects you may affect by yourself is Huge, but each additional character with this feat cooperating with you to produce this effect increases the maximum size of the object that may be cloaked by one size category. The maximum number of objects you may cloak at one time is equal to your character level.

Special: Once bestowed upon an object or objects, the effects of this feat last for one hour or until you use a free action to uncloak the object(s). You cannot maintain the effect of this feat while performing the Ritual of Life feat *(page 140)*.

CLOAK OTHERS

You can make other characters and creatures invisible.

Prerequisites: Nox only, Cloak Objects.

Benefit: You may target moving objects and other beings with your Cloak Objects feat. The recipient of this feat may take any actions they desire, including attacking, without revealing themselves. Hurled weapons and projectiles become visible after leaving contact with the cloaked individual unless individually targeted with the Cloak objects feat. Unwilling characters may make a Reflex save (DC of 10 + your character level) to avoid being cloaked.

Special: Once bestowed upon a character or creature, the effects of this feat last for an hour or until you use a free action to uncloak the subject. You cannot maintain the effect of this feat while performing the Ritual of Life feat *(page 140)*.

COMMUNICATE

You can telepathically communicate with other Ohnes.

Prerequisite: Ohnes only.

Benefit: You can telepathically communicate with other characters of your species within a range of 60 feet. Further, a successful Will save (DC 15) allows you to communicate with other telepathic characters.

Vitality Point Cost: 2 per minute.

CONTROL DEVICE

You can operate technological devices using mental commands only.

Prerequisites: Nox only, character level 3+, Electronics 4+ Mechanics 4+.

Benefit: As a free action, you can activate and operate technological devices of any kind, within line of sight. Once under your control, devices ignore commands from their control systems (such as a computer's keyboard). In the case of mechanical devices, your control overpowers that of the device's operator (a driver operating a car controlled via this feat would be unable to turn the steering wheel).

Special: This feat cannot be used to activate or control devices built by the Ancients. This feat does not grant you any skill to operate a device properly. For example, using this feat to control an aircraft does not grant you the Pilot skill.

CONTROL STARGATE

You can operate the Stargate without need of a dialing device of any kind.

Prerequisites: Nox only, Control Device.

Benefit: You can activate the Stargate and open a wormhole between your current location and any other Stargate within the gate network to which you know the proper address. The Stargate activates automatically when you use this ability; there is no need to dial the address. Opening the gate using this feat requires one full action.

ELECTROMAGNETIC ADAPTATION

You can maintain your focus while on worlds of strong or weak electromagnetic fields longer thanks to time spent on other planets.

Prerequisites: Unity only, Constitution 13+, Concentration 2+.

Benefit: You may double your Constitution bonus for the purpose of determining the length of time before you suffer the effects of a strong or weak electromagnetic field.

ELECTROMAGNETIC CONTROL

You can manipulate the electromagnetic field and cause severe damage to electronic devices.

Prerequisites: Unity only, character level 3+.

Benefit: As a half action, you may make ranged touch attack against an electronic device. If successful, you deal 6d6 points of damage to that device.

Vitality Point Cost: 4 vitality.

ENERGY HEALING

You are capable of using your knowledge of another's physical form and your own mastery over energy to heal another being that has been wounded.

Prerequisites: Unity only, Mind Scan.

Benefit: As a full action you may heal an adjacent character of 1 wound point of damage.

Vitality Point Cost: 4 vitality.

HIDE POSSESSION

You are adept at hiding evidence of your presence in a host body from physical sensory attempts to spot you.

Prerequisite: Goa'uld or Tok'ra only, Bluff 2+, Disguise 2+.

Benefits: You may spend one or more action dice to increase the all DCs for detecting your presence in a host body by an amount equal to 1/2 the character levels of your symbiote per action die (round down). This includes detection through technological means, such a MRI or other sense-enhancing device. Further, when you spend an action die on Bluff and Disguise checks to conceal your control over a host, you roll two dice and add the results of both to your check total. Finally, you need not produce the "hollow" voice characteristic of Goa'uld of Tok'ra control when speaking through your host.

HUSK DECEPTION

You can make it appear as if you have died when in fact you have only shed a useless husk of dead skin.

Prerequisite: Goa'uld or Tok'ra (or symbiote feat), Hide Possession.

Benefits: You gain a +2 bonus on all Bluff and Disguise checks to conceal you control over a host. Further, given at least one day to prepare, you may create the physical evidence of a dead symbiote within your host. If removed, these remains will appear to be a deceased symbiote to any visual inspection. A detailed analysis may reveal that the remains are not a genuine carcass (DC 20).

IMPROVED ENERGY BLAST

You have improved your mastery over the energy you project and can propel more powerful bolts than those that have not.

Prerequisites: Unity only.

Benefit: As a half action, you may make touch attack against an enemy. If successful you deal 4d6 points of radiation damage to that opponent.

Vitality Point Cost: 6 vitality.

MIND SCAN

You have honed your telepathic ability to the point where you may read the minds of other individuals.

Prerequisites: Unity only, Character level 6+.

Benefit: By spending a full action, you may scan the mind of any being within 10 feet. Thereafter, you may make inspiration and education checks as though you had all the knowledge of the character you had mind scanned, and permanently gain a +2 psion bonus to all Sense Motive checks targeting that opponent. If you mind scan another character, you lose the ability to make those checks based on the mind of the previously scanned being (you may only hold the knowledge of one character at a time). This ability may only be used on sentient beings, and the target may make a Will save (DC 20) to resist the scan.

Vitality Point Cost: 4 vitality.

PSYCHIC BLAST

You can focus your telepathic powers to unleash a massive mental shriek that affects all minds around you.

Prerequisites: Ohnes only. Charisma 13+, Communicate.

Benefit: Once per round as a full action, the character can create a psychic blast that affects all visible characters within 50 feet (including allies). Targets within the target area must make a Willpower save (DC 20) or be disoriented for 2d10 minutes. Disoriented characters are considered staggered, but do not need to make a Fortitude save each round *(see the Stargate SG-1 core rulebook, page 378-379)*.

Vitality Point Cost: 2d4.

READ SURFACE THOUGHTS

You can read the surface thoughts of another character.

Prerequisites: Nox only, Sense Motive 4+ ranks, Absorb Language.

Benefit: When within 10 feet of another character, you can make a Sense Motive check (DC 15 plus the target's Charisma modifier). If successful, you can read the thoughts on the surface of the character's mind, such as what they were about to say or how they react to something you say to them. It also allows you to determine the character's disposition towards you. This feat does not allow you read the character's mind; it only reveals immediate surface thoughts.

RITUAL OF LIFE

Along with the aid of at least two others, you can heal others' injuries.

Prerequisites: Nox only, First Aid 8+.

Benefit: To use this feat you and 3 other characters with this feat must meditate over a character for 1 minute before you make a First Aid check. The DC is based on the current condition of the target as follows:

CONDITION	DC	REST REQUIRED
Fatigued	10	1 hour
Unconscious	15	2 hours
Dying (−1 to −9 wounds)	20	3 hours
Dead (−10 to −24 wounds)	25	4 hours

If the check succeeds, the character is fully healed (vitality and wound points restored to their full values). The character must rest for a number of hours based on his previous condition after the ritual is complete in order to fully heal, if they do not, they are reduced to their previous stat or 0 wounds, whichever is better.

You can use this feat on any damaged character, so long as they have not been reduced to a condition of Destroyed (-25 wounds). When using this feat on Dead characters, you must perform the Ritual within one hour of the character becoming Dead (when their wound points are equal to or less -10).

Special: The Cloak Self and Shift Self feats cannot be used while performing the Ritual of Life. Cloaked and/or shifted characters become visible and shift back into normal space when using this feat *(see Nox Technology, page 150 for more information)*. Use of this feat requires that healing powder be sprinkled over the subject's body. At the GM's discretion, this feat may only be available to NPCs, unable to be taken by player characters.

SHIFTING

You can shift yourself into sub-space.

Prerequisites: Nox only, Character level 6+, Cloaking.

Benefit: As a half action, after cloaking yourself, you can shift your own body and carried items into the parallel dimension of sub-space. This has the effect of rendering you intangible in normal space. Once shifted, you may perform any actions normally available to you. You can shift back into normal space at any location within your line of sight at the time you shifted. Because sub-space is a parallel to normal space, you can also see and hear what happens in normal space as if you were still present, but you cannot interact with anything in normal space while in sub-space. There is no limit to the length of time you can spend in sub-space. Shifting from sub-space to normal space is a free action.

Special: You cannot maintain the effect of this feat while performing the Ritual of Life feat *(see left)*.

SHIFT OBJECTS

You can shift inanimate objects into sub-space.

Prerequisites: Nox only, Cloak Objects, Shifting.

Benefit: As a half action, you can shift any number of non-moving, inanimate objects you have cloaked into the parallel dimension of sub-space, effectively making the objects disappear. Shifted objects go into a small pocket of sub-space from which they can be retrieved at a later time. This prevents shifted objects from simply falling to the ground in sub-space. Objects operate in sub-space the same way they do in normal space.

Special: Stargates shifted into sub-space can still connect to other gates in normal space.

SHIFT OTHERS

You can shift other characters into sub-space.

Prerequisites: Nox only, Cloak Others, Shift Objects.

Benefit: As a half action, you can shift any number of other characters you have cloaked into the parallel dimension of sub-space, effectively making the characters disappear. Non-Nox characters shifted into sub-space through use of this feat may not take actions, and retain no memory of the shift or of the intervening time spent in sub-space. You can shift characters back into normal space at any location within line of sight. Due to their pacifistic nature, Nox may not use this ability to place other characters in harm's way.

STUNNING BLAST

You have tuned your ability to project blasts of energy to only stun your opponents rather than causing them real damage.

Prerequisites: Unity only.

Benefit: By making a successful touch attack against an enemy, you may deal 3d6 points of subdual damage to that opponent. Doing so requires a half action and costs 4 vitality points.

NEW TERRAIN FEATS

The following feats are considered part of the gear feat tree (see the Stargate SG-1 core rulebook, page 259).

FIREFIGHTER TRAINING

You are trained as a professional firefighter, and are not only used to dealing with flames, but almost at home amongst them.

Prerequisite: Survival skill 5+ ranks.

Benefit: When exposed to extreme heat, you only make Fortitude saves half as often (i.e. every 2 hours, 20 minutes, or 10 minutes). When immersed in a fire, you still make a Reflex save, but the DC is only 20. You ignore terrain effects caused by ash clouds and view things within heavy smoke as if they had one-quarter concealment (instead of one-half).

Finally, you gain a +4 bonus to the following saves and skill checks:

- Reflex saves to avoid catching fire, to put yourself out if on fire, and to avoid volcanic bombs.

- Fortitude saves to avoid choking from smoke inhalation.

- Survival checks to avoid poisonous gas clouds.

NBC TRAINING

You are experienced in the use of chemical warfare protective gear and techniques for survival in contaminated environments.

Prerequisites: Concentration 2+ ranks, Survival (any) 2+ ranks.

Benefits: Concentration is always a class skill for you. Further, the error ranges of your skill checks made while operating in a deadly environment are not increased by 2 (see below). Finally, you may don a chemical protection mask as free action.

RADIATION TOLERANCE

Your body is better able to resist the adverse effects of radiation exposure.

Prerequisite: Con 13+, Survival (any) 2+ ranks.

Benefits: You gain a +2 bonus to all Fortitude saves made specifically to resist the effects of radiation. This bonus comes in addition to any other bonuses you may get from taking precautions (like sunscreen, protective eyewear, etc.) and other feats, such as Great Fortitude.

DEADLY ENVIRONMENTS

The prospect that a tiny rip or brushing up against a heavy object could kill you is more than a little disconcerting. Characters operating in an environment that would be lethal to them without protective gear face several penalties due to the extra care they must take.

- All skill uses take 50% longer than normal (round down).

- The error range of all skill and attack checks is increased by 1.

- You may not take 10 on any check, even if you have a special ability to do so while under stress, unless that ability specifically refers to deadly environments.

Characters may roll an action die to ignore these effects for a number of minutes equal to the result of the action die.

NEW HUMAN EQUIPMENT

The following equipment is available to all SGC personnel should the situation warrant.

NEW PROTECTIVE GEAR

Field Protective Mask: A field protective mask, when worn with the accompanying hood, provides respiratory, eye, and head protection against all chemical and biological agents, toxins, radioactive fallout particles, and battlefield contaminants; no save is required. When the air has a low-oxygen content, such as in tunnels or caves, or when the air has a high level of smoke, the mask will not protect the wearer. Due to the hood, the wearer suffers a -2 to all Listen check while wearing the mask. The canister filter must be changed every 12 hours. Filters may not be changed in a contaminated environment. The mask comes with five extra filters. Additional filters may be purchased at ten filters per one gear pick. The mask requires one full action to don. A field protective mask is included in the standard SG team bundle at no additional cost.

Handheld Decontamination Apparatus: This device decontaminates small areas – such as the steering wheel or other equipment that must be touched – of all known biological and chemical agents. It looks like a small fire extinguisher and holds enough decontaminant to cover 135 sq. ft. or 6 people in MOPP4 gear. The contents are under pressure and are very flammable.

Off-World Decontamination Modules: The SGC has a few modular collective-protection equipment systems or MCPEs. These systems are actually large boxes, the size of a small cargo container, that are used on other worlds where teams may need to be decontaminated immediately or repeatedly. Each module comes with a single stage airlock and other medical and decontamination equipment. Within 12 hours one of these units can be set-up and ready for use.

Portable Decontaminating Apparatus: This devise functions similar to the handheld decontamination apparatus, except that it has a five gallon container of decontaminant, with a hose attached to the container at one end and a scrub brush at the end of a five foot rod. This devise may not be used at range. A portable decontaminating apparatus can decontaminate an area up to 1,200 sq. ft. of all known chemical and biological agents. It is used on such things as vehicles. The contents are not under pressure and must be pumped out using the rod and brush. However, the liquid is very flammable.

Sensor, Chemical Agent Detector Paper: This item contains two types of chemical agent detector paper. The first type can detect the presence of liquid chemical agents and can be attached to most equipment, including clothing, using the adhesive on its reverse. The second type of paper comes in booklets allowing the character to identify what kind of chemical agent the first paper has detected. This item grants a +4 gear bonus with Search checks made to locate and identify liquid chemical agents. Because the detection papers use colors to signify their results, they are useless on any world that has a non-white light emitting sun, or are used in an enclosed space without sufficient white light. Each unit of this item comes with 25 sheets of both types of detection paper and brief instructions on its use. This item is added to the standard SG team bundle at no additional cost.

Shots: These new shots are administered in the same manner as those in the core rulebook. See page 318 of the Stargate SG-1 core rulebook for further details.

- *Convulsant Antidote for Nerve Agents (CANA):* The CANA is a disposable autoinjector for intramuscular delivery of diazepam to a fellow character who is incapacitated by nerve agent poisoning. The CANA must be used on another character after he has begun to suffer from a nerve agent's primary phase effects, but before the secondary phase effects start.

- *Nerve Agent Antidote Kit (NAAK):* NAAKs prevent the effects of any nerve agents to which a character has been exposed, but only if it is administered before the character suffers from the primary phase damage of the agent. Three NAAKs are included in every standard SG team bundle at no additional cost.

Skin Decontamination Kit: The skin decontamination is designed for chemical decontamination. It consists of a flexible outer pouch containing six individual skin decontaminating packets. Each packet consists of a foil-packaged, laminated fiber material containing a reactive resin with a strong anti-bacterial solution. These wipes contain solutions that neutralize most nerve and blister agents, as well as preventing infections. One wipe can decontaminate a single character's hands, face, ears, and neck once. The kit is attached to the gas mask or "sea bag" in the standard SG team bundle, to which this item may be added at no extra cost.

Suit, Battledress Over-garment (BDO): The BDO is a camouflage colored expendable two-piece over-garment consisting of one coat and one pair of trousers, a pair of gloves, a helmet cover, and footwear cover all worn over a character's usual clothing. The BDO is a cheaper version of the NBC suit. When worn, a BDO provides a +4 equipment bonus to all saves against the effects of any liquid chemical and biological agents, as well as radioactivity. This suit is usually worn in conjunction with a gas mask for greater protection. The duration this suit can protect the wearer is 30 days, calculated from the time it is removed from its bag, unless exposed to an agent the suit protects against. If exposed the duration the suit is effective is 24 hours from the moment of contact.

Suit, Chemical Protective Over-garment (CPOG): The CPOG is a suit similar to the BDO, but instead of protecting the wearer from liquids it protects from vapors. Also like the BDO, this suit is worn over a character's usual clothing. When worn, a CPOG provides a +4 equipment bonus to all saves against the effects of all vapor and liquid chemical and biological agents, as well as radioactivity. This suit is almost always worn with a gas mask. When both the CPOG and gas mask are worn, the suit provides complete protection from vapor chemical and biological agents; no saving throws are required. The duration this suit can protect the wearer is 30 days, calculated from the time it is removed from its bag, unless exposed to an agent the suit protects against. If exposed the duration the suit is effective is 24 hours from the moment of contact.

Suit, Contamination Avoidance and Liquid Protective (SCALP): The SCALP is an over-garment made of composite materials completely covering a person. It is worn over an NBC suit to provide extra protection by allowing the suit or the wearer to sustain a further 3 points of damage before becoming useless. A SCALP may also be worn over a CPOG or BDO providing an additional +4 equipment bonus to saving throws offered by the undersuit. In either case, when worn over another suit the SCALP has the equipment quality of awkward due to the confinement of wearing three sets of clothing, and if in a hot environment, the wearer suffers a -2 to his Constitution due to water loss from sweat. A SCALP worn on its own provides only a +2 saving throw

STARGATE COMMAND NUCLEAR, BIOLOGICAL, AND CHEMICAL PROCEDURES

As part of the Air Force, the SGC follows all of the same procedures, and use the same gear, as the rest of the United States military when it encounters, or has the potential to encounter, nuclear, biological, or chemical agents. The following rules detail how these procedures are used in the game.

When the possibility arises of an NBC agent being brought through the Stargate, the SGC implements several procedures, and uses decontamination equipment, to ensure the agent does not contaminate the base.

First, the embarkation room is sealed off from the rest of the base, allowing entry and exit through only one of the doors leading into the room.

Second, a single stage or double stage air-lock system is fixed to the door on the inside of the room. A single stage air-lock system usually has an aerosol anti-bacterial and chemical decontamination combined that is sprayed onto all persons entering the air-lock from the gate room. No person is allowed through the air-lock until this decontamination occurs. Decontamination in a single stage air-lock takes four rounds. A double stage air-lock system adds a further airlock after the decontamination spray where the air is pumped out and fresh air pumped in at the same time to ensure no airborne particulate agents are carried into the base. The double stage air-lock adds six rounds onto the time it takes to go through the entire airlock, for a total of ten rounds.

Third, a chemical wash spray-frame is set over the ramp leading into the Stargate. As people pass from the gate they are automatically sprayed with scalding hot water with a chemical decontaminant to wash the suits worn by the travelers. If no suits are worn, the spray is disengaged; otherwise the traveler could suffer severe chemical burns (1d4 points of wound damage per round) requiring medical attention immediately.

After the travelers have gone through the air-lock, their suits and clothes are taken and decontaminated, if possible. If not, the suits and clothes are destroyed.

Finally, the travelers are given a thorough medical exam to test for any possible signs of known symptoms to the contaminants. If the agent is not known, a complete physical, with blood-work, is performed. Almost always, these medical exams are overseen or performed by the chief medical officer of the base. Sometimes travelers are restricted to the base (or certain levels of the base if there is a possibility of unknown effects or the contagion spreading) for a minimum of 24 hours, usually no longer than two weeks.

Only after all of these precautions are taken are travelers allowed to continue with their duties.

The decontaminates used in these procedures neutralize or otherwise remove all known biological and chemical agents, as well as nuclear fallout dust and particulates, from a person. However, many of the diseases encountered by SG teams are not known to Earth doctors. It is basically up to the GM whether the decontamination process works or not.

against liquid chemical and biological agents, as well as radioactivity. The duration this suit can protect the wearer is 14 days, calculated from the time it is removed from its bag, unless exposed to an agent the suit protects against. If exposed the duration the suit is effective is six hours from the moment of contact.

Suit, NBC: A character who wears this NBC (Nuclear, Biological, and Chemical) suit may operate in any environment contaminated with radioactive, chemical, or biological agents, and is immune to the effects of disease and gases. This suit's breathing filters must be replaced every 6 hours or its benefits are lost. The suit's benefits are also lost if either it or the character within suffers 3 or more points of damage.

NEW HUMAN WEAPONS

Dan-Inject CO2 Injection Rifle: This compressed gas dart rifle is used to inject targets at a distance. Made of black anodized aluminum and stainless steel, this CO2-powered rifle has a telescopic sight and can fire up to 3 shots on a single gas cartridge, taking a full action to reload both the magazine and gas charge. The 1.5ml darts can be loaded with any liquid. This weapon may be used in single-shot mode only.

Special: If the target does not take any of the projectile's 1d4 in damage (wound or vitality), the dart has failed to penetrate and the liquid does not enter the target's system. A standard attack action requires one full action (in order for the character to take advantage of the weapon's increased accuracy).

NEW ALIEN DEVICES

SGC teams have encountered numerous intelligent alien races with a wide range of technological advancement. This section includes an overview of the technological approaches of several of the more advanced races, and individual devices and weapons encountered during the first season. Items listed with a Resource Point cost are expensive or exotic even on their world of manufacture; some are beyond even the SGC's ability to procure. Items with a gear pick cost are available to SG teams at the GM's discretion only if they have the low tech quality *(see below)*. Otherwise, the cost is listed in resource points instead of gear picks.

NEW QUALITIES

Low Tech (LT): This item can be reproduced by the Stargate Command with relative ease. SGC team members may requisition this item at its normal cost.

ALTAIRAN TECHNOLOGY (TIN MAN)

The Altairans utilize a series of high-tech device for defense.

Field NBC procedures (MOPP)

MOPP is an acronym for Mission-Oriented Protective Posture. It is a flexible system that provides maximum NBC protection for an individual with the lowest risk possible, and still maintains mission accomplishment.

Even though a character may not be carrying all of the gear mentioned in the MOPP levels below, he should put on all those he does possess. Each higher level assumes that the equipment worn for a lower level is still worn.

All teams begin at MOPP Ready if the possibility of encountering nuclear, biological, or chemical agent is present before the team begins a mission.

MOPP Ready: The characters carry their protective masks with the bundle container. Characters in MOPP Ready are highly vulnerable to persistent agent attacks and should automatically upgrade to MOPP Zero when the team leader determines that chemical weapons have been used or that the threat for use of chemical weapons has risen.

MOPP Zero: Characters carry their protective masks with their bundle. The character's BDO or CPOG and other equipment making up the character's MOPP gear are readily available by being stored within arms reach of the character or carried by the character. Characters in MOPP Zero are highly vulnerable to persistent agent attacks and should automatically upgrade to MOPP1 when the team leader determines that chemical weapons have been used or that the threat for use of chemical weapons has risen.

MOPP1: When directed to MOPP1, characters immediately don their BDO or CPOG. MOPP1 provides a great deal of protection against persistent agents. This level is automatically assumed when chemical weapons have been employed in an area of operations or when ordered by the team leader.

MOPP2: Characters put on their chemical protective footwear covers and the protective cover for their helmet if one is being worn. Note that chemical protective footwear covers (CPFCs) come with BDO and CPOG suits.

MOPP3: Characters put on their protective mask and hood.

MOPP4: Characters completely encapsulate themselves by closing their overgarments, rolling down and adjusting the mask hood, and putting on NBC gloves. Note that a set of NBC gloves comes with all BDO and CPOG suits. MOPP4 provides the highest degree of chemical and biological protection, but also has the most negative impact on an individual's performance.

Mask Only Command: Only the protective mask is worn. The Mask Only Command is given under these conditions:

- When riot control characters are being employed and no chemical/biological threat exists.

- In a downwind vapor hazard of a non-persistent chemical agent.

Altairan Weapons

Altairan Disintegrator: The Altairan disintegrator uses a basic battery pack capable of firing 20 shots before being recharged. Any object or creature without vitality points struck by a disintegrator is vaporized immediately when suffering damage and cannot be healed or repaired. Any living creature or character with vitality points takes damage as normal, but any time the character or creature loses any wound points it must make a Fortitude save (DC 15) or be disintegrated (reduced to -25 wounds). Any character or creature reduced to 0 wounds or less is automatically disintegrated.

Stun Field Generator: The stun field generator is placed in a single location and aimed in a 90-degree arc at a particular area. When activated, the stun field generator automatically deals damage to all characters and creatures within 30 feet at the end of each round. Characters passing through this field may make a Fortitude save (DC 15) to take half this damage. The stun field generator deals only subdual damage, and cannot cause any lethal damage.

Asgard Technology (Thor's Hammer)

Asgard technology is among the most powerful in the universe, with the ability to send ships across the galaxy or teleport matter without the use of a ring device. The Asgard rarely give their technology to less developed species (read: humanity), but may be persuaded to loan them out in certain circumstances (GM's discretion).

Asgard Equipment

Gate Controller Device (GCD): The Gate Controller Device can be used to alter the way a DHD interacts with the Stargate.

Resource Points: N/A. Used solely at Asgard (GM's) discretion.

Mechanics: The GCD must be connected to the DHD by pressing the tip of the GCD into a port on the side of the DHD (requiring a half action). Once the GCD has been connected in this manner, it then has two primary functions, whose mechanics are as follows:

Dial an Alternate Gate (Half Action): In the cases where the Stargate is dialing a world that has multiple Stargates, the DHD is configured to connect directly to the primary gate. If the character using the Gate Controller Device wishes to travel to a Stargate on a world other than the default gate, the GCD must be used. The character uses the touch-sensitive interface to draw the point of origin of they gate they wish to dial. The Stargate is then used as per the normal dialing rules, but the Stargate connects to the alternate gate instead.

Dial a Local Gate (Half Action): While on a world with multiple Stargates, dialing the address of the planet you are on usually results in the Stargate locking in place without establishing a wormhole. Using the GCD, the point of origin another gate on that world is drawn on the touch-sensitive interface and then the gate is dialed as normal. The Stargate connects to the local gate and establishes the wormhole, allowing instantaneous transport between two Stargates on the same planet.

Mjolnir Pendant: These pendants are worn around the neck, and are intended to repel Goa'uld possession.

Resource Points; 2.

Mechanics: Whenever a larval Goa'uld comes within 5 feet of a mjolnir pendant, the larva must make a Will save (DC 20) or take the withdraw action. Goa'uld already in a host body need not make this Will save.

Ramir: These devices are intended to prevent the operation of naquadah-powered equipment.

Resource Points: 12.

Mechanics: When an active ramir is in place, no weapons or equipment that use naquadah as a primary power source within 30 feet will function. If a character attempts to activate such a device while within the disabling bubble of the ramir, the item simply appears to be without power. Characters with naquadah in their blood may not spend vitality to power Goa'uld devices while in a ramir's area of effect.

Thor's Hammer: This is the catch-name for a generic device which the Asgard used to protect worlds with a Stargate from incursions by the Goa'uld.

Resource Points: N/A. The devices cannot be requisitioned by SGC personnel, nor can they be moved from the planets on which they are placed without the direct intervention of the Asgard.

Mechanics: Whenever a group of characters emerges on a planet where a Thor's Hammer device is placed near the Stargate, the device will automatically activate and begin scanning the group. Each round, the device scans 1d4 characters, chosen at random by the Gamemaster. If a character being scanned is the current host of a Goa'uld (including Tok'ra), or is a Jaffa carrying a larval Goa'uld, that character is immediately teleported (along with any characters in physical contact with that character) to the interior of the labyrinth. While inside the labyrinth, the characters may proceed to the Hall of Mjolnir where any character hosting or carrying a Goa'uld must confront Thor's Hammer. If such a character passes through the archway, the character suffers 2d8 points of subdual damage and the Goa'uld larva suffers 1d6 points of energy damage per round until he retreats back into the labyrinth. If the Goa'uld larva dies, the damage ceases and the character may proceed (if still conscious) through the exit of the labyrinth without suffering further damage.

ASGARD WEAPONS

Shock Spear: The shock spear only deals damage to characters with naquadah in their blood. Characters without the Weapon Group Proficiency (Rifle) feat suffer a –4 penalty to all attack rolls with this weapon.

BYRSA GEAR (COR-AI)

The Byrsa are a primitive people by Earth standards, but they have developed a unique weapon to help defend themselves (*see Cor-ai, page 55, for more information*).

BYRSA WEAPONS

Kest: This primitive sling-crossbow is considered a medium hurled weapon. Reloading a kest after each shot requires one half action. When a character requisitions this weapon, he gains enough kest bolts to last him the duration of the current mission (GM's discretion). Regular bolts may be used, with an additional –1 penalty to accuracy.

GOA'ULD GEAR

The Goa'uld have stolen or retrograded technology for centuries, making them extremely advanced by Earth standards. The illusion of godhood is most often facilitated through use of this technology.

Unless otherwise stated (or allowed by the GM), Goa'uld gear may not be requisitioned to SGC personnel or their allies.

PELOPS' NANOTECHNOLOGY (BRIEF CANDLE)

Pelops' nanocytes are microscopic devices capable of producing a variety of effects by altering their host's body chemistry and physiology. Though Pelops uses these nanocytes to create specific effects in different hosts, the nanocytes themselves are the same in all cases. The nanocytes can produce only one single effect at any one time. Pelops activates the nanocytes' different effects by transmitting specific radio frequencies. For instance, one specific frequency boosts to the subject's Strength ability score, another boosts the subject's Dexterity score, and a third frequency boosts the subject's Constitution. Pelops closely guards the specific frequencies that activate the nanocytes' effects, in no small part due to the fact that he himself carries nanocytes within his body.

While Pelops' nanocytes respond appropriately to specific frequencies, there is nothing unique about the transmitter devices Pelops uses. SG-1 was able to use an Earth technology transmitter to awaken the Argosians after they damaged the transmitter hidden in the base of the statue of Pelops on Argos. Pelops uses all manner of transmitters, ranging from the automated devices on Argos (now destroyed) and Tiryns, to hand-held devices that control the nanocytes in various test subjects on Sparta, as well as the nanocytes Pelops carries in his own body.

Without some sort of signal from one of Pelops' transmitters (or any transmitter broadcasting a valid frequency) at least once per day, nanocytes in a subject's body start to break down as their immune system attacks and destroys them. Jaffa infused with the technology carry a small transmitter used to keep the nanocytes active within their bodies. These transmitters broadcast only a set number of signals that activate specific effects (such ability enhancements and healing) and a signal that does nothing but keep the nanocytes from being attacked by the Jaffa's immune system (i.e., its symbiote).

When outside the human body, the nanocytes are much more resilient. Pelops installed default programs in the nanocytes that cause them to replicate themselves if subjected to external stimulus or probing. Captain Carter of SG-1 triggered his "safety feature" when examining the nanocytes taken from Argos, resulting in a near loss of containment in the SGC.

Resource Points: N/A. The SGC and its allies do not have access to Pelops' experiments.

Mechanics: Some of the nanocytes' specific effects include the following. Others may exist at the GMs' discretion.

Aging, Accelerated: Used on both Argos and Tiryns, accelerated aging increases the rate at which the host's body ages. The specific rate at which the aging occurs is adjustable, ranging from slight acceleration in which each day that passes ages the subject by one week, to extreme acceleration (as in the case of the Argosians and Tirynsians, where the normal human lifespan is shortened to only one hundred days).

Aging, Reversed: Reversed aging slows down the body's natural aging process by automatically repairing, healing, and replacing dying cells as needed to keep the body in a more or less constant level of health. In game terms, this effect is similar to the Long Life ability of the Symbiote feat *(see page 265 in the Stargate SG-1 core rulebook).* This effect is persistent in the host until intentionally shut off, or until a different effect is triggered in the host. Pelops uses this effect on himself as well his First Prime, who has served the Goa'uld for the last 200 years.

Enhanced Abilities: This effect can be used to boost one of the host's ability scores for a period of up to one hour. Each ability score bonus has a corresponding penalty, the result of the stress of such radical and rapid change in the host's body. The possible bonuses and corresponding penalties are as follows:

BONUS	PENALTY
+4 Str	−4 Dex
+4 Dex	−4 Con
+4 Con	−4 Cha
+4 Int	−4 Wis
+4 Wis	−4 to Int
+4 Cha	−4 Str

Healing: This effect boosts the character's normal natural healing rate, allowing the character to heal 1d6 vitality points per character level per hour of rest (for up to three hours, after which time the character heals normally), and 1d4 wound points per day of rest.

Injury and Disease: This effect can create any manner of injury to the host's body, including lesions, abrasions, burns, and other injuries. When inflicting this effect on a subject, roll the damage dice as normal for the type of injury. For instance, if mimicking a wound from a staff weapon, roll normal damage (6d6) and apply the damage to the subject.

In addition, this effect can mimic the effects of any poison or disease, and at an accelerated rate. When using this effect, the onset time of both the Primary and Secondary phases of a disease of poison are lowered to the next lowest unit of time: years become months, months become weeks, hours become minutes, etc. For example, the onset time of ebola when mimicked via Pelops' nanocytes is 2d10 hours instead of 2d10 days. All other effects of mimicked diseases and poisons, including saving throw DCs and damage/effect remain the same.

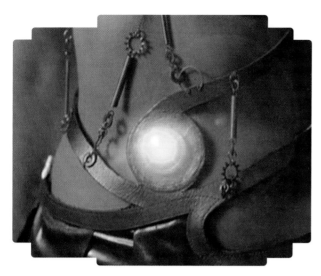

GOA'ULD GEAR (CHILDREN OF THE GODS)

Jaffa Creation Device: Although most Jaffa hail from the planet Chulak, this was not always so. In the past, the Goa'uld used many species as the incubators of their larvae, such as the Unas. These earlier incubators were not yet called Jaffa, but they functioned almost exactly like the Jaffa of later centuries. All such incubators, whether human or alien in origin, were initially created through a combination of surgery and genetic engineering at the hands of the System Lords. Once the Jaffa bred true, they became self-sustaining and the Goa'uld could simply choose from among their population when an incubator was needed. Of course, the technology to create new Jaffa continues to exist. A handful of Goa'uld further perfected this technology so that it could be easily transported and used at their leisure. Looking like an ornate belt with a central crystal, the creative device must be placed against the abdomen of the intended Jaffa-to-be. Within a few seconds, the crystal glows intently and creates a pouch in the abdomen into which a Goa'uld larva can be safely placed. The device does little permanent damage, but its effects are draining on those who undergo them.

Resource Points: N/A. Creation devices are not available to the SGC, nor may they be used by anyone save a Goa'uld.

Mechanics: The Jaffa creation device cannot be used in combat. It must be held against an helpless or unresisting target for a period of 10 seconds in order to function properly. At the end of that period, the potential Jaffa must make a Fortitude save (DC 12) or suffer 1d6 points of wound damage. After this damage heals, the target will become a true Jaffa if a larva is implanted within his newly-created abdominal pouch. In that case, he then gains the symbiote feat but loses the next level-based feat he would otherwise gain.

If a larva is not implanted, the target retains his original species characteristics except that he no longer has an immune system of his own. The abdominal pouch likewise remains present. These changes to the target's racial make-up can only be removed through the use of a sarcophagus or other advanced medical technology, such as that of the Asgard. A character without an immune system suffers all the problems that a normal Jaffa would should his symbiote be removed.

Kash'ta: The *kash'ta* is another form of inhaled chemical favored by the Goa'uld to affect their enemies in adverse ways. Unlike the more common *nish'ta,* the kash'ta enrages those who inhale it and instinctively turns them against their allies. While in this enraged state, they temporarily become stronger and hardier due to the adrenaline surge the chemical causes in their bloodstream. A victim affected by kash'ta will attack no one but those he formerly considered friends and allies prior to his being affected. For this reason, Goa'uld use this chemical when they wish to throw their enemies into disarray so as to provide any opening for their own attacks (or to flee). Kash'ta is sufficiently rare even among the Goa'uld that even some System Lords are unaware of its properties.

Resource Points: 8, but kash'ta is not normally available to the SGC.

Mechanics: A character exposed to kash'ta temporarily gains a +4 bonus to Strength, a +4 bonus to Constitution, and a +2 morale bonus on Will saves, but takes a –2 penalty to Defense. The increase in Constitution increases the character's vitality points by 2 points per level; when the kash'ta wears off, the extra vitality points are lost and the character's Constitution score drops back to normal. These extra vitality points are not lost first the way temporary vitality points are. While under the influence of kash'ta, a character cannot use any Charisma-, Dexterity-, or Intelligence-based skills (except for Balance, Escape Artist, Intimidate, and Ride), the Concentration skill, or any abilities that require patience or concentration. He can use any feat he has except those whose prerequisites are based on high Charisma, Dexterity, or Intelligence.

With regards to the saving throws to avoid its effects, kash'ta functions exactly like nish'ta *(see the Stargate SG-1 core rulebook, page 418).* However, unlike nish'ta, kash'ta's effects last for only 2d6+1 rounds per use. Each individual affected by the fumes will, if he fails his checks, fall under its influence for a different length of time. Thus, two characters affected at the same time will not necessarily shake off its effects at the same time. As with nish'ta, a strong electrical shock will eliminate the chemical's effects.

Healing Device, Modified: Other than being powered by the same naquadah power cell as a staff weapon, this tool appears identical to the standard healing device. Its function is limited, however, to scanning an adjacent character's current and maximum vitality and wound point totals, and sterilization of the surface of an object. Both functions take a full round each, and consume a charge. The power cell must be replaced after 25 uses.

Resource Points: 14.

Mechanics: As per Stargate SG-1 core rulebook.

Lotus Pollen: The System Lord Nirrti developed this contagion many years ago when a large populace needed to be exterminated, and used it against Cassandra's people in the episode *Singularity (see page 59).* Its effects are similar to pneumatic plague (boils, lesions, etc.) but the onset time is much faster. Instead of days, the disease affects its victim within hours. Because of the short incubation period, lotus pollen is not usually transmitted from person to person as they die too quickly. The best means of infecting a population with lotus pollen is to scatter it through the air for it to be inhaled or absorbed through the victim's orifices.

Resource Points: N/A. Lotus pollen is unavailable to the SGC or its allies

Mechanics: See Table 3.5: Lotus Pollen

Miniature Naquadah Bomb, Improved (Scarab): Nicknamed the "scarab" because of its ability to create itself from nothing, the improved miniature naquadah bomb can be lodged in a victim's body the same as a normal version. Its size is much smaller until it is activated, however, making it far more difficult to detect. After it has "grown" to its full size, the scarab acts like the standard version, unless it is removed from the presence of a Stargate.

Resource Points: N/A. This device is not available to the SGC or its allies.

Mechanics: This device activates, growing to the size of a penny, after the victim passes once through a Stargate. It takes 4d12 hours for the scarab to grow to its full size. Immediately upon growing to full size, the scarab will explode, inflicting 5d10 + 40 normal damage with a 100-ft. blast increment. Should any square touched by this blast contain at least one gallon of naquadah (or a solid equivalent, such as a Stargate), the explosion's damage is tripled and its blast increment is increased to one mile (calculated from its original ground zero).

If the victim is moved more than a half mile away from a Stargate, the scarab will be reabsorbed into the bloodstream in the same amount of time it has taken to grow to its current size.

Because of the way in which the scarab works, it is linked with a vital organ (usually the heart) of the victim, making its removal nearly impossible.

Detecting a scarab requires a successful First Aid check (DC 30 -1 per hour after the scarab begins to grow) using a sensor capable of scanning the victim's internal organs (e.g. an ultrasound, an X-ray, etc.). Removing it requires a second successful First Aid check (DC 25). If the removal check fails the victim dies. Unlike the normal version, the scarab does not need to be disarmed after its removal as its growth is immediately halted. A scarab cannot be disarmed while still inside a victim using current human technology except by moving the victim away from the presence of any Stargate.

Radiation Shield: The radiation shield is a device the Goa'uld used on worlds whose atmosphere was too thin or damaged to protect its inhabitants from ultraviolet (and other forms of) radiation. The shield was intended as a stopgap measure until such time as the Goa'uld properly terraformed the world. That is, it was never meant for long-term use, although "long-term" is relative in meaning. Given that terraforming could take centuries or more, a radiation shield might find itself in constant use for some time.

The shield consists of two identical portable stations. Each station includes an activation device, as well as an input device that allow the user to alter its settings. The two stations must be placed no more than 30 miles from each other and no less than 10 miles. When activated, the stations each emit an orange-colored force field stream that quickly finds its mate emitted from the other station. When the two streams meet, they then create a hemispherical shield whose diameter is equal to the distance between the two stations. This shield filters out all damaging radiation and allows those who live beneath it to walk about freely without fear of radiation poisoning.

Goa'uld radiation shields were most commonly used on worlds with an immediate use to the System Lords. Rather than being patient and doing the necessary terraforming work, the Goa'uld would set up a radiation shield (or several), so that they could establish an immediate presence on the planet. The SGC has discovered only a handful of worlds with active or even inactive radiation shields (a good example is the planet of Avnil, in the episode *The First Commandment; see page 21 for more information*). In almost every case, it has been a world with some resource of great value to the System Lords, such as a naquadah mine or a cache of Ancient technology.

Resource Points: N/A. This device is not currently available to the SGC or its allies.

Mechanics: Activating a radiation shield station requires 1 half action. The force field stream then travels upward from the station at a rate of 3 miles a second. Since both stations emit a stream, they will meet halfway between their locations fairly quickly. Once they meet, the shield forms at a similar rate. Anyone within the shield's radius is immediately rendered immune to the effects of any radiation that comes from the outside. Thus, for example, UV radiation no longer has any effect. However, should there be a source of radiation within the shield's area itself (such as a bomb or a radioactive isotope) it remains as a dangerous as ever.

Both parts of the device must be functioning for the shield to be generated. If one of the portable stations isn't working, then the second simply will not activate.

GOA'ULD ARMOR

Jaffa Armor, Standard: Jaffa armor is tough and resilient, designed to repel all but the most powerful forms of kinetic damage. The exact design varies from System Lord to System Lord, but in game terms, they all provide the same benefits.

Jaffa Helm, Standard: The very symbol of a System Lord's might, the external design of the helms of his Jaffa are unique each lord. However, all Jaffa helms possess some of the following special qualities, as dictated on Table 3.26.

TABLE 3.5: LOTUS POLLEN

		------- Primary Phase -------			------- Secondary Phase -------		
CONTAGION	CR	ONSET TIME	SAVE	DAMAGE/ EFFECT	ONSET TIME	SAVE	DAMAGE/ EFFECT
Lotus Pollen*	16	1d4 hours	Fort (DC 30)	1 Con	1d2 hours	Fort (DC 32)	2d6 Con

* After 1d6 hours the bacteria settles into the ground where it waits to infect a victim in the soil, crops, and water if ingested (such as food or water) or inhaled (in dust). All bacteria not infecting a victim dies after 2d12 weeks.

Communicator(C): This gear has an internal system that allows the character to communicate with other communication devices of the same type. In the case of Jaffa helmets, the internal communications system only connects Jaffa belonging to the same faction.

Intimidating (IN): Whenever a character meets a Jaffa in a helmet for the first time, that Jaffa is granted a +2 gear bonus to Intimidate checks on that character. However, the accompanying sound effects reduce the DC of all Listen checks to detect the helm wearer by 5.

Limited Vision (LV): Using this gear restricts the character's field of view, making him more vulnerable to the unexpected. While using an item with the limited vision quality, the character suffers a -2 gear penalty to all Reflex saves.

Night Vision (NV): The Jaffa helmet allows the wearer to see in dim light or total darkness when the night vision filter is activated. This filter offers a +4 bonus to Spot checks in near darkness and a +6 bonus to Spot checks in total darkness. Any character that uses the night vision filter in the daytime is blinded for 1 round while his vision clears.

Powered (PW): The gear operates under an internal power source and may fail under field conditions. It works normally for 5 minutes (50 rounds) but each time it is used thereafter without a recharge the user must roll a d20. This roll initially has an error range of 1. With a roll of 20, the error range increases by 1 (first to 1–2, then to 1–3, and so on). If the character rolls an error, the Gamemaster may spend an action die to cause the item's power to run down, requiring a new power source or a recharge. Replacing the power source of such a device requires 1 full action. Recharging requires 1d10+2 rounds. Either method refreshes the cycle, offering the character another 5 minutes of use before he must roll again, and resetting the roll's error range to 1. The Jaffa helmet only expends one round of power when a special quality requiring the helmet's internal power (such as night vision or the pressure seal) is used.

Pressure Seal (PS): The gear contains a pressure seal that can be activated with a half action. If the pressure seal is in place, the Jaffa is immune to damage and negative effects of gases, chemicals, sandstorms, and other environ-mental conditions that can be eliminated by an advanced air filter. While in use, the pressure seal incurs a -2 gear penalty to endurance-related checks and Fortitude saves due to restricted air flow.

Proximity Alarm (PA): The gear contains a special sensor that allows the user to tell when other combatants are approaching in secret. Whenever the user of this gear is being flanked, all his opponent's bonuses for flanking that character are halved (rounded up).

GOA'ULD WEAPONS

Dragon Talons: These short blades are carried in pairs by the Dragon Guard. The advanced material used in their construction grants them the armor piercing quality, but they may not be repaired in any way.

Lightning Cannon (nek'sed): Lightning cannons do not use standard ammunition, but are instead powered by a portable naquadah generator. Additionally, the lightning cannon can only be fired once every two rounds, requiring one round between shots to recharge the energy coils.

Lightning Staff: The staff weapons carried by Raiden's Lightning Guards can be fired in two modes, normal mode and lightning mode. In normal mode, the weapons act as standard staff weapons (see the Stargate SG-1 core rulebook, page 346). In lightning mode, the weapon's blast appears as a bolt of lightning. Characters struck by this attack take normal staff weapon damage (6d6), and must make a Fortitude save (DC 18) or be staggered (see page 379 in the Stargate SG-1 core rulebook) for 1d6 rounds. Lightning staves can only fired in lightning mode once every four rounds, and firing a lightning staff in lightning mode uses up 5 shots.

Raiden's Kara Kesh: Characters struck by Raiden's "thunder" must make Fortitude save (DC 20) or be deafened and stunned (see pages 378-379 in the Stargate SG-1 core rulebook) for 2d6 rounds. In addition, characters within 10 feet of the target must make Fortitude save (DC 15) or be deafened for 1d6 rounds. Characters struck by Raiden's "lightning" must make Fortitude save (DC 22) or be staggered (see page 379 in the Stargate SG-1 core rulebook) for 1d6 rounds.

Sunburst Grenade (ra'kek): The sunburst grenade fires bolts of energy out in all directions from protruding nozzles. However, when those nozzles are retracted the device looks like a communication sphere (but cannot be fired without spending a half-action to ready the device).

Thunder Staff: The staff weapons carried by Raiden's Thunder Guards can be fired in two modes, normal mode and thunder mode. In normal mode, the weapons act as standard staff weapons (see the Stargate SG-1 core rulebook, page 346). In thunder mode, the weapon fires a sonic attack along with its normal blast. Characters struck by this attack take normal staff weapon damage (6d6), and must make a Fortitude save (DC 18) or be deafened (see the Stargate SG-1 core rulebook, pages 378-379) for 4d6 rounds. In addition, characters within 10 feet of the target must make Fortitude save (DC 12) or be deafened for 2d6 rounds. Thunder staves can only fired in thunder mode once every three rounds, and firing a thunder staff in thunder mode uses up 3 shots.

Nox Technology (The Nox)

Though you'd never know to look at them, the Nox are a highly technological species, possessing technology that rivals that of the Asgard, possibly even the Ancients. The Nox have not allowed the advance of technology to compromise their world's ecosystem, or to change the fundamental values of their society, limiting the outward signs of their advancement. Where the advance of their civilization or technology might encroach on the wilderness, the Nox instead pursued alternative solutions, such as relocating their industries into the floating cities, leaving the surface pristine. Similarly, while their technology could produce devastating weapons, the Nox remain completely steadfast in their adherence to absolute pacifism.

Nox technology is based on the manipulation of energy fields of different sorts, including light, gravity, and electromagnetic energy. This is an extension of their natural ability to interact with and manipulate the bio-electrical energy fields of living beings. Their natural abilities are limited to individual energy fields, but through technology, they are able to interact with and manipulate external energy fields, granting them astounding capabilities.

Most prominent among the Nox's technological achievements is their ability to make themselves and others invisible and intangible. This ability is in fact two distinct effects, known to Nox scientists as cloaking and shifting, and these two effects are the basis for many of the Nox's technological capabilities.

Cloaking creates an energy field around the subject that is undetectable by Earth sciences and which causes light that would otherwise reflect off a subject to bend around the subject, creating an effect equivalent to invisibility. The Nox use this effect to defend themselves when necessary, but they also use it to defend the creatures of their world from off-world hunters, such as the Fenri, who the Nox have cloaked from Goa'uld hunters for centuries.

Shifting transfers a subject from the dimension of normal space to that of a parallel dimension know to Earth scientists as sub-space by manipulating the energy fields that define the boundary between normal and sub-spaces. This has the effect of making the subject effectively disappear from normal space. The Nox can shift themselves, as well as inanimate objects, and other beings into and out of sub-space at will. Most non-Nox retain no memory of entering sub-space when shifted, nor do they recall anything of the time spent in sub-space. Objects and beings shifted into sub-space can be shifted back into normal space at any location the Nox performing the shifting can see, allowing the Nox to seemingly teleport across great distances. The Nox often shift themselves when visitors arrive on their world, that they may observe the visitors, and also occasionally use this ability to defend themselves and the creatures of their world from outside threats, similar to the way they employ cloaking. Beings and objects in sub-space cannot normally interact with those in normal space in any way. The only exception are shifted Stargates, which can connect to other Stargates within normal space.

Beyond cloaking and shifting, the Nox technology also provides them the ability to interact with and control other technological devices, including those of non-Nox design. This control comes from manipulating the physical, electri-

cal (or nuclear, or quantum) energy used by the device. This capability has virtually no limit, and can control devices as simple as a bicycle or as complex as the Stargate. This latter use is one of the more common, though specialized, uses of this ability, allowing the Nox to open the Stargate without need of using a dialing device.

One other capability granted the Nox by their technology is that of anti-gravity, accomplished by counteracting the natural forces of gravity in a localized area. Unlike other Nox technological capabilities, anti-gravity is not used by individual Nox on an as needed basis, but is instead permanently applied to a specific object, such as the floating cities on which much of the Nox population live.

The mechanism by which the Nox employ their technology is unlike that of most other species. Whereas most species employ devices of one sort of another, the Nox do not carry gear or equipment of any kind. Instead, the technology they employ lives within their bodies, and is as much as part of them as individual Nox are part of the world around them. The components of Nox technology are microscopic organisms that, when living within Nox physiology strengthen the natural bio-electric energy field in their bodies and grant them the ability to manipulate the external energy fields around them to create the technological effects of cloaking, shifting, and controlling technology. Nox scientists bred these organisms, using cells from the Nox and many of the plants and trees on Gaia, and they are attuned specifically to Nox physiology. They offer no benefit to other species. Activating most capabilities requires no more than thought on the part of the Nox, though controlling technology often requires gestures.

The Nox implant their children with these organisms at the age of 5 or 6. The Nox learn to control and master the abilities of their technology over time, beginning with the ability to cloak themselves and gradually adding more and more abilities until they've mastered all that their technology offers.

Mechanics: In game terms, most of the capabilities offered by Nox technology, including cloaking, shifting, and controlling technology are accessible by acquiring specific feats, which are detailed in the appropriate section on page 137.

Cloaking and Shifting Characters

Cloaking and shifting convey no adverse affects on subjects, apart from mild disorientation upon being shifted back into normal space after more than a few moments in sub-space (-1 to all rolls on the round following their return to normal space). In this case, non-Nox characters feel as though they have lost track of time, (which is in fact, exactly what happens) and have no memory whatsoever of their time in sub-space. Individual feat descriptions include specific game effects of being cloaked and/or shifted.

Ohnes Technology (Fire and Water)

The Ohnes have mastered many forms of technology, including the ability to probe other species' minds and the ability to create viable pockets of renewable air within their underwater structures.

MEMORY TECHNOLOGY

The Ohnes's memory technology provides means for altering a subject's memories, as well as helping a subject retrieve memories long buried in his or her subconscious.

Resource Points: N/A. This technology is not normally available to the SGC or its allies. Even off-world Ohnes must normally return to their home world to use it.

Memory Alteration: The Ohnes' memory alteration technology can implant false memories into a subject, or alter existing memories. Implanting or altering a memory takes two hours, and involves strapping the subject onto a chair that keeps the subject immobile. The technology utilizes a laser beam that directly alters cells in the subject's brain. This alteration can be detected on an MRI scan, showing up as a dark mark on the subject's brain tissue.

Once the procedure is complete, the implanted or altered memory seems as real to the subject as actual memories. The subject can relate details of the memory as though he had lived it himself. However, characters subjected to this procedure often experience flashbacks, most often triggered by sights similar to key aspects of the implanted/altered memory. For instance, when Nem implanted the memory of Daniel Jackson's death in O'Neill, Carter, and Teal'c, the three of them experienced flashbacks when they saw bubbles, which reminded them of the air bubbles they saw while in Nem's underwater lab. When a character with an implanted/altered memory sees or otherwise experiences something that might trigger a flashback (at the GM's discretion), they must make a Will saving throw (DC 10). If the character succeeds, he experiences a flashback and is considered stunned *(see page 379 in the Stargate SG-1 core rulebook)* for 1d42 rounds.

Implanted memories are often not without flaws. After a character suffers a memory flashback, the GM should make another Will saving throw (DC 12, minus one per flashback) for the character. If the saving throw succeeds, the character begins to doubt the reality of the memory, feeling that something is "wrong" about it. The specifics of how this doubt manifests are up to the GM.

Implanted/altered memories can be circumvented through hypnosis and focused concentration. Once put under hypnosis, if the character succeeds at a Will save (DC 12), the character realizes that implanted memories are false, and accurately recalls any altered or supplanted memories. Only one Will save is allowed per hypnosis session (subject to approval by the GM).

Memory Retrieval: Like the memory alteration procedure, the Ohnes' memory retrieval technology uses a laser beam interacting with the subject's brain, stimulating dormant memories. To recall a dormant memory, the subject makes an Education check against a base DC equal to the number of years since the memory took place. If the check succeeds, the character recalls portions of the memory based on the result of the check as follows:

EDUCATION CHECK

RESULT	LEVEL OF RECALL
Base DC	Partial details of the memory
Base +5	50% recall of the memory
Base +10	Total recall of the memory

The result of the check is increased by the power level of the memory retrieval device. This power level starts at 5, but can be increased as needed to further stimulate the subject's memories, up to a maximum setting of 50. The character can make more than one check to attempt to recall more information about the memory, but only after an increase in the power level.

The memory retrieval procedure is extremely painful, and can cause permanent brain damage and even death. After each check, the character must make a Fortitude saving throw against a DC equal to 10 plus the power level. If the character fails, he loses a number of vitality points equal to the power level. If the test succeeds, the character loses a number of vitality points equal to one quarter (rounded down) of the power level.

Example: Lt. Wilson is trying to recall a memory from 15 years ago with the help of the Ohnes. He makes an Education check, adding 5 (the base power level) to the result for a total of 16, and recalls only partial details of the memory. Lt. Wilson then makes a Fortitude save (DC 15) and succeeds, losing 1 vitality point (5 divided by 4 = 1.25, rounded down). Because he really needs to recall more about the memory, he decides to try again. The power level increases to 15 and he makes another check, this time with a total result (including the power level bonus) of 25, meaning he recalls the entire memory. However, when he makes his Fortitude saving throw, he fails and loses 15 vitality points.

Note: The equipment required to use this technology is very heavy (meaning it cannot normally be transported), and normally limited to the Ohnes' labs on their home world. Operating it requires a successful Electronics check, DC 25. Ohnes characters who have used such equipment before reduce the DC to 10. Success indicates that the device may be used as stipulated above. Failure means it cannot.

OHNES GEAR

Ohnes Hydrator: Ohnes scientists developed a device used by explorers known as a hydrator that allows them to remain out of water for prolonged periods of time. The device includes a salt-water tank connected to a series of small hoses connected to a module that oxygenates the water stored in the tank. The Ohnes wear this device around their necks, and the hoses have adapters that fit over the wearer's gills allowing the wearer to breathe the water in the tank. Water stored in the hydrator can be re-oxygenated for up to five days before it needs to be replaced with fresh water.

Ohnes Stargate Alarm: The Stargate on the Ohnes world is equipped with a motion sensor.

Resource Points: N/A. This device is not available to the SGC or its allies.

Mechanics: The target area of the sensor is a 30 ft. × 30 ft. square in front of the Stargate. A successful Electronics check (DC 24) disables the sensor, but this can only be done once through the Stargate (first-time arrivals through the gate will automatically set off the sensor). The Ohnes do not take kindly to visitors disabling the security measures.

OHNES WEAPONS

The Ohnes use sidearms and rifles that fire pulses of coherent sound. These weapons are equivalent to Earth shotguns: capable of hitting adjacent targets and losing 1d4 points damage per range increment. They are more effective underwater, where their range increments double. Ohnes vibration weapons are considered shotguns for purposes of feats and weapon specialization.

Ohnes Sonic Pistol: This is the most common Ohnes weapon, a sidearm used by Ohnes warriors that utilizes concussive vibration to inflict damage.

Ohnes Sonic Rifle: This is a rifle-sized blaster used by Ohnes warriors, similar to the sonic pistol.

SIMARKAN TECHNOLOGY (EMANCIPATION)

During SG-1's visit to Simarka, the Shavadai villagers showed them a number of medicines created from local plant life. Among these was an anesthetic salve that, when applied to open wounds not only relieved the pain of the wound, but also greatly reduced the healing time. SG-1 took samples of this salve and the plants from which it was created back to Earth for study, where subsequent research revealed anesthetic and healing properties beyond those witnessed by SG-1.

As a result, a number of science teams from the SGC traveled to Simarka for further study of the local fauna in hopes of finding other plants with potential medicinal properties. In three months of off-world study, the SGC science and medical teams have discovered more than six Simarka plants with healing and anesthetic properties. Specimens of each have been brought to Earth and attempts at growing these plants in greenhouses at Area 51

have proved moderately successful. Though the plants are growing and surviving, they don't appear to thrive in Earth's atmosphere and soil as they do on Simarka. Precise reasons for these differences have yet to be isolated, and identifying them are among the chief goals of the SGC's off-world science teams.

Beyond study of the local plant life, the SGC teams also work with the locals to learn the process the Shavadai used to create the anesthetic salve and other local medicines. The hope is that the SGC and Area 51 scientists can eventually reproduce these processes using Earth-grown Simarkan plants. Though likely still a few years off, potential applications of these medicines are very promising.

In addition to the anesthetic salve, the Simarkans also produce a poultice that stops bleeding in all but the most serious wounds, powerful anti-venoms effective against scorpion stings and pit viper bites, and remedies for local diseases, including forms malaria and yellow fever.

Applying a Simarkan salve requires a First Aid check *(see page 137)*.

SIMARKAN GEAR

Simarkan Anesthetic Salve: This salve can only be used on characters that have suffered one or more wounds. When successfully applied to an open wound *(see Apply Salve Check, page 137)*, this salve heals 1d4 vitality points. A critical success when applying this salve heals 2d4 vitality points.

Simarkan Healing Salve: This salve is only useful on characters that are dying *(see page 381 in the Stargate core rulebook)*. When successfully applied to an open wound *(see Apply Salve Check, page 137)*, this salve stabilizes the character. A critical success when applying this salve stabilizes the character and heals 1d4 wound points.

Simarkan Anti-venom: When successfully applied to a sting or bite *(see Apply Salve Check, page 137)*, this anti-venom grants the character a +4 bonus to saves against the applicable poison (scorpion or pit viper). A critical success when applying the anti-venom increases the save bonus to +6.

Simarkan Fever Cure: A character who ingests this remedy gains a +4 bonus to saves against the applicable disease (malaria/yellow fever).

TOLLAN TECHNOLOGY (ENIGMA)

Technologically, the Tollan began developing at roughly the same time that Earth did. However, they did not experience a Dark Age the way we did after the fall of Rome, and thus their technology is several hundred years ahead of ours.

TOLLAN GEAR

Fission Generator (Tollan): This cylinder-like device, able to easily be fit inside a moderately-sized backpack, is actually an extremely powerful energy source. Utilizing a particle-enriched induction coil, it splits discrete particle elements, through artificial disintegration, into a usable energy form via fission. The most amazing aspect of this Tollan device is the utter lack of any byproduct of the reaction, made possible by the artificial nature of the fission – a key concept of Tollan quantilibrum mechanics. Because the particles are artificially charged, the effective fuel of the generator is never consumed, providing for limitless energy.

The effective output of the generator – in Earth terms – is approximately 5.3×10^{24} watts, or nearly 1% of the Earth's sun or 50 megatons. With the alteration of the fission regulator built into the generator, the theoretical output of the generator increases to 2.55×10^{25} watts – enough discharge to destroy an entire world if used improperly.

Resource Points: 15.

Mechanics: The fission generator is very much a deus ex machina that transcends the necessity for statistics in a Stargate campaign. The generator can provide limitless power for an entire world, or just as easily destroy one. At this time all fission generators are closely guarded by the Tollan and absolutely no alien species would be granted access without the approval of the Curia and the entire ruling body of the Tollan. Even then, it may be used only under special dispensation and regulatory controls (e.g. constant Tollan presence). For purposes of resisting damage, the fission generator has the following rules:

Hardness 10, Damage Thresholds 5/15/20/30, Break DC 30, Concealment DC15.

Modifying the generator into a bomb requires a DC 30 Electronics check to modify the control mechanism, a DC 30 Knowledge (nuclear/quantilibrum physics) test to properly make the alterations without disabling the device permanently, then followed by a DC 10 Demolitions check to set the detonator. Each test (sans the Demolitions check) consumes 1 + (DC – test result) hours to perform; a retry requires 1d4 days to attempt.

Phase Device (Tollan): This small device is worn on a character's arm, similar to an armband and is activated via a key sequence. The phase device projects an invisible phase inversion field directly ahead of the wearer, allowing the wearer to walk through matter. While in such a state the wearer can move freely through doors, walls, and even people. The alignment of the field discriminator prevents the wearer from falling through the floor. Energy also has no effect and passes harmlessly through the wearer, as do weapons. The phase device normally only affects the wearer and any equipment on their person. The wearer can also affect up to two additional humanoid-sized beings and their gear, but these beings must be in directly physical contact with the wearer at all times.

Resource Points: 8

Mechanics: The device takes one action to activate and operates for a maximum duration of 10 rounds before the unit must shut off and recharge the inversion field. On rounds 8, 9, and 10 a warning light on the unit flashes, indicating that the wearer needs to extract themselves from any matter. On round 10, if the wearer is within solid matter, a DC 20 Reflex save must be made to exit in time. Failure indicates that wearer receives 2d10 wound points; on a critical failure the wearer is killed instantly. Any passengers suffer the same effects as the wearer and must make similar checks should they lose contact/let go of the wearer. The device recharges in ten minutes, or by the next scene – whichever is longer.

Inverted Phase Communicator (Tollan): This Tollan communication device allows for faster-than-light communication by phasing through the folds of space, traversing great distances in a matter of moments. There is no theoretical limit to the range of the communication device; although programming the transmission beyond one's appreciable sensory range is difficult. The communicator can transmit verbal, text, or even holographic images, although the latter requires more precise transmission coordinates; both the verbal or text mediums can broadcast with a margin of error measured in light-years.

Resource Points: 5

Mechanics: It takes a full round to set up and activate the communicator, provided the message has already been programmed in. Simple messages take one round, complex messages two rounds, and holographic messages three rounds respectively to program. The transmission medium of the communicator is sufficiently advanced that it will function as long as some rudimentary sensory or receiving equipment is available at the destination (e.g. radio, television, microwave detection, etc). If the programmer is familiar with the destination or has star charts available, a DC 20 Knowledge (Astrophysics) check is required. For more distant transmissions or without specific coordinates, the DC is raised to 30.

Recall Device (Tollan): A multifunction device capable of recording visual and audio stimuli, the recorder is most known for its ability to record (and playback) emotions. This small, handheld device has a storage capacity of nearly 24 hours of data without loss or degradation under normal operating conditions. The user may select to record visual or audio stimuli (or both) through their point-of-view, or record their own emotions. Although the device can record all three simultaneously, such ability is disabled by the Tollan due to privacy concerns.

Playback merely requires the activation of the device any physical contact with its transmission induction surfaces. Imagery projected by the recorder is more easily absorbed by closing one's eyes and tuning out external distractions.

The nature of the device is such that undesired use (e.g. recording) is possible without the target's consent it somehow the target is surreptitiously connected to the device.

Resource Points: 6

Mechanics: Free action to activate recording or playback. Playback can be disorienting, such as receiving visual playback while trying to drive a vehicle simultaneously. In such a case where a distraction may be possible, a DC 15 Will save can allow the wearer to perform normally at a -2 penalty to all actions. Those unknowingly forced to experience emotion playback without their knowledge must make a DC 10 Will save to differentiate their feelings from those of playback.

MISCELLANEOUS RULES

FORCING A GATE (SOLITUDES)

Whenever an SG team wishes to force the wormhole to jump to a secondary Stargate on a world but does not have an Asgard gate controller device, they may attempt to recreate the conditions that sent Colonel O'Neill and Captain Carter to the Antarctic Stargate. A Mechanics check (DC 25) must be made in order to hook up a portable generator to the Stargate. A second Mechanics check (DC 20) must be made while the wormhole is active in order to force the jump. If successful, then the wormhole jumps to an alternate gate (on the same world if one exists, or one a different world if one does not) and all travelers appear at this new location.

In the case of failure, the Gamemaster should roll 1d100 on the following table to determine the result.

ROLL	RESULT
1–50	The Stargate deactivates and the established wormhole closes.
51–70	The Stargate deactivates and the established wormhole closes; additionally, the DHD malfunctions and must have its power reset before being used again.
71–80	The Stargate remains active but each traveler through the gate has a 50% chance of being sent to the default location.
81–90	The Stargate deactivates and the established wormhole closes; additionally, the DHD is damaged and requires 1d6 hours of work to repair.
91–95	The Stargate deactivates and the established wormhole closes; additionally, the Stargate is damaged and requires 1d10 hours of work to repair.
96–100	The Stargate deactivates and the established wormhole closes; additionally, the Stargate is damaged and cannot be repaired.

ELECTROMAGNETIC FIELD CHART FOR PLANET GENERATION (COLD LAZARUS)

In campaigns involving a Unity, world generation may be modified to include information on the planet's electromagnetic field. The following table may be used to determine the effects of a planet's electromagnetic field on a Unity.

TECH LEVEL	LOW EM	MEDIUM EM	HIGH EM
Primordial	1–25	26–90	91–100
Primitive	1–20	21–80	81–100
Industrial	1–15	16–70	71–100
Advanced	1–10	11–60	61–100

Low EM: The Unity suffers a -2 penalty to all ability scores and related checks for 4 hours. After 4 hours, the Unity begins losing 1 wound point per hour.

Medium EM: The Unity suffers no negative effects.

High EM: The Unity suffers a -4 penalty to all Ability scores and related checks for 4 hours, After 4 hours, the Unity begins losing 1 wound point per 10 minutes.

THE DECAYING ORBIT OF HELIOPOLIS (THE TORMENT OF TANTALUS)

The orbit of Heliopolis is slowly decaying into its sun. The rate at which it is doing this is very slow, so it is unlikely that it will affect any missions on the planet. However, a clever GM can always speed things up, and the information could be useful for campaigns set in the far future, or distant past. In addition, other planets with decaying orbits may be affected in a similar manner.

The following changes occur to the planet's statistics at the rate on the chart below. All rates of change are listed in Earth years.

ELEMENT	CHANGE & RATE
Thermosphere	+1% per 100 years
Atmosphere	−1% per 50 years
Hydrosphere	−1% per 50 years
Geosphere/Basic Terrain	None
Geosphere/Tectonic Activity	+1% per 50 years, up to the activity for a roll of 99
Biosphere/Climate-Based Terrain	+1% per 50 years*
Biosphere/Seasons	+1% per 25 years

* Remember to change the biosphere effects as the temperature and hydrosphere change.

Note: The different elements of the planet are affected at different rates. This reflects the subtle and gradual changes over time. Also, as the planet grows closer to its sun, the faster the rate of changes will occur. For every 1,000 years in the future, halve the speed of the rate of change. Likewise, for every 1,000 years in the past double the speed of the rate of change.

THE ATMOSPHERE OF OANNES (FIRE AND WATER)

The atmosphere of the Ohnes' world contains volcanic gases that cause severe sensitivity to light in humans. After fifteen minutes of exposure to the atmosphere, human characters must make a successful Fortitude check (DC 20) or their eyes become extremely sensitive to light. Characters who fail this save and look directly at any sort of light are considered blinded *(see page 378 in the Stargate SG-1 core rulebook)* for 1d4-2 rounds.

NEW DISEASES

The following section details several new diseases and contagions covered in Season One.

INITIAL GOA'ULD IMPLANTATION (CHILDREN OF THE GODS)

Upon implantation of a Goa'uld for the first time during the *Prim'ta,* a Jaffa's body reacts as if to a disease. If the symbiote is removed before the secondary phase, a Fortitude save (DC 20 before the Primary Phase, 25 during) must be made by both Jaffa and symbiote. Failure indicates the shock of the separation causes a loss of 2d10 + 4 Con damage, and is potentially fatal. Success indicates the immune system is not irreparably damaged, and the individual will recover. After the onset of the secondary phase, removal of the symbiote is as per the Symbiote feat (*see the Stargate SG-1 core rulebook, page 265*).

THE TOUCHED SYNDROME (THE BROCA DIVIDE)

The Touched virus is a contagious parasitic/histaminolytic virus that feeds on chemical transmitters in the body. Once infected, the individual exhibits aggressive behavior in the primary phase. With judgment also affected, Will saves (DC 20) are needed for the victim to overcome the impulse to act on any whim or repressed desire, or to respond to any perceived slight with violence. The GM has discretion on what triggers such an impulse.

As the disease enters the secondary phase, the victim develops a swollen brow and additional hair growth reminiscent of some forms of prehistoric mankind. The violent and aggressive behavior increase substantially (Will saves of DC 30 are now required) as all but the most primitive portions of the mind are blocked. In this phase speech is beyond the victim unless a concentration check (DC 25) is made. This stage continues as long as there is sufficient histamine in the victim's body.

The cure is to lower the histamine level of the body for at least 1d6+2 hours, which causes the virus to die and be flushed from the system. The easiest way to accomplish this is to administer large doses of antihistamine. The size of the dose required is itself dangerous, requiring a Fortitude save (DC 6) to avoid cardiac arrest due to shock. Chlorpheniramine maleate has been used to good effect, though a side effect of the dosage is unconsciousness for 1d4 hours is unless a Fortitude save (DC15) is made.

Sedatives administered during the primary and secondary phases add a +5 circumstantial bonus to Will saves made to avoid taking aggressive actions. Similarly, during the secondary phase, strong sedatives can allow an individual to speak, albeit with difficulty. Again the dosage required is high, with a Fortitude save needed to remain alert enough to speak. A dose giving a +2 bonus to the Concentration check requires a DC 12 Fortitude save. Larger doses that increase the bonus by each additional +2 also increase the Fortitude save DC by +4.

There is a naturally occurring antihistamine mixed in with the grain harvested on the light side of P3X-797. It comes from a mold that commonly infests the stockpiles, and is incorporated into many of the foods the Untouched eat. This protects them from the "curse" of the Touched Syndrome to varying degrees. The level of antihistamine present in an individual depends on a variety of factors, from diet to weather to the time since the most recent harvest. When an Untouched person is exposed to the virus, the natural protection affords a bonus of 3d6+3 to the Fortitude save against contracting the disease. Those who fast or otherwise avoid foods made from the grain are without his protection, as are most off-worlders. Over-the-counter antihistamines administered prophylactically, however, provide nearly complete immunity if taken regularly. A single dose protects for 2d4 +2 hours, granting a +20 bonus to saves.

MINOTAUR SYNDROME (THE BROCA DIVIDE)

This variant of the virus acts in a similar manner to the original though with much greater deformation of the face and greater hair growth. In addition to the ability damage (half of which is permanent in the secondary phase), the increased hormone production caused by the infection actually increases both Strength and Constitution for the duration. Also, starting in the primary phase, victims are extremely photosensitive, and will stay well clear of the Land of Light.

The cure for this strain is more complicated than for the more common variety. In addition to removing the histamine from a victim's blood, the melatonin cycle must be reset to normal. While under the influence of the virus, the victim has no apparent need to sleep, and the production of melatonin drops to extremely low levels. If the victim's normal cycle is restored, either artificially by injection or by forcing him to sleep at regular intervals, and his histamine level kept low throughout this period (1d4 days for a normal human, 2d4 days for one of the Untouched), the victim is cured.

TABLE 3.6: NEW DISEASES

| | | | Primary Phase | | | | Secondary Phase | |
CONTAGION	CR	ONSET TIME	SAVE	DAMAGE/ EFFECT	ONSET TIME	SAVE	DAMAGE/ EFFECT
Initial Goa'uld Implantation	16	1d12 minutes	Fort (25)	1 Str, 1 Con, Fever (+1d6°F)	1d4 hours	Fort (30)	Immune System Destroyed
Touched Syndrome*	15	1d20 hours	Fort (22)	1 Int, 1 Wis, 1 Cha	1d6 hours	Fort (24)	2d4 Int, 2d4 Wis, 2d4 Cha
Minotaur Syndrome	18	1d4 days	Fort (20)	1 Int, 1 Wis, 1 Cha +1 Str	1d6 days	Fort (22)	2d4 Int, 2d4 Wis, 2d4 Cha; +1d4 Str, +1d4 Con

New Templates

The following templates may be applied to the appropriate characters or creatures.

Android Template

Should a character ever be converted to an android by the Altairan process (*see Tin Man, page 65*), the following template may be used to represent the changes between the original character and the new android. Apply these changes to the character's statistics:

Wounds: Double the points gained by the character's Constitution score.

Vitality: Same as the character.

Speed: Increase speed by 10 feet.

Defense: Same as the character.

Damage: Same as the character.

Special Qualities: The following special qualities are added to characters that have the android template:

Limited Range: An android can only survive for a short amount of time when away from its natural power source. Once an android is out of the power source's range, the android may function normally for 4 hours. After 4 hours, the android suffers a -4 penalty to all Strength, Dexterity, and Constitution checks and all related skill rolls. The character may function in this capacity for 2 hours, after which the android shuts down and may not be reactivated until its power cells are completely recharged.

Support and Maintenance: The character loses RP equal to one half his character level (to a minimum of 0).

Robot: All androids are considered to be of the robot type (*as defined in the Stargate SG-1 core rulebook, page 480*) but with a few minor changes. A character with the "robot" type requires no sleep, air, nourishment, or water,

and cannot suffer subdual damage or critical hits. It is immune to level drain, ability damage, and all non-physical attacks. Unlike the standard robot type, however, androids possess vitality points and do suffer penalties for possessing no vitality. The android makes Will saves as normal. Any other abilities, feats, or special qualities that affect creatures or characters with the robot type affect androids as well.

Saves: +2 bonus to Fortitude saves.

Abilities: +6 to Strength, +6 to Constitution, +4 to Intelligence.

Skills: Same as the character.

Feats: Same as the character.

Altairan Mutant Template

Should a creature ever spend any length of time on the surface of the Altair (*see Tin Man, page 65*), the following template may be used to represent the changes in the creature to a mutated version of its former self. Note that this template may not be applied to any creatures that are of the robot (or android) type. Apply these changes to the creature's statistics:

Wounds: Same as the creature.

Vitality: Same as the creature.

Speed: See Special Qualities.

Defense: See Special Qualities.

Damage: See Special Qualities.

Special Qualities: The Altairan mutants have several different mutations that are typical of the environment in which they evolved. Choose one of the following mutations, and apply its effects to the chosen creature.

Acute Senses: Thanks to extra eyes, overdeveloped ears, or an exaggerated sense of smell, the mutant has developed an increased awareness of its surroundings. The creature gains a +2 bonus to all Reflex saves thanks to its acute senses.

Carapace: The mutant has developed a chitin or scale carapace that acts as a natural defense against the evolved predators on Altair. The creature gains a +2 natural armor bonus to Defense and is covered in an armored carapace.

Extra Legs: The mutant has grown more legs than it naturally has, and can bound across the landscape at incredible speeds. The creature gains a +10 foot bonus on its natural movement rate thanks to its extra limbs.

Jagged: Claws, fangs, or spikes have grown out of the creature where there were none before. A mutant with this special quality adds +2 to all damage rolls made with natural weapons.

Rugged: Millennia spent on the dangerous surface of Altair have given the mutant a toughness not possessed by most creatures. The mutant gains a +2 bonus to all Fortitude saves due to its ability to survive in the harshest environment.

Saves: See Special Qualities.

Abilities: -2 to Charisma, otherwise same as the creature.

Skills: Same as the creature.

Feats: Same as the creature.

NEW NPC CLASSES

The following abbreviated classes offer GMs a means to populate his world with a wider variety of characters.

ABYDONIAN DESERT FIGHTER

Desert fighters are the stealthy warriors who defend the city of Nagada and its inhabitants. They are taught from a young age to survive in the open desert, as well as to use subterfuge to gain an advantage over their enemies. In addition, they act as guards for the map building, the Stargate, and any other important artifacts and locales on Abydos. The desert fighters are quite zealous in their duties, seeing themselves as the first line of defense against outside incursions.

FULL SKILLS

The desert fighter's full skills and key abilities are:

FULL SKILL	KEY ABILITY
Hide	Dex
Move Silently	Dex
Survival (desert)	Wis

HALF SKILLS

The desert fighter's half skills and key abilities are:

Half Skill	Key Ability
Climb	Str
Diplomacy	Cha
Jump	Str
Search	Int
Spot	Wis
Tumble	Dex

CLASS FEATURES

All of the following are class features of the Abydonian desert fighter.

Starting Feats: The Abydonian desert fighter begins play with the following feats.

Armor Group Proficiency (Light)
Weapon Group Proficiency (Hurled)
Weapon Group Proficiency (Melee)
Weapon Group Proficiency (Rifle)*

* This feat is available only to those desert fighters who have been trained by Dr. Daniel Jackson or Colonel Jack O'Neill during their time on the planet both during and immediately after Ra's fall from power. However, due to their limited access to more advanced weaponry, most Abydonian desert fighters rarely get the opportunity to use this feat.

Desert Training: At 1st level, the Abydonian desert fighter gains the Desert Training feat.

Stealthy: At 2nd level, the Abydonian desert fighter gains the Stealthy feat.

Uncanny Dodge: Starting at 4th level, the Abydonian desert fighter gains the ability to react to danger before his senses would normally permit him to even be aware of it. He retains his Dexterity bonus to Defense (if any) even when flat-footed or struck by an invisible attacker (he still loses his Dexterity bonus to Defense if immobilized).

At 8th level, the Abydonian desert fighter may no longer be flanked, since he can react to opponents on opposite sides as easily as he can respond to a single attacker. This defense denies scouts and others with the sneak attack ability the opportunity to use flank actions to sneak attack the desert fighter unless the attacker is at least four levels higher than the desert fighter.

Sneak Attack: Starting at 6th level, the Abydonian desert fighter inflicts extra damage when either flanking a target *(see Stargate SG-1 core rulebook, page 369)* or attacking a target who's currently denied his Dexterity bonus to Defense (such as a character who is flat-footed or immobilized). The extra damage inflicted is +1d6 at 6th level and +2d6 at 10th level.

Ranged attacks normally gain this bonus only if the target is within one range increment. Beyond that, it's difficult to hit the target's vitals.

The Abydonian desert fighter may make a sneak attack with any weapon (or unarmed attack), even one that deals subdual damage. However, he cannot use a weapon that deals normal damage to inflict subdual damage during a sneak attack, even by applying the standard -4 penalty *(see the Stargate SG-1 core rulebook, page 380)*, nor may he use strafe when sneak attacking.

Finally, the Abydonian desert fighter may not sneak attack targets who are immune to critical hits, who have total concealment, or whose vitals are out of reach.

TABLE 3.7: THE ABYDONIAN DESERT FIGHTER (NPC CLASS)

LvL	VITALITY POINTS	BASE ATT	FORT SAVE	REF SAVE	WILL SAVE	DEF BON	INIT BON	SPECIAL
1	6	+1	+2	+1	+0	+0	+1	Desert Training
2	9	+2	+3	+2	+0	+1	+1	Stealthy
3	13	+3	+3	+2	+1	+1	+2	
4	16	+4	+4	+2	+1	+2	+2	Uncanny dodge
5	20	+5	+4	+3	+1	+2	+3	
6	23	+6	+5	+3	+2	+2	+4	Sneak Attack +1d6
7	27	+7	+5	+4	+2	+3	+4	
8	30	+8	+6	+4	+2	+3	+5	Uncanny dodge
9	34	+9	+6	+5	+3	+4	+5	
10	37	+10	+7	+5	+3	+4	+6	Sneak Attack +2d6

Asura

The asuras are the Jaffa of Vritra and fight in his name. They are fast, subtle warriors, who favor attacking from the shadows rather than directly confronting their foes. Their tools of battle include poison and assassination, in addition to more traditional swordplay. For that reason, they are greatly feared even within Vritra's territory.

Full Skills

The asura's full skills and key abilities are:

Full Skill	Key Ability
Craft (Poison)	Int
Hide	Dex
Move Silently	Dex

Half Skills

The asura's half skills and key abilities are:

Half Skill	Key Ability
Balance	Dex
Bluff	Cha
Climb	Str
Jump	Str
Spot	Wis
Tumble	Dex

Class Features

All of the following are class features of the asura:

Starting Feats: The asura begins play with the following feats.

Armor Group Proficiency (Light)
Weapon Group Proficiency (Hurled)
Weapon Group Proficiency (Melee)
Weapon Group Proficiency (Rifle)

Jaffa Warrior: At 1st level, the asura gains all the special talents listed for the Jaffa macro-species, as well as those listed fir any one Jaffa sub-specialty except shol'va rebel *(see the Stargate SG-1 core rulebook, page 148).*

Poison Basics: At 1st level the asura gains the Poison Basics feat.

Expertise: At 2nd level, the asura gains the Expertise feat.

Darting Weapon: At 4th level, the asura gains the Darting Weapon feat.

Assassin: At 6th level, the asura gains the Assassin feat.

Sneak Attack: Starting at 8th level, the asura inflicts extra damage when either flanking a target *(see the Stargate SG-1 core rulebook, page 369).* Or attacking a target who's currently denied his Dexterity bonus to Defense (such as a character who is flat-footed or immobilized). The extra damage inflicted is +1d6.

Ranged attacks normally gain this bonus only if the target is within one range increment. Beyond that, it's difficult to hit the target's vitals.

The asura may make a sneak attack with any weapon (or unarmed attack), even one that deals subdual damage. However, he cannot use a weapon that deals normal damage to inflict subdual damage during a sneak attack, even by applying the standard –4 penalty *(see the Stargate SG-1 core rulebook, page 380),* nor may he use strafe when sneak attacking.

Finally, the asura may not sneak attack targets who are immune to critical hits, who have total concealment, or whose vitals are out of reach.

Master Assassin: At 10th level, the asura gains the Master Assassin feat.

Table 3.8: The Asura (NPC Class)

Lvl	Vitality Points	Base Att	Fort Save	Ref Save	Will Save	Def Bon	Init Bon	Special
1	6	+0	+1	+0	+1	+1	+1	Jaffa warrior, Poison Basics
2	9	+1	+2	+0	+2	+2	+1	Expertise
3	13	+2	+2	+1	+2	+3	+2	
4	16	+3	+2	+1	+2	+3	+2	Darting Weapon
5	20	+3	+3	+1	+3	+4	+3	
6	23	+4	+3	+2	+3	+5	+4	Assassin
7	27	+5	+4	+2	+4	+6	+4	
8	30	+6	+4	+2	+4	+6	+5	Sneak attack +1d6
9	34	+6	+4	+3	+4	+7	+5	
10	37	+7	+5	+3	+5	+8	+6	Master Assassin

DIVINE MINION

On many worlds, the native near-humans are primitive – or superstitious – enough to accept that more technologically advanced visitors are gods. This is a natural enough belief, given that the Goa'uld and even the Asgard have passed themselves off as divine beings (although admittedly for very different reasons). Divine minions are near-humans who have given themselves over fully to their masters. They have perfect loyalty and will fight with incredible zeal, even to the death.

FULL SKILLS

The divine minion's full skills and key abilities are:

FULL SKILL	KEY ABILITY
None	N/A

HALF SKILLS

The divine minion's half skills and key abilities are:

HALF SKILL	KEY ABILITY
Climb	Str
Hide	Dex
Intimidate	Str or Cha
Jump	Str
Move Silently	Dex
Spot	Wis
Survival (choose one)	Wis
Any one other skill	Varies

CLASS FEATURES

All of the following are class features of the divine minion:

Starting Feats: The divine minion begins play with the following feats.

Armor Group Proficiency (Light)
Armor Group Proficiency (Medium)
Weapon Group Proficiency (Hurled)
Weapon Group Proficiency (Melee)

Stone Cold: At 1st level, the divine minion gains the Stone Cold feat.

Bonus Feat: At 2nd and 6th levels, the divine minion gains any one basic or ranged combat feet (for a total of two basic or ranged combat feats from this class over the course of his career).

Divine Madness: Starting at 4th level, when using a standard attack action, the divine minion may accept a penalty of up to -5 to his Defense and add the same number (up to +5) to his base attack bonus as a competence bonus. The number shifted in this manner may not exceed the character's Defense bonus and lasts until his Initiative count during the following round.

Glint of Madness: At 8th level, the divine minion gains the Glint of Madness feat.

Loyal Unto Death: At 10th level, as a free action, the divine minion may choose to offer himself up as sign of his devotion to his god. When doing so, the character suffers only minimum damage from all attacks (i.e. assume all damage dice roll 1s).

Even after the divine minion drops to 0 wounds, he may act against his enemies – when between 0 and -9 wound points, he may take a half action per turn.

If at the end of the combat, the divine minion still has wound points remaining, he immediately drops to -1 wound points.

Once the divine minion begins his last stand, he automatically fails all stabilization checks, but he cannot die until he has publicly sung the praises of his divine master.

EYE OF HATHOR

In one of her many guises, Hathor was known as the "eye of Ra," since she acted as her lord's eyes and ears throughout his domain. Since his destruction, Hathor has abandoned that title but seen fit to train individuals to act as her eyes and ears. They are among her most trusted Jaffa and travel to many worlds on missions of importance to her. Though well versed in the arts of war, they are also quite adept at subterfuge and espionage. Indeed, the eyes of Hathor more often act as spies and saboteurs for her cause than as warriors, although they would be more than a match for most in a direct confrontation. Many eyes of Hathor are Netjerians – part of Hathor's plan to reclaim her lost throne world for herself.

FULL SKILLS

The eye of Hathor's full skills and key abilities are:

FULL SKILL	KEY ABILITY
Bluff	Cha
Surveillance	Wis

TABLE 3.9: THE DIVINE MINION (NPC CLASS)

LvL	VITALITY POINTS	BASE ATT	FORT SAVE	REF SAVE	WILL SAVE	DEF BON	INIT BON	SPECIAL
1	8	+1	+1	+0	+2	+1	+1	Stone Cold
2	12	+2	+2	+0	+3	+2	+1	Bonus feat
3	17	+3	+2	+1	+3	+3	+2	
4	21	+4	+2	+1	+4	+3	+2	Divine madness
5	26	+5	+3	+1	+4	+4	+3	
6	30	+6	+3	+2	+5	+5	+4	Bonus feat
7	35	+7	+4	+2	+5	+6	+4	
8	39	+8	+4	+2	+6	+6	+5	Glint of Madness
9	44	+9	+4	+3	+6	+7	+5	
10	48	+10	+5	+3	+7	+8	+6	Loyal unto death

HALF SKILLS

The eye of Hathor's half skills and key abilities are:

HALF SKILL	KEY ABILITY
Climb	Str
Hide	Dex
Innuendo	Wis
Move Silently	Dex
Search	Int
Sense Motive	Wis
Spot	Wis
Any one other skill	Varies

CLASS FEATURES

All of the following are class features of the eye of Hathor.

Starting Feats: The eye of Hathor begins play with the following feats.

Armor Group Proficiency (Light)
Armor Group Proficiency (Medium)
Weapon Group Proficiency (Melee)
Weapon Group Proficiency (Handgun)
Weapon Group Proficiency (Rifle)

Jaffa Warrior: At 1st level, the eye of Hathor gains all the special talents listed for the Jaffa macro-species, as well as those listed for any one Jaffa sub-specialty except shol'va rebel *(see the Stargate SG-1 core rulebook, page 148)*.

Specialty: At 1st level, the eye of Hathor gains 3 ranks in any one class skill.

Stealthy: At 2nd level, the eye of Hathor gains the Stealthy feat.

Uncanny Dodge: Starting at 4th level, the eye of Hathor gains the ability to react to danger before his senses would normally permit him to even become aware of it. He retains his Dexterity bonus to Defense (if any) even when flat-footed or struck by an invisible attacker (he still loses his Dexterity bonus to Defense if immobilized).

At 8th level, the eye of Hathor may no longer be flanked, since he can react to opponents on opposite sides as easily as he can respond to a single attacker. This defense denies scouts and others with the sneak attack ability the opportunity to use flank actions to sneak attack the eye of Hathor unless the attacker is at least four levels higher than the eye of Hathor.

Field Operative: At 6th level, the eye of Hathor gains the Field Operative feat for free, even if he does not meet the prerequisites.

Advanced Skill Mastery: At 10th level, the eye of Hathor gains the Advanced Skill Mastery for his Stealthy feat.

FREEDOM FIGHTER

Freedom fighters engage the System Lords on planets throughout the galaxy, leading resistance movements and aiding other races as they battle the Goa'uld.

FULL SKILLS

The freedom fighter's full skills and key abilities are:

FULL SKILL	KEY ABILITY
Demolitions	Int
Hide	Dex
Listen or Spot	Wis
Survival	Wis

HALF SKILLS

The freedom fighter's half skills and key abilities are:

HALF SKILL	KEY ABILITY
First Aid	Wis
Move Silently	Dex
Search	Int
Any one other skill	Varies

CLASS FEATURES

All of the following are class features of the freedom fighter.

Starting Feats: The freedom fighter begins play with the following feats.

Armor Group Proficiency (Light)
Armor Group Proficiency (Medium)
Weapon Group Proficiency (Melee)
Weapon Group Proficiency (Handgun)
Weapon Group Proficiency (Rifle)

Combat Instincts: At 1st level, the freedom fighter gains the Combat Instincts feat.

Coolness Under Fire: At 2nd level, the freedom fighter gains the Coolness Under Fire feat.

Lead: At 4th level, the freedom fighter gains the Lead class ability as a pointman *(see the Stargate SG-1 core rulebook, page 160)*, once per session.

At 8th level, he may use this ability twice per session.

TABLE 3.10: THE EYE OF HATHOR (NPC CLASS)

LvL	VITALITY POINTS	BASE ATT	FORT SAVE	REF SAVE	WILL SAVE	DEF BON	INIT BON	SPECIAL
1	6	+0	+1	+1	+1	+1	+1	Jaffa Warrior, specialty
2	9	+1	+2	+2	+2	+1	+1	Stealthy
3	13	+2	+2	+2	+2	+2	+2	
4	16	+3	+2	+2	+2	+2	+2	Uncanny dodge
5	20	+3	+3	+3	+3	+3	+3	
6	23	+4	+3	+3	+3	+4	+4	Field Operative
7	27	+5	+4	+4	+4	+4	+4	
8	30	+6	+4	+4	+4	+5	+5	Uncanny dodge
9	34	+6	+4	+4	+4	+5	+5	
10	37	+7	+5	+5	+5	+6	+6	Advanced Skill Mastery (Stealthy)

Explosives Basics: At 5th level, the freedom fighter gains the Explosives Basics feat.

Command Decision: At 9th level, the freedom fighter gains the Command Decision feat.

JAFFA PRIEST

These Jaffa lead the everyday worship of their gods, maintain the safety and well being of the larval Goa'uld, and perform the rites and rituals associated with daily life under the rule of the gods.

FULL SKILLS

The Jaffa priest's full skills and key abilities are:

FULL SKILL	KEY ABILITY
Bureaucracy	Cha
Concentration	Wis
Profession (Priest)	Wis
Sense Motive	Wis

HALF SKILLS

The Jaffa priest's half skills and key abilities are:

HALF SKILL	KEY ABILITY
Bluff	Cha
First Aid	Int
Intimidate	Str or Cha
Knowledge (Goa'uld)	Dex
Listen	Wis
Mechanics	Int
Spot	Wis
Survival	Wis

CLASS FEATURES

All of the following are class features of the Jaffa priest.

Starting Feats: The Jaffa priest begins play with the following feats.

Armor Group Proficiency (Light)
Armor Group Proficiency (Medium)
Weapon Group Proficiency (Melee)
Weapon Group Proficiency (Hurled)

Jaffa Clergy: At 1st level, the Jaffa priest gains all the special talents listed for the Jaffa macro-species *(see the Stargate SG-1 core rulebook, page 148)*, as well as those listed for the Jaffa clergy sub-specialty *(see page 123)*.

Specialty: At 1st level, the Jaffa priest's Bureaucracy skill is increased by 3 ranks.

Symbiote: At 2nd level, the Jaffa priest gains an additional ability from the symbiote feat *(see the Stargate SG-1 core rulebook, page 265)*. He gains an additional ability from the symbiote feat at 6th and 10th levels.

Goa'uld Tech: At 4th level, the Goa'uld clergy gains training in the operation of various Goa'uld devices usable by non-Goa'uld. The Jaffa priest gains a +4 competence bonus to any Knowledge (Goa'uld) and Mechanics checks dealing with the use of these items.

Rapid Healing: At 8th level, the Jaffa priest gains the Rapid Healing feat.

TABLE 3.11: FREEDOM FIGHTER (NPC CLASS)

LvL	VITALITY POINTS	BASE ATT	FORT SAVE	REF SAVE	WILL SAVE	DEF BON	INIT BON	SPECIAL
1	6	+1	+1	+1	+2	+1	+1	Combat Instincts
2	9	+2	+2	+2	+3	+1	+1	Coolness Under Fire
3	13	+3	+2	+2	+3	+2	+2	
4	16	+3	+2	+2	+4	+2	+2	Lead 1/session
5	20	+4	+3	+3	+4	+3	+3	
6	23	+5	+3	+3	+5	+4	+4	Explosives Basics
7	27	+6	+4	+4	+5	+4	+4	
8	30	+6	+4	+4	+6	+5	+5	Lead 2/session
9	34	+7	+4	+4	+6	+5	+5	
10	37	+8	+5	+5	+7	+6	+6	Command Decision

TABLE 3.12: THE JAFFA PRIEST (NPC CLASS)

LvL	VITALITY POINTS	BASE ATT	FORT SAVE	REF SAVE	WILL SAVE	DEF BON	INIT BON	SPECIAL
1	6	+0	+1	+0	+1	+1	+1	Jaffa clergy, specialty
2	9	+1	+2	+1	+2	+2	+1	Symbiote
3	13	+2	+2	+1	+2	+3	+2	
4	16	+2	+3	+2	+3	+3	+2	Goa'uld tech
5	20	+3	+3	+2	+3	+4	+3	
6	23	+3	+3	+3	+4	+5	+4	Symbiote
7	27	+4	+4	+3	+4	+6	+4	
8	30	+5	+4	+4	+5	+6	+4	Rapid Healing
9	34	+6	+5	+4	+5	+7	+5	
10	37	+7	+5	+4	+6	+8	+6	Symbiote

LIGHTNING GUARD

Lightning Guards are one of two elite class of Jaffa (along with Thunder Guards) who serve Raiden. Lighting guards are among the quickest and most agile Jaffa in the service of any Goa'uld, including the System Lords.

FULL SKILLS

The Lightning Guard's full skills and key abilities are:

FULL SKILL	KEY ABILITY
Concentration	Wis

HALF SKILLS

The Lightning Guard's half skills and key abilities are:

HALF SKILL	KEY ABILITY
Balance	Dex
Intimidate	Str or Cha
Spot	Wis
Survival (choose 2)	Wis
Tumble	Dex

CLASS FEATURES

All of the following are class features of the Lightning Guard.

Starting Feats: The Lightning Guard begins play with the following feats.

Armor Group Proficiency (Light)
Armor Group Proficiency (Medium)
Weapon Group Proficiency (Melee)
Weapon Group Proficiency (Rifle)

Jaffa Warrior: At 1st level, the Lightning Guard gains all the special talents listed for the Jaffa macro-species, as well as those listed for the Serpent Guard Jaffa sub-specialty *(see the Stargate SG-1 core rulebook, page 148)*.

Symbiote: At 1st level, the Lightning Guard gains the Symbiote feat *(see the Stargate SG-1 core rulebook, page 265)*. The Lightning Guard gains the Symbiote feat one additional time at 3rd level and for every 3 levels gained thereafter (i.e. a second time at 3rd level, a third time at 6th level, and a fourth time at 9th level).

Lightning Staff: At 2nd level, each Lightning Guard is issued a lightning staff *(see page 175)* and 4 energy cells.

Lightning Strike: At 4th level, the Lightning Guard gains the Speed Trigger feat.

Improved Initiative: At 7th level, the Lightning Guard gains the Improved Initiative feat.

Visage of Terror: At 8th level, the Lightning Guard is issued a standard Jaffa Helm *(see page 175)*.

Lightning Reflexes: At 10th level, the Lightning Guard gains the Lightning Reflexes feat.

MARUT

Marut are the holy warriors who fight on behalf of Indra. Though not Jaffa themselves, they behave as if they were indeed the special servants of their long-gone Goa'uld master. They typically arm themselves with swords and other pointed weapons, but all receive training in the use of the staff weapon. Very few of these weapons still exist on Prakiti; this has not stopped the marut from being familiar with their use in battle. These warriors fight fanatically and to the death, as they believe that Indra will learn of any cowardice they show in battle and punish them when he returns in glory.

FULL SKILLS

The marut's full skills and key abilities are:

FULL SKILL	KEY ABILITY
None	N/A

HALF SKILLS

The marut's half skills and key abilities are:

HALF SKILL	KEY ABILITY
Balance	Dex
Handle Animal	Cha
Intimidate	Str or Cha
Jump	Str
Sport	Str or Dex
Spot	Wis
Survival	Wis
Any one other skill	Varies

TABLE 3.13: THE LIGHTNING GUARD (NPC CLASS)

LvL	VITALITY POINTS	BASE ATT	FORT SAVE	REF SAVE	WILL SAVE	DEF BON	INIT BON	SPECIAL
1	8	+1	+0	+2	+1	+1	+1	Jaffa warrior, Symbiote
2	12	+2	+0	+3	+2	+1	+2	Lightning staff
3	17	+3	+1	+3	+2	+2	+3	Symbiote
4	21	+4	+1	+4	+2	+2	+3	Lightning strike
5	26	+5	+1	+4	+3	+3	+4	
6	30	+6	+2	+5	+3	+4	+5	Symbiote
7	35	+7	+2	+5	+4	+4	+6	Improved initiative
8	39	+8	+2	+6	+4	+5	+6	Visage of terror
9	44	+9	+3	+6	+5	+5	+7	Symbiote
10	48	+10	+3	+7	+5	+6	+8	Lightning reflexes

CLASS FEATURES

All of the following are class features of the marut.

Starting Feats: The marut begins play with the following feats.

Armor Group Proficiency (Light)
Armor Group Proficiency (Medium)
Weapon Group Proficiency (Hurled)
Weapon Group Proficiency (Melee)
Weapon Group Proficiency (Rifle)

Weapon Focus: At 1st level, the marut gains the Weapon Focus feat.

Iron Will: At 4th level, the marut gains the Iron Will feat.

Weapon Specialization: At 7th level, the marut chooses one weapon with which he's proficient (such as "dagger" or "sword") to specialize in. When wielding that weapon, he inflicts an additional +2 damage. If his choice is a ranged weapon, this bonus damage applies only if the marut is within one range increment of his target.

Improved Iron Will: At 10th level, the marut receives an additional +2 to all Will saves. This bonus stacks with the bonus from the Iron Will feat.

NOX WANDERER

Many Nox travel the galaxy, learning everything they can about different worlds and the beings which inhabit them. They use their abilities to remain hidden most of the time, but are sometimes persuaded to lend aid to needy causes if it doesn't violate their pacifistic beliefs.

Only Nox may belong to this class.

FULL SKILLS

The wander's full skills and key abilities are:

FULL SKILL	KEY ABILITY
First Aid	Wis
Handle Animal	Cha
Xeno-Languages	Int
Any one skill	Varies

HALF SKILLS

The wanderer's half skills and key abilities are:

HALF SKILL	KEY ABILITY
Knowledge (Choose 2)	Int
Sense Motive	Wis
Spot	Wis
Survival (choose 2)	Wis
Any two skills	Varies

CLASS FEATURES

All of the following are class features of the Nox wanderer.

Starting Feats: The Nox wanderer begins play with the following feats. Note again that all Nox are extreme pacifists and will under no circumstances turn a weapon on another living creature.

Armor Group Proficiency (Light)

Species Feat: At each level, the Nox wanderer gains one feat from the species feat tree. The Nox wanderer must meet all prerequisites for these feats.

TABLE 3.14: THE MARUT (NPC CLASS)

LvL	VITALITY POINTS	BASE ATT	FORT SAVE	REF SAVE	WILL SAVE	DEF BON	INIT BON	SPECIAL
1	10	+1	+1	+0	+2	+0	+1	Weapon Focus
2	15	+2	+2	+0	+3	+1	+1	
3	21	+3	+2	+1	+3	+1	+2	
4	26	+4	+2	+1	+4	+2	+2	Iron Will
5	32	+5	+3	+1	+4	+2	+3	
6	37	+6	+3	+2	+5	+2	+4	
7	42	+7	+4	+2	+5	+3	+4	Weapon specialization
8	48	+8	+4	+2	+6	+3	+5	
9	53	+9	+4	+3	+6	+4	+5	
10	59	+10	+5	+3	+7	+4	+6	Improved Iron Will

TABLE 3.15: THE NOX WANDERER (NPC CLASS)

LvL	VITALITY POINTS	BASE ATT*	FORT SAVE	REF SAVE	WILL SAVE	DEF BON	INIT BON	SPECIAL
1	4	+0	+2	+0	+2	+1	+0	Species feat
2	6	+0	+3	+0	+3	+1	+1	Species feat
3	9	+0	+3	+1	+3	+2	+1	Species feat
4	11	+0	+4	+1	+4	+2	+2	Species feat
5	14	+0	+4	+1	+4	+3	+2	Species feat
6	16	+0	+5	+2	+5	+4	+2	Species feat
7	19	+0	+5	+2	+5	+4	+3	Species feat
8	21	+0	+6	+3	+6	+5	+3	Species feat
9	24	+0	+6	+3	+6	+5	+4	Species feat
10	26	+0	+7	+3	+7	+6	+4	Species feat

* The Nox are absolute pacifists and do not gain attack bonuses when they advance in levels in any class.

RESPECTED ELDER

Often the advisors and power brokers behind the scenes, if not leaders themselves, these individuals are valued for their experience.

FULL SKILLS

The respected elder's full skills and key abilities are:

FULL SKILL	KEY ABILITY
Bluff	Cha
Bureaucracy	Cha
Diplomacy	Cha
Gather Information	Cha
Knowledge (choose)	Int
Sense Motive	Wis

HALF SKILLS

The respected elder's half skills and key abilities are:

HALF SKILL	KEY ABILITY
Concentration	Wis
Listen	Wis
Spot	Wis
Any two other skills	Wis

CLASS FEATURES

All of the following are class features of the respected elder.

Starting Feats: The respected elder begins play with the following feats.

Armor Group Proficiency (Light)
Weapon Group Proficiency (Melee)
Weapon Group Proficiency (Hurled)

Boosted Charisma: At 1st level, the respected elder's Charisma score rises by 2.

Ordinary Past: At 1st level, the respected elder gains the Ordinary Past feat.

Persuasive: At 2nd level, the respected elder gains the Persuasive feat.

Charmer: At 4th level, the respected elder gains the Charmer feat.

Boosted Wisdom: At 6th level, the respected elder's Wisdom score rises by 2.

Advanced Skill Mastery: At 8th level, the respected elder gains the Advanced Skill Mastery feat linked to his Persuasive feat.

Boosted Intelligence: At 10th level, the respected elder's Intelligence score rises by 2.

SIMARKAN WARRIOR

Simarkan warriors are those who defend the tribes of Simarka. These warriors wield primitive swords, knives, and bows, and wear light armor.

FULL SKILLS

The Simarkan warrior's full skills and key abilities are:

FULL SKILL	KEY ABILITY
Craft (choose)	Int
First Aid	Wis
Search	Int
Survival (choose 3)	Wis

HALF SKILLS

The Simarkan warrior's half skills and key abilities are:

HALF SKILL	KEY ABILITY
Handle Animal	Cha
Move Silently	Dex
Any two other skills	Varies

CLASS FEATURES

All of the following are class features of the Simarkan warrior.

Starting Feats: The Simarkan warrior begins play with the following feats.

Armor Group Proficiency (Light)
Weapon Group Proficiency (Hurled)
Weapon Group Proficiency (Melee)
Weapon Group Proficiency (Archaic)

Track: At 1st level, the Simarkan warrior gains the Track feat.

Terrain Training: At 1st level, the Simarkan warrior gains one of the following feats: Desert Training, Forest Training, Mountain Training, or Swamp Training. All pre-requisites requisites for this feat – including skill ranks – are waived.

The Simarkan warrior gains an additional feat from this list with the same conditions at 4th, 7th, and 10th level.

TABLE 3.16: THE RESPECTED ELDER (NPC CLASS)

LVL	VITALITY POINTS	BASE ATT*	FORT SAVE	REF SAVE	WILL SAVE	DEF BON	INIT BON	SPECIAL
1	4	+0	+0	+0	+2	+1	+1	Charisma +2, Ordinary Past
2	6	+1	+0	+1	+2	+2	+1	Persuasive
3	9	+1	+1	+1	+3	+3	+2	
4	11	+2	+1	+2	+3	+3	+2	Charmer
5	14	+2	+1	+2	+4	+4	+3	
6	16	+3	+2	+3	+4	+5	+4	Wisdom +2
7	19	+3	+2	+3	+5	+6	+4	
8	21	+4	+2	+4	+5	+6	+5	Advanced Skill Mastery
9	24	+4	+3	+4	+6	+7	+5	
10	26	+5	+5	+4	+6	+8	+6	Intelligence +2

THUNDER GUARD

Thunder Guards are one of two elite class of Jaffa (along with Lightning Guards) who serve the Goa'uld Raiden. Thunder Guards are among the strongest and toughest Jaffa in the service of any Goa'uld, including the System Lords.

FULL SKILLS

The Thunder Guard's full skills and key abilities are:

FULL SKILL	KEY ABILITY
None	N/A

HALF SKILLS

The Thunder Guard's half skills and key abilities are:

HALF SKILL	KEY ABILITY
Concentration	Wis
Intimidate	Str or Cha
Spot	Wis
Survival (choose)	Wis

CLASS FEATURES

All of the following are class features of the Thunder Guard.

Starting Feats: The Thunder Guard begins play with the following feats.

Armor Group Proficiency (Light)
Armor Group Proficiency (Medium)
Armor Group Proficiency (Heavy)
Weapon Group Proficiency (Melee)
Weapon Group Proficiency (Rifle)

Jaffa Warrior: At 1st level, the Lightning Guard gains all the special talents listed for the Jaffa macro-species, as well as those listed for the Serpent Guard Jaffa sub-specialty *(see the Stargate SG-1 core rulebook, page 148)*.

Symbiote: At 1st level, the Thunder Guard gains the Symbiote feat *(see the Stargate SG-1 core rulebook, page 265)*. The Thunder Guard gains the Symbiote feat one additional time at 3rd level and for every 3 levels gained thereafter (i.e. a second time at 3rd level, a third time at 6th level, and a fourth time at 9th level).

Thunder Staff: At 2nd level, each Thunder Guard is issued a thunder staff *(see page 175)* and 5 energy cells.

Thunder Strike: At 4th level, the Thunder Guard gains the Speed Trigger feat.

Endurance: At 7th level, the Thunder Guard gains the Endurance feat.

Visage of Terror: At 8th level, the Thunder Guard is issued a standard Jaffa Helm *(see page 175)*.

Great Fortitude: At 10th level, the Thunder Guard gains the Great Fortitude feat.

TABLE 3.17: THE SIMARKAN WARRIOR (NPC CLASS)

LvL	VITALITY POINTS	BASE ATT*	FORT SAVE	REF SAVE	WILL SAVE	DEF BON	INIT BON	SPECIAL
1	6	+0	+2	+1	+1	+0	+0	Terrain training, Track
2	9	+1	+3	+2	+2	+1	+1	
3	13	+2	+3	+2	+2	+1	+1	
4	16	+3	+4	+2	+2	+2	+2	Terrain training
5	20	+3	+4	+3	+3	+2	+2	
6	23	+4	+5	+3	+3	+2	+2	
7	27	+5	+5	+4	+4	+3	+3	Terrain training
8	30	+6	+6	+4	+4	+3	+3	
9	34	+6	+6	+5	+5	+4	+4	
10	37	+7	+7	+5	+5	+4	+4	Terrain training

TABLE 3.18: THE THUNDER GUARD (NPC CLASS)

LvL	VITALITY POINTS	BASE ATT	FORT SAVE	REF SAVE	WILL SAVE	DEF BON	INIT BON	SPECIAL
1	10	+1	+2	+0	+1	+0	+0	Jaffa warrior, Symbiote
2	15	+2	+3	+0	+2	+1	+1	Thunder staff
3	21	+3	+3	+1	+2	+1	+1	Symbiote
4	26	+4	+4	+1	+2	+2	+2	Thunder strike
5	32	+5	+4	+1	+3	+2	+2	
6	37	+6	+5	+2	+3	+2	+2	Symbiote
7	42	+7	+5	+2	+4	+3	+3	Endurance
8	48	+8	+6	+2	+4	+3	+3	Visage of terror
9	53	+9	+6	+3	+5	+4	+4	Symbiote
10	59	+10	+7	+3	+5	+4	+4	Great Fortitude

WARRIORS OF AKKAD

The Warriors of Akkad include the most loyal and best trained of Sargon's Jaffa. Though not especially well versed in the technology of the Goa'uld, these warriors more than compensate with their martial abilities.

FULL SKILLS

The warrior of Akkad's full skills and key abilities are:

FULL SKILL	KEY ABILITY
Balance	Dex

HALF SKILLS

The warrior of Akkad's half skills and key abilities are:

HALF SKILL	KEY ABILITY
Intimidate	Str or Cha
Spot	Wis
Survival (desert)	Wis

CLASS FEATURES

The following are class features of the warrior of Akkad.

Starting Feats: The warrior of Akkad begins play with the following feats.

Armor Group Proficiency Light
Armor Group Proficiency Medium
Weapon Group Proficiency Melee
Weapon Group Proficiency Rifle

Jaffa Warrior: At 1st level, the warrior of Akkad gains all the special talents listed for the Jaffa macro-species, as well as those listed for Horus Guard Jaffa sub-specialty *(see page 148 in the Stargate core rulebook).*

Symbiote: At 1st level, the warrior of Akkad gains the Symbiote feat *(see page 265 in the Stargate core rulebook).* The warrior of Akkad gains the Symbiote feat one additional time at 3rd level and for every 3 levels gained thereafter (i.e. a second time at 3rd level, a third time at 6th level, and a fourth time at 9th level).

Combat Instincts: At 2nd level, the warrior of Akkad gains the Combat Instincts feat.

Desert Training: At 4th level, the warrior of Akkad gains the Desert Training feat.

Training: At 6th level, the warrior of Akkad gains the Training feat. He gains this feat again at 10th level.

Stone Cold: At 9th level, the warrior of Akkad gains the Stone Cold feat.

ADDENDUM: SGC ARMORY

Despite being shrouded in secrecy, Stargate Command is an element of the United States Air Force, which in turn is part of one of the world's strongest militaries. This provides SG teams with an unprecedented degree of logistical support – subject, of course, to the twin concerns of funding and security. This appendix provides clarifications and expansion material for Chapter Nine of the *Stargate SG-1* core rulebook.

STANDARD-ISSUE WEAPONS

SG teams are issued a variety of armaments, depending on their primary assignment. GMs who prefer a more heavily-armed SG team should replace the "FN P90..." line in the standard SG team bundle with "standard-issue weapons." This includes one sidearm, one primary weapon (if the team member is qualified to use it), and the team member's choice of a bayonet or a survival knife.

STANDARD-ISSUE SIDEARMS

Per standing orders, no SG team member is allowed to leave Earth unarmed. All SG team personnel are issued sidearms. In the unlikely event that an individual who is not proficient with handguns (e.g. a near-human from a primitive society) is assigned to an SG team, the team commander is responsible for ensuring that the team member in question follows proper procedures regarding his weapon.

- Every member of a non-Russian SG team receives a Beretta M9 with 45 rounds (3 15-round magazines).

- Every member of a Russian SG team receives a Makarov PM with 40 rounds (5 8-round magazines).

STANDARD-ISSUE PRIMARY WEAPONS

Every SG team member who is qualified to use a submachinegun or rifle (e.g. has Weapon Group Proficiency (Rifle)) is issued one in addition to his sidearm. The type of primary weapon issued to each team depends on that team's mission profile. If a character does not receive a primary weapon, he instead receives a doubled ammunition

TABLE 3.19: THE WARRIOR OF AKKAD (NPC CLASS)

LVL	VITALITY POINTS	BASE ATT	FORT SAVE	REF SAVE	WILL SAVE	DEF BON	INIT BON	SPECIAL
1	6	+1	+1	+0	+1	+1	+1	Jaffa warrior, Symbiote
2	9	+2	+2	+0	+1	+2	+1	Combat Instincts
3	13	+3	+3	+1	+2	+3	+2	
4	16	+4	+3	+1	+2	+3	+2	Desert Training
5	20	+5	+4	+1	+3	+4	+3	
6	23	+6	+5	+2	+4	+5	+4	Training
7	27	+7	+6	+2	+4	+6	+4	
8	30	+8	+6	+2	+5	+6	+5	Stone Cold
9	34	+9	+7	+3	+5	+7	+5	
10	37	+10	+8	+3	+6	+8	+6	Training

allotment for his sidearm. A character who selects a weapons bundle containing an assault rifle, machine gun, shotgun, sniper rifle, or submachinegun may carry that weapon in addition to or in place of his standard-issue primary weapon.

Diplomatic, Engineering, Medical, and Scientific teams are not expected to engage in frontline combat operations, though they should be capable of defending themselves if need be. They are issued primary weapons and ammunition loads suitable for their low-threat (for the SGC) mission profiles. At present, this is an H&K MP5A3 with 120 rounds (4 30-round magazines).

Exploration teams encounter a wide variety of hazards, some of which require a solution in the form of deadly force. There has been much debate in the SGC regarding the proper primary weapons for exploration teams. Although some officers maintain that exploration teams should be issued more powerful primary weapons due to the frequency of hostile contacts that these teams experience, SGC's highest echelons discourage the issue of assault rifles or other recommended options exactly because of these combat situations. The mission of an exploration team (SG-1's record notwithstanding) is to gather information and survive to return that information to Earth, not to engage in protracted firefights with numerically and technologically superior opponents. To this end, exploration teams are issued weapons and ammunition loads suitable for self-defense – but not for extended offensive operations. Prior to 2002, this was an H&K MP5A3 with a tactical flashlight, 2× telescopic sight, magazine clamp, and 150

rounds (5 30-round magazines). In 2002, this changed to an FN P90 with a tactical flashlight and 150 rounds (3 50-round magazines).

Covert Ops and Search and Rescue teams are expected to engage in offensive operations as necessary to complete their mission objectives. They are frequently deployed in hostile territory, and may be required to operate off-planet for several days at a time. The standard-issue primary weapon of these teams is a Colt M4A1 with 210 rounds (7 30-round magazines) and each team member's choice of a day/night sight or a red dot sight.

Marine Combat Unit teams, like Covert Ops and Search and Rescue teams, often conduct offensive operations. Unlike the aforementioned teams, who must engage in combat in order to accomplish other objectives, SGC marines usually engage in combat as their primary objective. The standard-issue primary weapon of these teams is a Colt M16A3 with 300 rounds (10 30-round magazines) and each marine's choice of a 2× telescopic sight or red dot sight.

Russian teams are technically tasked with much the same wide mission profile as exploration teams. However, under the terms of the agreement that allows Russian personnel access to Cheyenne Mountain, they are allowed to bring their own equipment. The Russian authorities overseeing their teams have chosen national products over SGC standard arms and equipment as a not-so-subtle gesture of independence. The standard-issue primary weapon for Russian teams is a Kalashnikov AKS-74U with 210 rounds (7 30-round magazines).

TABLE 3.20: STANDARD-ISSUE WEAPONS

TEAM TYPE	PRIMARY WEAPON	AMMO	ACCESSORIES
Covert Ops	Colt M4A1	210 rounds	day/night or red dot sight
Diplomatic	H&K MP5A3	120 rounds	
Engineering	H&K MP5A3	120 rounds	
Exploration (pre-2002)	H&K MP5A3	150 rounds	tactical flashlight, 2× telescopic sight, magazine clamp
Exploration (2002 and later)	FN P90	150 rounds	tactical flashlight
Marine Combat Unit	Colt M16A3	300 rounds	2× telescopic sight or red dot sight
Medical	H&K MP5A3	120 rounds	
Russian	Kalashnikov AKS-74U	210 rounds	
Scientific	H&K MP5A3	120 rounds	
Search and Rescue	Colt M4A1	210 rounds	day/night or red dot sight

NEW AND REVISED WEAPON BUNDLES

CLOSE COMBAT BUNDLE (REVISED)
- Franchi SPAS-12 shotgun or Daewoo USAS-12 shotgun
  with assault sling
  with 60 rounds 12 gauge (slugs or shot)
- Earplugs

FIRE SUPPORT BUNDLE
- FN M249 SAW machine gun
  with 600 rounds 5.56×45mm NATO FMJ
  with standard sling

FIRE SUPPORT BUNDLE, MARINE
- FN M240G machine gun
  with 150 rounds 7.62×51mm NATO FMJ

FIRE SUPPORT BUNDLE, RUSSIAN
- Kalashnikov PK machine gun
  with 300 rounds of 7.62×54mm Soviet FMJ
  with standard sling

FRONTAL ASSAULT BUNDLE, RUSSIAN
- Kalashnikov AK-74 assault rifle
  with standard sling
  with 210 rounds of 5.45×39mm Soviet FMJ
- 2 smoke grenades

HEAVY ASSAULT BUNDLE, RUSSIAN
- KBP GP-25 grenade launcher
- 6 fragmentation grenades
- laser sight (for weapon on which GP-25 is mounted)

SNIPER BUNDLE (REVISED)
- H&K MSG-90 sniper rifle
  with 60 rounds 7.62×51mm NATO FMJ
  with 20 rounds 7.62×51mm NATO AP
  with standard sling
  with bipod

SNIPER BUNDLE, ANTI-MATERIAL
- Barrett M82A1 "Light Fifty" sniper rifle
  with 24× telescopic sight
  with standard sling
  with 20 rounds .50 BMG FMJ

SNIPER BUNDLE, MARINE
- Face paint, 3 applications
- Ghillie suit
- Remington M40A1 sniper rifle
  with 60 rounds 7.62×51mm NATO FMJ
  with 20 rounds 7.62×51mm NATO AP
  with standard sling

SNIPER BUNDLE, RUSSIAN
- Dragunov SVD sniper rifle
  with 60 rounds 7.62×54mm Soviet FMJ
  with standard sling
- Light amplification binoculars

New Weapon Accessories

Magazine Clamp: As the name implies, this device clamps two magazines for an assault rifle or submachine-gun side-by-side, holding one at the ready while the other feeds the weapon. This allows the character to perform one reload for the weapon as if he had the Quick Reload feat. However, if the character drops the firearm on a hard surface or uses it as an improvised melee weapon, the GM may spend an action die to declare that the feed lips of the ready magazine are bent, rendering it unusable.

Note: Due to the weapon's unconventional configuration, a magazine clamp may not be used with FN P90 magazines.

Picks: –

Weight: –

Weapon Sight, Red Dot: A red dot sight is a non-magnifying optical sight that projects an illusory red dot in the user's field of vision, giving the shooter the visual assistance of a laser without the telltale beam or dot. When using a weapon with a red dot sight, the character gains a +2 gear bonus with all ranged attack checks made against targets within 100 ft. Unless otherwise specified, a red dot sight may only be attached to a bow or a firearm's rail mount. A red dot sight provides no bonus if the user's line of vision is not aligned with its optics.

Picks: 2

Weight: ½ lb.

New Weapon Qualities

Bull Barrel (BB): The weapon has a heavier "bull" barrel than its design would normally call for. This makes it more resistant to abuse. Increase all four of its wound thresholds, adding +6 to the first, +8 to the second, and +10 to the third and fourth. This quality may only be added to assault rifles, sniper rifles, and shotguns, and costs 1 gear pick to add.

Custom Stock (CU): The firearm's stock and grip are modified to meet the exact requirements of an individual shooter. At the start of each combat, a character firing a weapon with a custom-fitted stock gains a +1 masterwork bonus to his initiative total. This bonus is added only once, at the start of combat. When anyone other than the character to whom the weapon is fitted uses the weapon in combat, the +1 bonus is replaced by a –1 penalty. This quality costs 1 gear pick to add.

Discreet (DT): Through compact size or unusual shape, this weapon is difficult to find. The DCs for all Spot and Search checks to notice it are increased by 2. This quality cannot be added to a weapon.

New Weapons

Pistols

SIG Sauer P226: This ultra-reliable Swiss-made weapon is the standard-issue sidearm of the NID, and is also in service with several legitimate government agencies and the US Navy's SEAL teams. The P226 can be acquired in three different calibers: 9mm, .357 SIG, or .40 S&W.

Assault Rifles

Colt M4A1: The M4A1 is the fully automatic carbine version of the M16 assault rifle. It is six inches shorter and a pound lighter than current-generation M16s, featuring a shorter barrel and an adjustable four-position telescoping stock. The M4A1 also replaces the M16's carrying handle with a flat top suitable for mounting a variety of optics. The M4A1 can accept virtually any accessory or under-barrel weapon that the M16 can, including the M203 grenade launcher, and uses the same magazines as the M16.

The M4A1's adjustable stock allows any Medium-sized character with an average or near-average human physique (total Strength and Constitution between 20 and 32) to spend a full action to adjust the weapon to fit his arm length and shooting stance. A character who has done this gains the benefits of the custom stock (CU) quality.

Kalashnikov AK-74: The modernized version of the classic AK-47 design shares its parent's reputation for durability, but is re-tooled for the modern 5.45×39mm round.

Sniper Rifles

Dragunov SVD: This highly accurate rifle has been standard issue for the Russian (formerly Soviet) Army since its introduction in 1963. It was developed as what is now called a "designated marksman's rifle." Soviet infantry organizational procedures called for a marksman armed with an SVD in every rifle squad, rather than the American deployment of smaller numbers of independent sniper teams. Russian SG teams try to follow their accustomed doctrine and deploy with a designated marksman carrying an SVD if a qualified shooter is available.

H&K MSG-90: The latest in H&K's series of sniper rifles based on the venerable G3 platform, the MSG-90 is in limited US military service. This includes the SGC, where it is the standard sniper rifle for most SG teams.

Remington M24 Sniper Weapon System: Like its elder brother, the M40A1, the US Army's M24 is based on the Remington Model 700. Most M24s are chambered for the military standard 7.62×51mm NATO round, but a few have been adapted to .300 Winchester Magnum instead. The M24 is not SGC standard-issue, but does see rare use in the hands of Army sharpshooters who, like their Marine counterparts, prefer to go with what they know.

Remington M40A1: Based on the venerable Remington Model 700 hunting rifle, the M40A1 has been the standard-issue sniper rifle for the US Marine Corps since the 1970s. Snipers attached to Marine Combat Unit SG teams use this weapon in place of the MSG-90.

Note: The Barrett M82A1, Dragunov SVD and SVU, and H&K MSG-90 have detachable magazines and can be reloaded with a single half action. The Remington M24 and M40A1 have internal magazines which must be loaded with individual rounds at a rate of three per half action.

SHOTGUNS

Franchi SPAS-12: The predecessor of the SPAS-15, the SPAS-12 has a more civilian appearance, with an eight-round tube magazine under the barrel rather than its descendant's detachable box magazine.

Daewoo USAS-12: Vaguely similar in overall appearance to the M16 series of assault rifles, the USAS-12 is a fully automatic shotgun fed from a drum magazine. Extensive use of polymer in its construction keeps its weight down, which is a blessing to the SGC personnel who carry it in the field – but automatic fire makes it recoil like a jackhammer.

Mossberg Model 500 Bullpup: This civilian-market pump-action shotgun saw brief use during the first US Air Force mission to Abydos, prior to the establishment of the first SG teams. It is no longer a first choice weapon, but several Model 500s remain in the SGC's armories.

Note: The Daewoo USAS-12 and Franchi SPAS-15 have detachable magazines and can be reloaded with a single half action. The Benelli M1 Super 90, Franchi SPAS-12, Gurza KS-23, Ithaca MAG-10 Roadblocker, and Winchester 1300 have internal magazines which must be loaded with individual shells at a rate of three per half action.

SUBMACHINEGUNS

H&K MP5K: The -K (for *kurz*, or "short") variant of the MP5 is small enough to be slung under an overcoat or carried in a briefcase. This stripped-down SMG has no stock and a minimal barrel just long enough to mount a vertical grip to give the shooter some semblance of control. The MP5K is not in SGC use, but is one of the standard weapons of NID agents desiring portable fully automatic firepower. MP5Ks can use standard MP5 magazines, but are more frequently seen with discreet 15-round magazines instead.

IMI Micro-Uzi: The smallest member of Israel Military Industries' venerable Uzi family is extremely easy to maintain and operate. Its balance and small size make it easy to fire with one hand, though controllability in fully automatic mode is something of a joke. Like the MP5K, the Micro-Uzi is an NID weapon and is not found in SGC hands.

Kalashnikov AKS-74U: This compact derivative of the AK-74 was originally designed for vehicle crews and airborne troops, providing them with the power of an assault rifle without the bulk. Its reduced mass makes it extremely difficult to control when fired in fully automatic mode. The AKS-74U is the standard-issue primary weapon of Russian SG teams.

MACHINEGUNS

Browning M2HB: The Browning "Ma Deuce" .50 caliber heavy machine gun has been in service since World War II with only minor changes to its design. This weapon is technically man-portable in the sense that it can be picked up and moved, but its design makes it impossible to use unsupported. The M2HB must be mounted on a tripod (44 pounds, included in any requisition), vehicle, or other solid structure to be fired. Unlike most machine guns, the M2HB can be fired in single-shot mode, and has seen limited use as a sniping weapon.

The SGC does not typically issue M2HBs to SG teams due to these limitations, outside of specific situations where FREDs can be used in offensive roles. Typically, M2HBs are emplaced as part of the standard defenses of the gate room, the Alpha Site, and other critical fixed positions.

FN M249 SAW: The Belgian-made M249 SAW (Squad Automatic Weapon) is the standard 5.56×45mm light support weapon of the American military. It is normally fed from a 200-round disintegrating belt held under the weapon in either a cloth bag or a plastic case, but can accept standard M16 magazines in a pinch.

FN M240G: The 7.62×51mm M240 medium machine gun was introduced in the 1990s to replace the aging M60E4 in US service. It has none of its predecessor's reputation for unreliability and has been favorably received as both a vehicle-mounted weapon (in its M240B configuration) and an infantry support weapon. The M240G sees limited use in the SGC, primarily in the hands of Marine Combat Unit teams whose commanders want a heavier base of fire than that provided by the M249.

GRENADE LAUNCHERS

KBP GP-25: The Russian underbarrel grenade launcher is very similar in basic function to the American M203. It fires 40mm ammunition, which is not interchangeable with American 40mm grenades. The GP-25 sacrifices range for decreased weight, and will only attach to an AK-series assault rifle or submachinegun.

ROCKET LAUNCHERS

Raytheon FIM-92 "Stinger" Anti-Aircraft Missile Launcher (corrected): The FIM-92 Stinger has been the standard US man-portable surface-to-air missile since 1982, when it replaced the Vietnam-era Redeye. The Stinger uses dual infrared and ultraviolet tracking to defeat countermeasures, and its Mach 2 airspeed and high-explosive warhead have been repeatedly proven in battle. The most recent variant, Stinger-RMP (Reprogrammable MicroProcessor) Block II, can accept tracking software upgrades in order to be deployed against new threats. The SGC has taken full advantage of this capability in deploying Stingers against Goa'uld death gliders, whose low combat airspeed places them fully within the Stinger's kill envelope.

Despite cinematic evidence to the contrary, the Stinger is incapable of acquiring ground targets and is highly ineffective against them even if fired "dumb" (1–10 error range and –8 to attacks). The Stinger launcher/guidance unit itself weighs 5 pounds, and each individual rocket in its disposable launch tube (2 gear picks per rocket) weighs 23 pounds.

ALIEN WEAPONS

Staff Weapon (corrected) (Goa'uld, Jaffa): The Jaffa warrior's primary offensive weapon, a staff weapon emits a focused plasma charge that can penetrate most forms of body armor with ease. It may also be used as a close combat weapon similar to a quarterstaff. Staff weapons are inaccurate and brutal, epitomizing the Goa'uld martial philosophy of rule through fear.

Resource Points: 6

Mechanics: A staff weapon is a Large-sized two-handed weapon. It may be used as a melee weapon or a ranged weapon, as follows.

For purposes of melee combat, a staff weapon is considered a quarterstaff *(see the Stargate SG-1 core rulebook page 328).* As per the standard rules for two-handed melee weapons, the character's Strength modifier is applied to all attack checks, and 1.5× his Strength modifier (if positive, rounded up) is applied to all damage rolls with the weapon. If the character does not possess the Weapon Group Proficiency (Melee) feat, he suffers a -4 penalty with all melee attack checks made with a staff weapon.

For purposes of ranged combat, a staff weapon is considered a hurled weapon (in the same sense that a bow is) for all purposes except the application of damage effects and damage reduction, for which it is considered an energy weapon. As per the standard rules for hurled weapon, the character's Dexterity modifier is applied to all attack checks, and no ability modifier is applied to damage rolls with the weapon. If the character does not possess the Weapon Group Proficiency (Hurled) feat, he suffers a -4 penalty with all ranged attack checks made with a staff weapon. Finally, a staff weapon used in ranged combat uses the statistics offered below.

Staff weapons are notoriously imprecise, and are hazardous to fire at targets in close proximity to friendly personnel. The Increased Precision and Precise Shot feats have no effect on ranged attacks made with staff weapons. In addition, whenever a character scores an error with a staff weapon attack against a target located adjacent to one or more bystanders, the GM may spend 2 action dice to activate the critical miss as a successful attack against one bystander adjacent to the target. If the bystander is located within the same square as the target (e.g. they're grappling), this critical failure may be activated at the cost of only 1 action die.

A staff weapon may only be fired in single-shot mode and may only be fired once per round as a full action, unless the character possesses the Speed Trigger feat *(see the Stargate SG-1 core rulebook page 251)* or another feat which specifically affects the modes in which he may fire a staff weapon. If a character is capable of firing a staff weapon in burst or strafe mode, he gains a +2 gear bonus to attacks made using these fire modes, as the energized plasma blasts are as visible as conventional tracer ammunition *(see the Stargate SG-1 core rulebook page 337).* The Jaffa call the technique of rapidly firing a staff weapon *kel'no'pah* (literally, "lightning strike").

Using the aim action with a staff weapon requires a full action, not a half action as normal. Staff weapons are not ergonomically designed for precision use.

A staff weapon derives its destructive energy from a small naquadah power cell which energizes an array of capacitors. This capacitor array stores enough energy for 50 shots. The power cell recharges the capacitors at the rate of one shot every 30 seconds (5 combat rounds). Power cells are typically good for several thousand shots before they need to be replaced, and such replacement is part of routine maintenance for both Goa'uld forces and the SGC.

Finally, the wielder of a staff weapon gains a +2 gear bonus to Intimidate checks against anyone who has seen a staff weapon fired but has never defeated an opponent wielding a staff weapon. Staff weapons are one of the primary symbols of Goa'uld dominance and their subjects and enemies alike are frequently cowed by the display of raw power that a staff weapon master can present.

TABLE 3.21: FIREARMS

NAME	PICKS	RECOIL	ACCURACY	DAMAGE	ERROR	THREAT	INCREMENT	RANGE AMMO	QUALITIES	SIZE	WEIGHT
Pistols											
SIG Sauer P226											
9mm P	2	13	–	1d10+1	1	20	25 ft. (max 250 ft.)	15	DP, RG	S	2 lb.
.357 SIG	2	15	–	2d6	1	20	25 ft. (max 250 ft.)	12	DP, RG	S	2 lb.
.40 S&W	2	19	–	1d12	1	20	25 ft. (max 250 ft.)	12	DP, RG, TD	S	2 lb.
Assault Rifles											
Colt M4A1											
5.56×45mm NATO	4	0	–	4d4	1–2	20	100 ft. (max 1,000 ft.)	30	no strafe mode, IN adjustable stock*	L	7 lb.
Kalashnikov AK–74											
5.45×39mm Soviet	5	12	–	3d6+1	1	20	175 ft. (max 1,750 ft.)	30	RG	L	9 lb.
Sniper Rifles											
Dragunov SVD											
7.62×54mm Soviet	6	13	+1	2d10+1	1–2	18–20	200 ft. (max 2,000 ft.)	10	IN 6× telescopic sight	L	10 lb.
H&K MSG-90											
7.62×51mm NATO	6	0	+1	4d4+2	1–2	18–20	175 ft. (max 1,750 ft.)	20	AA, BB, IN 12× telescopic sight	L	14 lb.
Remington M24											
7.62×51mm NATO	5	10	–	4d4+2	1	18–20	200 ft. (max 2,000 ft.)	5	IN 12× telescopic sight, bipod	L	13 lb.
.300 Winchester Magnum	6	10	–	3d6+2	1	18–20	250 ft. (max 2,500 ft.)	5	IN 12× telescopic sight, bipod	L	13 lb.
Remington M40A1											
7.62×51mm NATO	5	0	–	4d4+2	1	18–20	200 ft. (max 2,000 ft.)	5	IN 10x telescopic sight	L	15 lb.
Shotguns											
Daewoo USAS-12											
12 gauge shot	4	12	–	5d4	1–3	20	30 ft. (max 150 ft.)	20	single-shot, burst, or strafe mode	L	12 lb.
12 gauge slug	4	14	–	2d12	1–3	19–20	30 ft. (max 150 ft.)	20	single-shot, burst, or strafe mode	L	12 lb.
Franchi SPAS-12											
12 gauge shot	5	16	–	5d4	1–2	20	30 ft. (max 150 ft.)	8	CS, DP, RG	L	10 lb.
12 gauge slug	5	19	–	2d12	1–2	19–20	30 ft. (max 150 ft.)	8	CS, DP, RG	L	10 lb.
Mossberg Model 500 Bullpup											
12 gauge shot	4	21	–	5d4	1–2	20	30 ft. (max 150 ft.)	6	BP, DP	L	7 lb.
12 gauge slug	4	25	–	2d12	1–2	19–20	30 ft. (max 150 ft.)	6	BP, DP	L	7 lb.
Submachineguns											
H&K MP5K											
9mm P	3	10	–3	1d10+1	1–2	20	30 ft. (max 300 ft.)	15 or 30	DP, DT; single-shot, burst, or strafe mode	M	4 lb.
IMI Micro-Uzi											
9mm P	1	10	–3	1d10+1	1–2	20	30 ft. (max 300 ft.)	20	CS, DT	S	4 lb.
Kalashnikov AKS-74U											
5.45x39mm Soviet	3	22	–2	3d6+1	1	20	45 ft. (max 450 ft.)	30	CS, RG; single-shot, burst, or strafe mode	M	120
Special Weapons											
Dan-Inject JM Standard	2 + ammo	–	+1	1d4/Special	1	19 –20	30ft. (max.300 ft.)	3	–	M	6 lb.

* See weapon description for additional rules.

TABLE 3.22: FIREARMS AMMUNITION

AMMUNITION TYPE	PICKS	EFFECT
Darts		
Empty	1 per 30 shots	No special effect
Succinylcholine Chloride	1 per 9 shots	Muscle relaxant, Fortitude Save (DC 20) or unconscious for 2d4 hours
Chlorpheniramine Maleate	1 per 15 shots	Antihistamine, Fortitude Save (DC 15) or unconscious for 1d4 hours, no allergies for 1d4 days

Note: All Picks include a sufficient supply of CO2 cartridges for the number of darts acquired.

NAME	PICKS	RECOIL	ACCURACY	DAMAGE	ERROR	THREAT	INCREMENT	RANGE AMMO	QUALITIES	SIZE	WEIGHT
Machineguns											
Browning M2HB											
.50 BMG	8	–	2d12+2	1–2	18–20	300 ft. (max 3,000 ft.)	–	50	AK, AP, DP, RG; single-shot, burst, or strafe mode	L	84 lb.
FN M249 SAW											
5.56×45mm NATO	4	–	4d4	1	20	100 ft. (max 1,000 ft.)	–	200	–	L	15 lb.
FN M240G											
7.62×51mm NATO	6	–	4d4+2	1–2	19–20	150 ft. (max 1,500 ft.)	–	100	AK, DP	L	24 lb.
Grenade Launchers											
KBP GP-25	3	–1	per grenade	per grenade	per grenade	40 ft. (max 400 ft.)	per grenade	1	–	M	3 lb.
Rocket Launchers											
FIM-92 Stinger	4	–	3d10+2	1–3	–	500 ft. (max 5,000 ft.)	10 ft.	1	AP	L	5 lb.

TABLE 3.24: EQUIPMENT

MEDICAL SUPPLIES	PICKS	DR	RANGE INCREMENT	DURATION	QUALITIES	WEIGHT
Handheld Decontamination Apparatus*	1	–	2 ft. (max. 8 ft.)	–	–	5 lb.
Portable Decontaminating Apparatus*	2	–	–	–	–	25 lb.

SHOTS	PICKS	DR	RANGE INCREMENT	DURATION	QUALITIES	WEIGHT
Convulsant Antidote for Nerve Agents*	1 per 2	–	–	–	–	–
Nerve Agent Antidote Kit*	1 per 2	–	–	–	–	–
Skin Decontamination Kit*	1	–	–	–	–	–

SENSORS	PICKS	DR	RANGE INCREMENT	DURATION	QUALITIES	WEIGHT
Chemical Agent Detector Paper*	1	–	–	–	–	–

SURVIVAL EQUIPMENT	PICKS	DR	RANGE INCREMENT	DURATION	QUALITIES	WEIGHT
Field Protective Mask*	2	–	–	–	–	1 lb.

SUITS	PICKS	DR	RANGE INCREMENT	DURATION	QUALITIES	WEIGHT
Battledress Overgarment*	1	–	–	24 hours/ 30 days	CM	5 lb.
Chemical Protective Overgarment*	1	–	–	24 hours/ 30 days	CM	5 lb.
NBC*	2	–	–	6 hours	–	20 lb.
SCALP*	1	–	–	6 hours/ 14 days	AK	1.5 lb.

* See item description for additional rules.

TABLE 3.25: ALIEN EQUIPMENT

OHNES GEAR	PICKS	DR	RANGE INCREMENT	DURATION	QUALITIES	WEIGHT
Ohnes hydrator	2	–	–	5 days	–	10 lbs.

SIMARKAAN GEAR	PICKS	DR	RANGE INCREMENT	DURATION	QUALITIES	WEIGHT
Simarkan anesthetic salve	1	–	–	–	LT	–
Simarkan healing salve	1	–	–	–	LT	–
Simarkan anti-venom	1	–	–	–	LT	–
Simarkan fever cure	1	–	–	–	LT	–

TABLE 3.26: ALIEN ARMOR

NAME	RP	DM	DR	WEAK	MDB	ACP	SPECIAL QUALITIES	SPEED	WEIGHT
Medium Armor									
Jaffa armor, standard	10	+1	8	C,E	+2	–4	–	Same	25 lb.
Helmets									
Jaffa Helm, standard	4	+2	1	F	–	–2	C, IN, LV, NV, PW, PS	–5 ft.	20 lb.
Jaffa Helm, Dragon	4	+2	1	F	–	–2	C, IN, LV, NV, PW, PS, PA	–5 ft.	20 lb.
Jaffa Helm, Horus	4	+2	1	F	–	–2	C, IN, LV, PS	–5 ft.	20 lb.
Jaffa Helm, Serpent	4	+2	1	F	–	–2	C, IN, LV, NV, PW, PS	–5 ft.	20 lb.
Jaffa Helm, Setesh	4	+1	1	F	–	–1	C, IN, LV, NV, PS	Same	20 lb

TABLE 3.27: ALIEN WEAPONS

NAME	RP	RECOIL	ACCURACY	DAMAGE	ERROR	THREAT	RANGE INCREMENT	AMMO	QUALITIES	WEIGHT
Altairan Weapons										
Disintegrator	8	12	–	3d6*	1-2	20	20 ft	20	–	½ lbs.
Stun field	12	–	–4	10d6**	–	–	–	10	–	6 lbs.
Asgard Weapons										
Shock spear	8	10	-2	3d6†	1	20	100 ft	100	DP, TD	8 lbs.
Byrst Weapons										
Kest	2	–	–1	1d8 +1	1-2	20	60ft.*	1	LT	4 lb.
Jaffa Weapons										
Staff Weapon (Corrected)	6	12	-4	6d6	1-2	18-20	30 ft.	50*	AP, AK, TD	8 lb
GOA'ULD WEAPONS										
Medium Melee Weapons										
Dragon talons	1	–	–	1d6+2	1	20	–	–	AP, 1-h	1lb
Small Hurled Weapons										
Ra'kek	10	–	–	6d6‡	1-6	–	10 ft	30 ft	–	5 lb.
Large Ranged weapons										
Lightning staff	7	12	–4	6d6+special	1-2	18-20	30 ft.	50*	AP, AK, TD	8 lb.
Nek'sed	8	14	–4	8d6Δ	1-4	20	60 ft	–	–	30 lbs.
Thunder staff	6	12	–4	6d6+special	1-2	18-20	30 ft.	50*	AP, AK, TD	8 lb.
Ohnes Weapons										
Ohnes sonic pistol	3	12	–	4d4	1-2	19–20	20Σ	10	–	4 lb.
Ohnes sonic rifle	5	10	–	6d4	1	19–20	100Σ	20	DP, RG	10 lb.

* See special rules for this weapon on page 172.

** Subdual damage.

† Max 5 increments.

‡ Blast Increment 30 ft.

Δ Additionally, any characters within five feet of an opponent hit by a lightning cannon suffer 3d6 points of secondary damage from the weapon's powerful blast.

Σ Double this value underwater.

THE OPEN GAME LICENSE

THE OPEN GAME CONTENT